HALACHAH
and
MEDICINE TODAY

HALACHAH
and
MEDICINE TODAY

SELECTIONS FROM
הלכה ורפואה
edited by Rabbi Moshe Hershler, זצ"ל

translated and edited by
Dr. Mordechai Koenigsberg

FELDHEIM PUBLISHERS
Jerusalem · New York
-»> «<-

REGENSBERG INSTITUTE
MACHON Ha'RAV HERSHLER
Institute for the Advanced Study of
Halachah and Medical Problems
Jerusalem • Chicago
5757 - 1997

First published 1997
Copyright © 1997 by Machon Ha'Rav Hershler

Rabbi E.R. Heisherik
P.O.B. 16005 / Jerusalem, Israel

ISBN 0-87306-796-7

FELDHEIM PUBLISHERS
POB 35002 / Jerusalem, Israel

200 Airport Executive Park
Nanuet, NY 10954

10 9 8 7 6 5 4 3 2 1

Printed in Israel

This *sefer* is dedicated to the memory of my parents

Rabbi Herschel Koenigsberg *z"l*

Mrs. Rose Elfenbein Koenigsberg *z"l*

and to
Oscar Buky, D.D.S., *z"l*
Florence Buky, M.D., *z"l*
Schmuel and Brina Buky, *z"l*
Rose and Seymour Novick, *z"l*
Margaret and Morris Lubinsky, *z"l*

Introduction

The field of medical ethics is exploding, because rarely does a day pass when we are not besieged by major advances in biomedical and therapeutic technology.

For the concerned physician there is a fundamental need for an up-to-date explanation of the Jewish viewpoint of today's bioethical problems. The question is how Halachah, based on its classic and ancient text, provides valid and objective answers to the bioethical problems of modern society.

Since Halachah does not operate in a spiritual or intellectual vacuum, this book is offered to the concerned world medical community, enabling its readers to encounter original halachic studies dealing with crucial problems of modern life without sacrificing the full flavor of the actual Talmudic reasoning presented in the original Hebrew articles.

Oscar A. Novick, M.D.

Foreword

...And a threefold cord is not quickly broken [Kohelet 4:12].

A threefold cord — if three participate together, there is nothing greater [*Metzudat David* commentary, ibid.]

There can be no better description of this latest book of the Regensberg Institute — Machon Ha-Rav Hershler than the words quoted above.

The dream of my father-in-law, our revered teacher, Ha-Gaon Rabbi Moshe Hershler, *zt"l*, was to share his knowledge of medicine and Jewish law with physicians and healthcare workers throughout the world. During his lifetime, five volumes of essays and responsa were published under the auspices of the Regensberg Institute, each of which was received with great accolade and enthusiasm by the Torah community.

Unfortunately, there were many in the broader community who, because of a lack of fluency in Hebrew, were unable to benefit directly from these books. As a result, before his passing Rabbi Hershler decided to translate his series of halachic works, a task that he entrusted to his dear friend Rabbi Dr. Mordechai Koenigsberg of New York.

Since then, Dr. Koenigsberg, a great Torah scholar and scientist in his own right, has dedicated himself to bringing Rabbi Hershler's dream to reality. As you will read in his preface and as you will see from the fruit of his labor, Dr. Koenigsberg's contribution to this volume is much more than mere translation. Rather, he has created a masterpiece, accessible to the English-speaking community and which preserves the depth and breadth of the original. He has proven to be an extraordinary editor and a most gifted writer.

Without flour (sustenance), there is no Torah.

The realization of Rabbi Hershler's dream and Dr.

Koenigsberg's efforts would not have been possible without the never-ending encouragement and assistance of Dr. Oscar and Bernice Novick of Chicago. Renowned patrons of Torah within their community and around the world, the Novicks contributed to this important endeavor and lent their own talents to reviewing the manuscript in detail, offering many insightful suggestions regarding its final form.

It was their efforts, combined with those of Dr. Koenigsberg and Rabbi Hershler, that created the "threefold cord" of this work.

Rabbi Elazar said: "During the story of the sale of the Cave of the Machpelah, the Torah referred to the 'children of Chet' ten times — reminiscent of the Ten Commandments, to teach us that whoever assists in the dealings of a righteous person is as if he fulfills the Ten Commandments."

These words of Rabbi Elazar are the tribute extended to our dear friends, Dr. and Mrs. Koenigsberg. For their efforts on behalf of Rabbi Hershler's dream, may Hashem grant them much *nachas* from their children and grandchildren and may He extend His Heavenly blessings to them and all of their continued efforts.

These too are the blessings extended to Dr. and Mrs. Novick, exceptional individuals who guaranteed that the "dealings of a righteous person" have become accessible to the entire Jewish world. May they merit the blessings of Torah, continue to enjoy *nachas* from their wonderful family and benefit from the blessings from on high in all their endeavors.

Dayan Eliyahu Refael Heisherik
Jerusalem, 575

Preface

Years ago, the renowned *gaon* Rabbi Moshe Hershler, *zt"l*, felt the need for an English-language version of *Halachah U'Refuah*, the excellent series he edited and published in Hebrew under the auspices of the Regensberg Institute. The series dealt with a variety of important topics that an Orthodox Jewish physician or health-care worker should be aware of and be knowledgeable about. Each essay analyzed and explained a particular theme, starting with the primary sources in the Talmud and following the issue through the *Rishonim* and *Acharonim*, finally arriving at the practical application of the Halachah. Many Torah leaders and luminaries contributed to these volumes, as well as physicians and others aware of current medical issues who are knowledgeable in Halachah.

Rabbi Hershler asked me to undertake the task of translating the original material and reworking it into a format which would appeal to both the professional and the layman who are not likely to struggle through the Hebrew essays. Every translator knows that much is lost in translation, and it is impossible to translate word for word. This is particularly true in dealing with halachic arguments and reasoning. Sometimes it is necessary to elaborate a concept, using many words to explain a short phrase; and, at other times, one can achieve a clearer understanding of the material by eliminating superfluous comments and peripheral remarks. Yet, as the book began to take shape in my mind, it became apparent that, although it would be important to reorganize the material in each article into a clearer, simpler structure, the crucial conceptual framework, proofs, and arguments should be retained, so that the English reader may experience and savor the halachic development of each topic.

I had initially intended to translate and edit all the articles in the first two volumes of *Halachah U'Refuah*. But, as I expended a great deal of effort revising and clarifying the English text, I realized that I would not complete this task in a timely fashion. To minimize the delay in bringing this material to the English-speaking public, I decided to present selections from the first two volumes of *Halachah U'Refuah*. In some instances, articles by different authors, as indicated in the Table of Contents, were combined and condensed to avoid redundancy and simplify the text. To this material, several articles were added that were originally authored in English, and these were also edited and reworked, to a greater or lesser extent.

The book is not meant to be merely a *Shulchan Aruch* for medically related problems, listing a series of dos and don'ts for each topic. It has been written for those who wish to understand more clearly the concepts and logical foundations which support these halachic rulings.

I wish to take this opportunity to express my appreciation to Rabbi Hershler, *zt"l*, for his encouragement and patience during the long gestation of this volume, which provided me with a unique opportunity to spread the word of Torah. After his untimely passing, I had the pleasure of working with his son-in-law, Rabbi Eliyahu Refael Heisherik, *shlita*, who prodded me to see this project through to its completion. My gratitude is further extended to a dear *chaver*, Rabbi Gedaliah Aaron Rabinowitz, *shlita*, for his guidance and many valuable suggestions. Thanks also to the friends who reviewed different sections of the material for clarity and readability.

My daughter Chana conscientiously and indefatigably entered the entire text into the computer, with some assistance from her sister, Aliza. This facilitated the later revisions of the manuscript. May they be blessed.

This is also a fitting occasion to thank my parents, Rabbi and Mrs. Herschel Koenigsberg, *z"l*, who spared no effort to raise me to love, study, and teach Torah. I know that this volume will give them special pleasure in *Gan Eden*.

My wife, Riki, deserves special recognition for her support of learning and constant encouragement of my efforts in acquiring and disseminating Torah. She has also carefully reviewed the entire text for clarity of expression and syntax. May Hashem grant her the merit to see generations walking in the path of Torah, toiling in the study hall and fulfilling the mitzvot.

I pray that my efforts for accuracy and clarity in presenting the words of the Torah scholars who prepared this material shall be successful, so that no one will err, Heaven forbid, in applying their conclusions and rulings in practice. May this volume enhance the understanding and love of Torah in the English-speaking world, and serve as an inspiration for the performance of mitzvot.

Mordechai Koenigsberg
Kew Gardens Hills, New York
Sivan 5756

Contents

May actions not directly associated with the saving of life be performed on Shabbat on behalf of the critically ill?

Translated and adapted from the article by
RABBI OVADIA YOSEF in *Halachah U'Refuah* II, 80-91

Rabbi Ovadia Yosef questions whether there are constraints with respect to the actions that can be performed for a critically ill patient. Must one refrain from employing any measure which would normally be forbidden on Shabbat as long as doing so does not impose a risk to the patient? Or do we say that, since the laws of Shabbat are set aside for one who is in life-threatening danger, it is permissible to perform any beneficial procedure which will contribute to the patient's ease and ameliorate his pain, even though it does not directly improve or stabilize the patient's critical status?

The Rambam states that, for a patient in life-threatening danger, Shabbat is treated like a weekday with regard to all procedures that the patient requires.[1] The *Maggid Mishneh* understood that the Rambam permitted all actions, even those that would not increase the risk to the patient if they were withheld.[2] R. Yosef Karo rules similarly in the *Shulchan Aruch*,[3] but in the *Beit Yosef* he cites Rashi's position that Shabbat may be profaned only for actions which would increase the risk to the patient were they not to be performed.[4]

Apparently this issue is linked to a controversy among the *Rishonim* as to the extent that Shabbat laws are set aside in order to save a life. Are Shabbat prohibitions pushed

---

1 *Hilchot Shabbat* 2:2.

2 Ibid., *Maggid Mishneh* 2:14.

3 *Orach Chayim* 328:4.

4 *Shabbat* 129a, Rashi: *Davar she-ein bo sakkanah.*

aside, *dechuyah*, only when they would interfere with life-saving maneuvers, or are the restrictions of Shabbat rendered completely permissible, *hutrah*, in dealing with an individual who is in a life-threatening situation? In a pragmatic halachic sense, the term *dechuyah* limits the setting aside of Shabbat to situations where there are no alternatives to performing the normally prohibited action, while *hutrah* conveys a broader dispensation which can be applied even when there are alternatives.

The Maharam of Rottenberg compares the laws of Shabhat in the face of danger to life to the laws of preparing food on *Yom Tov*.[5] Just as the Torah permitted all direct work involving preparation of food on *Yom Tov*, so too is all work permitted on Shabbat, as though it were a weekday, for a patient who is critically ill. In this manner, the Maharam explains why it is permissible to ritually slaughter an animal on Shabbat in order to feed one who is critically ill, even when it is possible to feed the patient from a *neveilah*, an unslaughtered carcass, which is a lesser Biblical offense. However, the Rashba[6] maintains that Shabbat laws are merely *dechuyah* for the sake of a critically ill patient, and wherever possible one should try to avoid profaning Shabbat on his behalf. Thus, if nonkosher food is available for the patient, it would not be permissible to ritually slaughter another animal, in contrast to *Yom Tov*, when work involving preparation of food is completely permitted, even when it is possible to do the cooking before the holiday.

Support for the position that Shabbat prohibitions are *hutrah* for life-threatening danger may be brought from R. Elazar ben Azaryah's response in the Talmud that the rule suspending the laws of Shabbat may be inferred from the

---

5 *Teshuvot Maharam mi-Rottenberg* (Cremona edition, 200; Bloch edition, *Mekitzei Nirdamin* II, 119:41). It is also cited in the Rosh, *Yoma* 88:14, in *Teshuvot Rosh* 26:5, and in the *Mordechai, Shabbat*, no. 466.

6 *Teshuvot Rashba* 689. Also see *Beit Yosef* and *Tur, Orach Chayim* 329, and the commentary of the Ran on *Beitzah* 17b.

laws of circumcision: "If circumcision, which involves only one of the organs of the human body, suspends the laws of Shabbat [so that the circumcision may take place], how much more so shall the saving of one's whole body suspend Shabbat!"[7]

Circumcision itself is treated as completely permissible on Shabbat[8] even according to authorities who maintain that for critically ill patients Shabbat laws are merely *dechuyah*. Thus the Ran states, "Even though with regard to performing work for a critically ill patient the rule is that wherever possible it should be performed in an unusual manner, there it is different because Shabbat prohibitions are not rendered completely permissible...but with regard to circumcision, even if it were possible to perform the ritual without profaning Shabbat, such as by doing it in an unusual manner, we do not preferentially seek to do so, because circumcision does not merely defer Shabbat. Rather, the strictures of Shabbat are rendered completely permissible with respect to this ritual, since the Torah specifically permitted circumcision on Shabbat."[9]

Other authorities maintain that the inference of the Talmud is not limited to circumcision. The restrictions of Shabbat are rendered completely permissible whenever there is danger to life, just as they are for the ritual of circumcision,[10] and, since Shabbat is treated as a weekday, it is not necessary to seek an otherwise permissible mode of action. (It is interesting that the Rama[11] does not follow the line of reasoning which extends the blanket permission for circumcision to life-threatening situations in general. He

---

7 *Yoma* 85b.

8 *Shabbat* 132b. This is derived from the verse, "And on the eighth day the flesh of his foreskin shall be circumcised" (*Vayikra* 12:3), which implies that circumcision is performed even when the eighth day is Shabbat.

9 *Chiddushei ha-Ran, Shabbat* 130b; and *Chiddushei ha-Ramban*.

10 Ri of Trani, *Shabbat* 130b; *Teshuvot ha-Tashbatz* III, 37.

11 *Teshuvot ha-Rama* 76.

derives the principle that Shabbat prohibitions are completely *hutrah* in cases of danger to life from the above-cited
reasons of the Rambam and the Maharam of Rottenberg.
Then, using the inference of the Talmud, he reverses the
comparison to equate circumcision in this respect to circumstances of danger to life.)

Yet, even with regard to circumcision there is no universal agreement that the prohibitions of Shabbat are completely *hutrah*. The *Shulchan Aruch* states that two
circumcisers should not share in performing the ceremony
on Shabbat, one to cut the outer skin and the other to tear
away the inner membrane; the entire procedure must be
completed by one individual.[12] From this rule Rabbi Yosef
concludes that, according to the *Shulchan Aruch*, the prohibitions of Shabbat are not *hutrah* with regard to circumcision
but, rather, that Shabbat is deferred for the ritual. Therefore, a circumciser who excises only one layer of the foreskin
has transgressed a Shabbat prohibition, since only the complete performance of the ritual is permitted.

The prohibitions of Shabbat would not be *hutrah* with
regard to circumcision also according to the Rashba, as cited
in *Tosafot*.[13] The Talmud notes that it once occurred that the
people forgot to bring a knife before Shabbat (for a circumcision which was to be performed on Shabbat), so they
brought it on Shabbat via roofs and courtyards (to avoid
carrying through a public domain). This was not to the liking
of R. Eliezer, who permitted carrying it even through a public
domain (since he holds that, in addition to the performance
of the ritual itself, preliminary arrangements for the ritual
of circumcision are also permitted). The Rashba asks, "Since
it is a general principle that whenever one is confronted by
both a positive and a negative commandment both should be
fulfilled if possible, and since it is possible to fulfill the

---

12 *Shulchan Aruch, Yoreh De'ah* 266:14. The Rama, of course, differs in his gloss
    on the text, as in his responsum cited above.

13 *Shabbat* 130a and 130b, *Tosafot: She-lo bi-retzon R. Eliezer.*

positive commandment [of performing a circumcision] by bringing the knife via roofs and courtyards [thereby avoiding the negative commandment of carrying in a public domain], perhaps R. Eliezer would agree that it should not be brought through the public domain?" From the question it is clear that the Rashba cannot hold that the prohibitions of Shabbat are *hutrah* with respect to circumcision, for if that were so there would be no negative commandment to avoid.

There is also some controversy in interpreting the Rambam's position concerning the suspension of Shabbat for one in life-threatening danger. We have already cited the *Maggid Mishneh* and the Rama, who maintain that the Rambam considered the prohibitions of Shabbat to be completely *hutrah* in this circumstance. Yet the Rambam specifically states, "Shabbat is *dechuyah* if there is danger to life,"[14] from which the *Kesef Mishneh* and others assume that the Rambam is of the opinion that Shabbat prohibitions are merely deferred, not completely permitted.[15] But the Rambam also states as a general rule, "with regard to a critically ill patient, Shabbat is like a weekday," whereby the Rama and the *Maggid Mishneh* infer that the prohibitions of Shabbat are completely permitted in a case of danger to life.[16]

According to this view one must say that, in using the term *dechuyah*, the Rambam does not intend to define the extent of the suspension of Shabbat technically. He used the language of the Talmud, which apparently was imprecise in this respect. The Gaon of Rogozov explains the Rambam in

---

14 *Hilchot Shabbat* 2:1.

15 Ibid., *Kesef Mishneh; Beit Yosef, Shulchan Aruch, Orach Chayim* 328; and *Biur ha-Gra, Shulchan Aruch, Yoreh De'ah* 265:25. *Aruch ha-Shulchan* contends that *Biur ha-Gra* concludes that the Rambam considered Shabbat prohibitions to be completely permitted for a critically ill patient (*Aruch ha-Shulchan, Yoreh De'ah* 266). But the Gra specifically states that "Shabbat is *dechuyah* and not *hutrah*" (*Yoreh De'ah* 155:24).

16 See also *Tzofnat Pa'ne'ach* on the early part of *Shabbat*, ch.2; *Teshuvot Chesed l'Avraham Te'umim*, 2nd ed., *Orach Chayim* 67; *Teshuvot Avnei Nezer, Orach Chayim* 455:5; and *Teshuvot Divrei Malkiel* IV, 15.

the following manner: When there is a critically ill patient, one should not consider that Shabbat prohibitions are extant and are set aside only because of the danger. Rather, the essence of Shabbat is canceled in a critical moment; therefore all [the patient's] needs are taken care of even though he will not die if they are not performed.[17] (The Tashbatz[18] also cautions that the term *docheh* as used in the Talmud is not necessarily restricted to mean "sets aside," but can also imply *huttar*, "permits." The language of other *Rishonim* is also imprecise in this respect, as some use the verb *lidchot* in conjunction with the statement that Shabbat is treated entirely like a weekday.)

The difficulty in interpreting the Rambam's position may be seen from the uncertainty of R. Yosef Karo. In the *Beit Yosef* he initially maintained that the Rambam rules as the Rashba and the Ran.[19] Yet, when he later compiled the *Shulchan Aruch*, he ruled that the prohibitions of Shabbat are completely permissible, as on a weekday.[20] Since it is known that R. Yosef Karo ruled according to the Rambam, we must assume that he realized subsequently that, despite the Rambam's use of the term *dechuyah*, there is no compulsion to maintain that he considers Shabbat prohibitions to be merely deferred and not permitted as on a weekday. Thus, he followed the more lenient interpretation of the *Maggid Mishneh*. (Others suggest that the Rambam holds that Shabbat prohibitions are completely permitted according to Biblical law, and that in using the term *dechuyah* he teaches us that the Sages are more stringent when it is possible to provide for the patient in a permissible manner with no delay.[21])

---

17 *Tzofnat Pa'ne'ach* on the early part of *Shabbat*, ch.2.

18 *Teshuvot ha-Tashbatz* III, 37.

19 *Tur, Orach Chayim* 328.

20 *Shulchan Aruch, Orach Chayim* 328:4.

21 *Nachal Eitan, Hilchot Shabbat* 2:1; *Teshuvot Chayim v'Chesed Musfaye* 17: Mabit, *Kiryat Sefer, Hilchot Ma'achlot Asurot,* ch.14.

Although there is no direct reference to the position of *Tosafot* regarding whether Shabbat prohibitions are set aside or rendered completely permissible, it may be inferred that *Tosafot* follows the latter opinion. The Talmud cites a difference of opinion regarding the culpability of one who bakes on *Yom Tov* for a weekday meal.[22] Rabba says that he should not be punished because of the principle of *ho'eel*, "since" (since it is possible for guests to visit him on *Yom Tov* at which time the food would be eaten on *Yom Tov* itself). *Tosafot* questions this line of reasoning, for by applying the principle of *ho'eel* you may evade all the prohibitions of Shabbat, "since" proscribed acts may be usable for a patient who may present as critically ill on Shabbat. To this *Tosafot* answers that a critically ill patient is not a usual occurrence and, therefore, we do not use the reasoning of *ho'eel* From the question, it may be inferred that *Tosafot* holds that the prohibitions of Shabbat are completely permitted for one who is critically ill, just as the work of preparing food is completely permitted on *Yom Tov*. Otherwise *Tosafot* should have answered that we do not use *ho'eel* with regard to the laws of Shabbat because the prohibitions of Shabbat are merely set aside for a critical patient, not completely permitted. Indeed, many authorities maintain that *Tosafot's* position is similar to that of the Maharam of Rottenberg.[23]

Despite the numerous lenient opinions, the *Mishnah Berurah* is inclined to follow the more stringent view that when it is clear that withholding a particular action will not increase risk to the patient, the procedure should be performed on Shabbat only by a non-Jew, as is the law regarding a noncritically ill patient.[24] Among the evidence marshaled

---

22 *Pesachim* 46b, and *Tosafot: Rabba amar.*

23 *Teshuvot Ateret Chachamim, Orach Chayim* 4; *Teshuvot Besamim Rosh* 39; *Teshuvot Or Gadol* 1; *Sho'el u'Meshiv,* 2nd series, II, 15; *Teshuvot Maharam Shik, Orach Chayim* 140: *Venira;* and Rabbi S. Z. Auerbach, *Me'orei Esh* 12b.

24 *Mishnah Berurah, Shulchan Aruch, Orach Chayim* 328:14; and the *Biur Halachah: Kol she-regilim.*

to support its position, the *Mishnah Berurah* includes
Rashi's explanation that the Mishnah's ruling that a sick
person is fed [on Yom Kippur] upon the opinion of experts
refers to a situation where doctors say he will be in danger
if he does not eat,[25] implying that Biblical prohibitions are
not rendered completely permissible for a critically ill patient. On the other hand, Rabbi Elchanan Wasserman[26]
points out that it is only Shabbat-related prohibitions that
are rendered permissible for a critically ill patient because
of the Talmud's inference from the laws of circumcision.
Other prohibitions, such as eating meat from an animal that
was not slaughtered according to the laws of *shechitah* or
eating on Yom Kippur, are merely deferred, i.e., they are set
aside only when there is actual danger to life in forgoing the
proscribed action.[27]

From a practical standpoint, it is possible to hold that
Shabbat prohibitions are merely deferred and still follow the
Maggid Mishneh's rule that even Shabbat-prohibited procedures which may be withheld with no increased risk to the
patient may be implemented on Shabbat. The Radbaz clearly
states that Shabbat prohibitions are not completely permitted for one who is critically ill,[28] yet he is inclined to be lenient
in practice for fear that the concern to avoid performing
treatments that are not urgently required may lead one to
withhold even needed procedures, thereby endangering the
patient.[29] The *Avnei Nezer*[30] also suggests that, as with

---

25 *Yoma* 82a, Rashi: *Al pi beki'in.*

26 *Kovetz He'arot* on *Yevamot* 18:5. See also Rabbi Yishmael Hakohen, *Teshuvot Zerah Emet.*

27 That is why the *Shulchan Aruch* (*Orach Chayim* 618:7) rules that on Yom
    Kippur a critically ill patient should, if possible, eat amounts smaller than that
    which would incur culpability, even though he is not eating in the manner in
    which he is accustomed to on a weekday.

28 *Teshuvot ha-Radbaz* IV, 130.

29 Ibid. IV, 66; and *Shulchan Aruch ha-Rav* 328:4, 13.

30 *Avnei Nezer, Orach Chayim* 453:5.

circumcision, which is deferred for a slight pain in the infant's eye,[31] one may be lenient in considering the possibility that any pain or discomfort resulting from withholding a noncritical procedure may augment to the danger to the patient.

Rabbi Yosef concludes that since many authorities hold that Shabbat prohibitions are completely permitted, *hutrah*, for a critically ill patient and, according to many, this is also the Rambam's view, one should be lenient in performing procedures which relieve the patient's pain, even though there would be no clear added risk to the patient were they withheld.

---

31 *Yevamot* 71b; *Shulchan Aruch, Yoreh De'ah* 262:2.

The observant physician and Shabbat

Translated and adapted from the article
by RABBI MOSHE FEINSTEIN in *Halachah U'Refuah* I, 127-30

Ha-Gaon Rabbi Moshe Feinstein addresses practical considerations regarding the manner in which an observant physician should discharge his professional responsibilities on
Shabbat. In citing the Rambam — "Shabbat is pushed aside
(*dechuyah*), with regard to danger to life"[1] — Rabbi Feinstein
follows the *Kesef Mishneh*'s conviction that the Rambam is
of the opinion that Shabbat prohibitions are not completely
permitted (*hutrah*).[2] Yet, when actually confronted with a
patient who is critically ill, one should not seek to minimize
and avoid prohibitions in assisting the patient. The Rambam
himself cautions that, although an individual not commanded to observe Shabbat is present, the necessary procedures and treatments should not be performed "by gentiles
and minors...but by adult Jews and their wise men,"[3] lest
onlookers conclude that there is no dispensation for those
obligated to keep Shabbat and thus be reluctant to assist
patients, or tarry in seeking an alternative, when a gentile
is not present.[4] Therefore, with regard to the need to seek
permissible modes of treatment, there is no apparent practical difference between the position that Shabbat prohibitions are *dechuyah* and the view that they are *hutrah*.

However, the fact that the prohibition which is set aside is

---

1 *Hilchot Shabbat* 2:1, and *Kesef Mishneh.*

2 See "May Actions Not Directly Associated with the Saving of Life Be Performed
on Shabbat on Behalf of the Critically Ill?" in this volume. Rabbi Ovadia Yosef
there cites the *Maggid Mishneh*, who maintains that the Rambam considers
the prohibitions of Shabbat to be completely *hutrah* in this circumstance.

3 Ibid. 2:3, and *Kesef Mishneh.*

4 See "Performing Shabbat-Prohibited Acts by Means of a Non-Jew" in this
volume, for a more complete discussion of this issue by Rabbi Yehoshua
Neuwirth.

still extant suggests to Rabbi Feinstein that, although one must not hesitate to respond when confronted by an emergency, according to the Rambam, a physician should not seek to make himself available in a community where there are other doctors. The observant physician's office should be closed, his home phone number not publicized, and he should not carry a paging beeper, unless he is the only physician in the area. A physician working in a hospital should attempt to have Shabbat as his designated day off, even where there is a possibility that a non-observant Jewish physician will be given a Shabbat assignment is his stead. If he has already been scheduled for Shabbat, he should try to exchange with a non-Jew. But when a non-Jew is not available, Rabbi Feinstein further posits that the observant physician should be permitted to exchange days with a non-observant Jew, because the non-observant doctor would in any case violate the laws of Shabbat at home and, in serving hospitalized patients, he might benefit by having his Shabbat infractions take place in authorized circumstances.

On the other hand, if the observant physician must be on duty in the hospital or if a patient came to him privately for a critical matter, he is surely obligated to treat him, without considering whether the patient is a potential Shabbat observer.[5] But, as suggested by the Rebbe of Klauzenberg,[6] one should not accept payment for providing medical service on Shabbat, since one may not profit from Shabbat violations.[7] Moreover, with no possibility of financial benefit to becloud his judgment, the physician would be less likely to overestimate the gravity of the illness.

---

5 For a more complete discussion of this issue, see "Treatment of a Non-Shabbat Observer on Shabbat," in this volume. Rabbi Feinstein takes issue with the *Mishnah Berurah* (330: 8), who remonstrates against Torah-observant physicians who violate even Biblical precepts in treating those who would surely not observe Shabbat in the future. He cites the *Chatam Sofer* (*Yoreh De'ah* 131), who maintains that where enmity can lead to a threat to Jewish life, even Biblical precepts may be violated.

6 Personal communication to Rabbi Feinstein.

7 See "Compensation for Medical Treatment on Shabbat," in this volume.

The concept of danger to life as it pertains to Shabbat and to fasting on Yom Kippur

Translated and adapted from the article by RABBI SHABTAI
AVRAHAM RAPPAPORT in *Halachah U'Refuah* II, 340-46

Rabbi Rappaport discusses an apparent contradiction between the Rambam's ruling regarding the laws of Shabbat for a patient who is in danger and his decision concerning the question of feeding such a patient on Yom Kippur. In *Hilchot Shabbat*, the Rambam states that Shabbat is treated like a weekday with regard to all procedures that the patient requires.[1] As discussed earlier, according to most authorities, the Rambam's intent is to permit all procedures which will benefit the patient, even those that would not increase the risk to the patient if they were withheld. Yet, with respect to eating on Yom Kippur, the Rambam is not so lenient. He requires a seriously ill patient to indicate that he believes his life will be endangered by fasting before he can be fed.[2]

The contrast between these two rulings is even more surprising when we consider that Rashi does, in fact, restrict the permission to minister to a seriously ill patient on Shabbat to those procedures that would avert a possible life-threatening danger, although the risk need not be imminent. The Mishnah states, "If one has pain in his throat, medicine may be poured into his mouth on Shabbat, because human life may be in jeopardy and for every possible risk to human life the laws of Shabbat are suspended."[3] The Talmud notes that the Mishnah adds "'for every possible risk to life the laws of Shabbat are suspended...' [to teach that the laws are suspended] not only where there may be life-threatening

---

1 *Hilchot Shabbat* 2:2.

2 *Hilchot Shevitat he-Asor* 2:8.

3 *Yoma* 83a.

danger on this Shabbat but even in a case of possible peril on the following Shabbat.... For example, if [physicians] estimated that eight days of treatment are needed to avert the danger and the first day falls on Shabbat, one might suggest that the treatment should be delayed until nightfall so that two Shabbatot would not be profaned. The Mishnah, therefore, informs us [that the treatment starts right away]."[4] Rashi explains that the suggestion to postpone treatment until nightfall refers to a situation in which it is certain that despite the delay the patient will not die on this Shabbat but, if treatment is not initiated immediately, there is a possibility that he will succumb on the following Shabbat. But the Rambam does not require the possibility of the patient expiring the following Shabbat in order to permit the initiation of treatment on the current Shabbat. He merely states that when a patient is estimated on Shabbat to need eight days of therapy, we do not wait until the termination of Shabbat to start the treatment in order to avoid desecrating two Shabbatot but, rather, commence therapy immediately.[5] According to the Rambam, the patients current perilous condition is sufficient to warrant present violation of Shabbat, even though no added risk will result from the deferral of treatment until nightfall.

Rashi and the Rambam differ similarly in explaining the dictum of "he shall live by them [i.e., the laws of the Torah] and not die because of them,"[6] by which the Talmud teaches that in the case of danger to human life the laws of Shabbat are suspended.[7] According to Rashi, the Torah's intent is that one should surely live by observing the commandments, and not come thereby to a possibility of losing one's life, even

---

4 Ibid. 84b, Rashi: *Lo sofek Shabbat.*

5 *Hilchot Shabbat* 2:2, The Rosh and the *Shulchan Aruch* (*Orach Chayim* 328:11) rule similarly.

6 *Vayikra* 18:5.

7 *Yoma* 85b. See Rashi: *D'Shemuel.*

if the danger is not immediate.[8] However, the Rambam
maintains that the text "he shall live by them" teaches that the
laws of the Torah are not meant to be vengeful but rather
merciful, kind, and peaceful.[9] It is, therefore, forbidden to
tarry in profaning Shabbat for a patient who is in danger, since
such a delay would not be consonant with mercy, kindness,
and peacefulness, and the Torah would not prevent the
saving of another's or one's own life. Since the Rambam does
not specifically link the dictum to a situation where tarrying
might increase the risk to the patient, it is inferred that any
beneficial act may be performed, even one for which there is
no concern that the patient might die if it is not implemented.

(A subsequent ruling of the Rambam at first appears
inconsistent with his lenient approach. For the Rambam
specifies that when oil is needed on Shabbat for a woman in
childbirth, it should preferably be brought in an unusual
manner (*shinui*).[10] But if Shabbat is treated like a weekday
with regard to the needs of one who is dangerously ill,[11] then
it should not be necessary to perform the act in an unusual
manner. The *Maggid Mishneh* explains that a woman in
childbirth is a normal state of affairs and, although there is
potential danger, the majority of women do not succumb.
Therefore, for such a patient's benefit, it may be necessary
to perform the proscribed act in an unusual manner. Rabbi
Rappaport, however, differentiates between an action or
treatment which is directly for the patient's benefit and one
which is preparatory, enabling those caring for the patient
to do their duties. Thus, smearing oil on the patient directly
benefits the individual at risk, while bringing the oil through
a public domain when there is none available in the patient's

---

8 *Tosafot* (*Yoma* 85a, *Tosafot: U'lefakeach ha-gal*) similarly notes that the
Torah's intent is that under no circumstance should it be possible to cause
someone's death by observing the commandments.

9 *Hilchot Shabbat* 2:3.

10 Ibid. 2:11; and in the *Maggid Mishneh*.

11 Ibid. 2:2.

immediate vicinity merely facilitates the treatment. For actions which directly benefit the patient in peril, Shabbat is like a weekday, but for bringing the oil we must consider minimizing the violation of the laws of Shabbat wherever possible. Indeed, the Rambam requires an unusual action only for bringing oil, but not for cutting and tying the umbilical cord, or for lighting a lamp, etc. But according to Rashi and *Tosafot*, Rabbi Rappaport notes, there would be no difference between bringing oil and any other act. For they maintain that violations of Shabbat are permissible only if withholding the action would increase the risk to the patient. According to this position, if an unusual manner of performing the deed would not increase the risk to the patient, then the action should be performed in its usual fashion.)

Why does the Rambam's principle that all may be done for the benefit of a patient in danger not apply to eating on Yom Kippur? Rabbi Rappaport explains that on Yom Kippur the intent of the Torah is to promote a sense of affliction through the discomfort of hunger pangs. Fasting is the order of the day and, even when one is ill, eating is permitted *only* when fasting will endanger the individual. It is, therefore, necessary for the patient or an attending physician to declare that the patient must eat in order for him to be fed.

Similarly, with regard to a woman after childbirth the *Shulchan Aruch*[12] rules that from the third to seventh day after delivery she should not be fed automatically on Yom Kippur but only if she specifically requests to be fed.[13] On Shabbat, however, our approach is different. Unless she specifically states that she does not need it, every procedure that is usually performed for her benefit is permitted routinely, as on a weekday, because she is a patient in danger.[14]

---

12 *Orach Chayim* 617:5; see the *Dagul me-Revavah.* See also Rosh, *Yoma* 8:10.

13 The first three days after delivery she is fed routinely even if she wishes to fast, because we assume that fasting will surely endanger her life.

14 *Orach Chaim* 330:4; see also the Rambam, *Hilchot Shabbat* 2:13, and the Rosh, *Shabbat* 18:5.

Are Shabbat restrictions set aside to save a fetus?

Translated and adapted from the article
by RABBI MOSHE HERSHLER in *Halachah U'Refuah* II, 57-64

The basic principle concerning this issue is stated in the Talmud regarding a woman who dies on Shabbat in the process of giving birth: "One may bring a knife through a public domain to cut open her abdomen and take out the fetus."[1] The Talmud further explains that the novelty of the ruling is that Shabbat may be desecrated in a case of doubt, even where there is no underlying presumption of life, since the fetus may not be viable if the birth is untimely.

The *Rishonim* disagree as to the interpretation of the Talmud, for the Mishnah declares that, when a woman is in difficult labor, a fetus in the womb may be cut up and brought out piece by piece to save the mother's life. It may not be harmed only if the head or the greater part of the fetus was already delivered, since one life cannot be dismissed for the sake of another.[2] Now, if the life of a fetus while it is in the womb is of no consequence, one should not be permitted to desecrate Shabbat on its behalf. Thus, the *Shittah Mekubetzet*[3] cites an opinion that it is permissible to desecrate Shabbat to save a fetus only when its head is born, but not if it is still completely within the womb. The Ritva,[4] however, differentiates between a fetus in the womb of a dead mother, which he considers as an already-born infant lying in an inanimate container, and a fetus in a living mother. Only in the latter case would it be forbidden to

---

1 *Erachin* 7a.

2 *Oholot* 7:6.

3 *Erachin* 7b, *Shittah Mekubetzet* 1.

4 Ritva, *Niddah* 44a.

desecrate Shabbat.

Tosafot,[5] on the other hand, points out that, even if the fetus were considered as unborn and not as an infant in a container with regard to the question of culpability for killing it, one should still be permitted to profane Shabbat on its behalf. For one may desecrate Shabbat for a mortally wounded person even though there would be no culpability in a court of law for killing him. The *Shittah Mekubetzet* also cites the *Tosafot ha-Rosh*,[6] which maintains that the fetus is considered as a life in doubt, and also for a doubtful case of saving life Shabbat is desecrated.

A similar controversy is also found among the *Rishonim* regarding a pregnant woman who smells the odor of food and develops a morbid desire for it on Yom Kippur. The Mishnah states that she must be fed until she is revived.[7] The Ramban[8] points out that according to the *Halachot Gedolot*,[9] which explains that the concern is that the fetus may be aborted if she does not eat, it is evident that Shabbat may be profaned even in the absence of danger to the mother. He cites another opinion which maintains that, although Shabbat cannot be desecrated for the fetus itself, the possibility of aborting imposes a risk on the mother herself. (This opinion also concurs with the Ritva in assuming that the fetus may be rescued on Shabbat from the womb of a woman who has died during delivery, because after the death of its mother it is viewed as already delivered.)

As a basis for the *Halachot Gedolot's* position, the Ramban proposes the axiom of R. Shimon ben Menassia: "Profane [for the sake of one in danger] one Shabbat so that he may keep many Shabbatot."[10] This principle would of course

---

5 *Niddah* 44a, *Tosafot: I'hu.*

6 *Erachin* 7a, *Tosafot ha-Rosh* 5.

7 *Yoma* 82a.

8 Ibid., *Chiddushei ha-Rambam*, and *Torat ha-Adam, Inyan ha-Sakkanah.*

9 *Halachot Gedolot*, in the latter portion of the laws of Yom Kippur.

apply to a fetus as well, for the efforts to ensure the fetus's well-being will enable it to survive to observe future Shabbatot. The Ritva also mentions this principle as an additional reason for saving the fetus. Perhaps the position of the *Tosafot ha-Rosh* may be explained in a similar manner, for, although the fetus's life is in doubt, efforts to ensure its survival may enable it to observe many Shabbatot in the future.

In practice, most later authorities accept the position of the *Halachot Gedolot*. However, the *Magen Avraham*[11] cautions that Shabbat can be desecrated only for a fetus which is likely to survive. He would, therefore, differentiate between a full-term fetus and a very premature one or one afflicted with life-threatening anomalies (which currently may be diagnosed in utero using ultrasound imaging). Rabbi Hershler suggests that the *Noda bi-Yehudah's*[12] ruling that Shabbat is not to be desecrated for a fetus when there is no risk to the mother probably derives from our ignorance as to the maturity of the fetus and its likelihood for survival. For when the woman is already in labor, the *Noda bi-Yehudah* decides that Shabbat restrictions may be overridden for the sake of the fetus alone (who is presumed to be at term). Rabbi Hershler further reasons that, since the dispensation is based upon R. Shimon ben Menassia's axiom, Shabbat laws should merely be deferred (*dechuyah*) for the fetus and not be rendered completely permissible (*hutrah*), so that alternative solutions minimizing the desecration should be sought.

(As a consequence of our contemporary success in caring for premature infants, it can be argued that Shabbat should be desecrated even for preterm fetuses, on the basis of "profane one Shabbat so that he may keep many Shabbatot.")

---

10 *Yoma* 85b.

11 *Shulchan Aruch, Orach Chayim* 330, *Magen Avraham* 15.

12 *Noda bi-Yehudah* II, *Choshen Mishpat* 59.

Regarding a physician traveling to a sick person on Shabbat

Translated and adapted from the article
by RABBI YEHOSHUA NEUWIRTH in *Halachah U'Refuah* I, 160-65

Rabbi Yehoshua Neuwirth stresses that a physician who expects to be called to travel to a dangerously ill patient on Shabbat should, whenever possible, prepare what he will need before Shabbat, in order to minimize the extent of Shabbat infractions. He compares the situation to that of a traveler crossing the desert who has forgotten when Shabbat should be observed. The Talmud says that from the day the traveler becomes aware of his confusion as to the proper time, he should count six days and rest on the seventh.[1] Rava explains that since any day may, in fact, be Shabbat, the traveler may only do enough work each day to attend to his needs and to get closer to his destination. This includes the day that he sets aside as Shabbat (which is merely hallowed by *Kiddush* and *Havdalah*). But, if he knew how many days ago he left civilization, then every eighth day from that time he may do as much work as he pleases, since he surely did not set out on Shabbat.[2] The authorities rule that in the latter case, if the traveler is able to take care of his needs for the entire week by working on every eighth day (the day of his departure on each recurring weekly cycle), it would be forbidden for him to work on any other day, lest it be Shabbat.[3]

Similarly, a soldier who is commanded to complete a task by the end of Shabbat must not rely upon the fact that a

---

1 *Shabbat* 69b.

2 By extension, if he knew he did not set out on Friday, he may also treat the ninth day of each cycle as a regular weekday.

3 *Mishnah Berurah* 344:11.

military command may defer the laws of Shabbat, but should make every effort to complete the task prior to the onset of Shabbat.[4] A pregnant woman approaching delivery is also advised to prepare every Friday for possible delivery on Shabbat, so as to minimize desecration of the holy day.[5]

From these rulings Rabbi Neuwirth infers that a doctor who is *on duty* in a hospital on Shabbat must remain at the hospital, since he will surely be called for one of the many critically ill patients who are hospitalized. If, however, he did not remain at the hospital and is called, he is surely permitted to travel to attend to a patient who is at risk, even though he has, at the outset, breached the demand that he not be far from the hospital.[6]

On the other hand, a doctor *on call* is not certain that he will be needed to treat a patient who is in danger and, therefore, is not required to abandon his family to remain in the hospital. However, it is preferable for physicians who are called to the hospital frequently to live in the vicinity, to avoid the recurring problem of desecrating Shabbat.

With regard to traveling to see a patient who is not required to observe Shabbat, Rabbi Neuwirth is of the opinion that, since the Talmud establishes the principle that one may desecrate Shabbat only for those who observe it, wherever possible an observant physician should try to avoid being placed in such a situation.[7] To avoid antagonism, it is permitted to violate Shabbat to attend to such a patient, but the authorities differ as to whether this applies only to

---

4 Ibid., *Sha'ar ha-Tziyun* 9.

5 *Mishnah Berurah* 330:1.

6 Similarly, it is preferable to defer a circumcision until after Shabbat if one has not prepared all that is needed for the procedure. Yet, if the *mohel* performed the procedure despite his lack of preparation, he may subsequently treat the infant who is in peril because of the operation (ibid. 331:24; *Iggrot Moshe, Orach Chayim* 131).

7 *Avodah Zarah* 25a. See also "The Observant Physician and Shabbat," and "Treatment of a Non-Shabbat Observer on Shabbat," in this volume.

Rabbinical restrictions[8] or even to Biblical precepts.[9] The *Penei Yehoshua* suggests that violating a Biblical precept to avoid physical harm or danger to oneself could be considered an action performed not for the defined purpose of the work categories involved but for an incidental benefit, and this would be forbidden only by Rabbinical edict.[10] However, a physician who can avoid desecrating Shabbat and chooses not to do so is considered culpable for his transgressions.[11]

It can be argued that the principle of authorizing desecration of Shabbat only for the sake of those who will observe it in the future should not extend to Jews who flaunt their habitual violation of Shabbat in public.[12] However, the *Chelkat Ya'akov* suggests that since it is permitted to violate Shabbat even when there is only doubt of danger, we should take into consideration the possibility that a Jew who is seriously ill may have thought of repentance.[13] In addition, he offers a number of other considerations for leniency: one whose Shabbat work is not agricultural in nature or one who is sufficiently embarrassed not to desecrate Shabbat in the presence of a Rabbi might not be considered a public violator of Shabbat; the possibility that equating Shabbat violators with those not required to observe Shabbat is only by Rabbinic edict, and that the comparison may not extend to a Jew who has never been properly educated to understand the gravity of violating Shabbat. At the present time, since most

---

8 *Mishnah Berurah* 330:8.

9 *Chatam Sofer, Yoreh De'ah* 131; *Divrei Chayim* II, 25; *Darchei Teshuvah, Yoreh De'ah* 154:9.

10 Novellae, *Shabbat* 72b. This is so particularly if the doctor accepts no compensation. Rabbi Yosef Colon (*Teshuvot Maharik* 137) adopts a similar position. (See "Treatment of a Non-Shabbat Observer on Shabbat," in this volume.)

11 *Mishnah Berurah* 330:400. See also *Chattam Sofer* VI, 194. The *Mishnah Berurah* (656:10) stresses that a physician is surely not permitted to violate Shabbat merely to avoid losing his livelihood.

12 *Mishnah Berurah* 329:9; *Peri Megadim* 328:6.

13 *Chelkat Yaakov* I, 45.

non-observant Jews have not been properly instructed concerning religious matters, we may consider them halachically as equivalent to Jewish children who had been taken
captive and raised by gentiles.[14] Although they habitually
violate Shabbat, nevertheless observant Jews are commanded to sustain them and, therefore, if necessary, even to
desecrate Shabbat for their benefit.

---

14 *Chazon Ish, Yoreh De'ah* 13:28.

Accompanying a patient to the hospital on Shabbat

Translated and adapted from the article
by RABBI CHAIM PORUSH in *Halachah U'Refuah* II, 239-44

In considering whether a relative may accompany a patient traveling to the hospital on Shabbat, Rabbi Porush notes that when the companion is needed to aid the patient, to arrange for medical care, or merely to hasten his treatment, there is no doubt that it is permissible and even required. The question arises when the patient is merely fearful to travel alone. May one violate Shabbat to accompany him?

The Talmud rules that, when the donor demands it, it is permissible on Shabbat to perform a *kinyan*, a formal act of acquisition, to transfer a gift from one who is lying ill and is in fear of dying to the recipient [even though the Rabbis forbade business transactions on Shabbat],...because of the possibility that the dying man's condition may deteriorate if he were to become anxious at the thought that his oral instructions were insufficient and he would have no opportunity to distribute his possessions.[1] The Rashbam and *Tosafot* explain that this ruling applies both when the donor distributes all his possessions [and formal acquisition accomplishes nothing, for the Rabbis ruled that a dying man's oral commands are as legally effective as a conventional *kinyan*] and when the sick man retains a portion of his estate [indicating his expectation to survive], in which case a *kinyan* by the recipient is necessary [as the Rabbis did not grant the donor any special consideration]. The Rosh, however,

---

1 *Bava Batra* 156b-157a. See the commentaries of the Rashbam, *Tosafot,* and the Rosh. The situations where special consideration is given to an ill person distributing his belongings include one who states that he expects to die soon, whether or not he specifies that this is his motivation for giving the gift, and one whose illness has taken a serious turn for the worse and it is clear that he is anticipating death, even though he makes no mention of it.

declares that the leniency of making the *kinyan* on Shabbat permitted by the Talmud does not apply when the estate is only partially distributed, for the Sages had no concern regarding possible mental anguish when the sick man expects to live.

The Rambam,[2] however, reasons that since, in reality, legal acquisition is not needed [for a dying man to distribute his possessions], if he requested that they be acquired by the recipient through a usual act of *kinyan*, we may do so even on Shabbat, for the act is meaningless, as it accomplishes nothing. But the *Lechem Mishneh* cautions that, according to the Rambam, legal acquisition could not be performed on Shabbat in a situation where it would be efficacious and is required to transfer the gift. The *Shulchan Aruch* similarly states, "If [a dying man] requested that his possessions be acquired from him legally, we do so even on Shabbat, because such acquisition [is a sham] as it is not necessary."[3]

Apparently the Rashbam, *Tosafot*, and the Rosh hold that it is permissible to violate a Rabbinic prohibition [that of acquisition on Shabbat] for the sake of the dying man's peace of mind, while the Rambam and the *Shulchan Aruch* maintain that it is not allowed. But, if so, why does the *Shulchan Aruch* rule that it is permitted to send a non-Jew outside the Shabbat limits (*techum*) to call relatives when it is requested by one who is very sick, even though this would normally be restricted by Rabbinic rule?[4] The *Magen Avraham* adds that one may even hire the non-Jew to go, so that the patient will not suffer mental anguish.[5]

Rabbi Porush suggests that, according to the Rambam and the Shulchan Aruch, valid legal acquisition is not per-

---

2 *Hilchot Zechiyah u'Mattanah* 8:3, and in the *Lechem Mishneh*.

3 *Choshen Mishpat* 254.

4 *Orach Chayim* 306:9.

5 *Magen Avraham*, note 18. Rabbenu Simchah is also quoted as having permitted the hiring of a person to call his relatives (see the gloss on the Rosh, *Bava Batra* 156b, and in the *Mordechai, Shabbat* 3:314).

mitted for a dying man because the circumstances where legal acquisition is required are such that we suspect that the patient does not really expect to die. Since we do not anticipate that he will become disturbed enough to aggravate his condition, an action on the part of a Jew, even one proscribed only by Rabbinic ordinance, cannot be permitted. However, the Rabbinic prohibition of asking a non-Jew to perform a Shabbat violation can be allowed, since it does not involve direct physical action on the part of a Jew.

From this discussion, one might assume that violation of a Biblical Shabbat prohibition for a patient's peace of mind would surely be forbidden. Yet the Talmud rules that when a blind woman in confinement says she needs the lamp lit, her companion may kindle it for her. Even though the blind woman cannot see the light, we permit it to "put her mind at ease, as she reasons [that the light is helpful], for if anything will be required, my friend will [more readily] take notice and do it for me."[6] It is, in fact, generally accepted by the authorities that even Biblical prohibitions are permitted to put a seriously ill patient's mind at ease. Indeed, the Rambam rules that for a patient who is dangerously ill, we view Shabbat "as though it were a weekday regarding all the things [the patient] needs."[7] The *Maggid Mishneh* adds, "even if withholding the thing that is being done for him would put him in no danger." The *Shulchan Aruch* rules similarly.[8] Why then do we require a non-Jew to call the relatives for one who is ill?

Rabbi Porush, therefore, suggests that the ruling allowing a gentile to call the relatives of an individual who is seriously ill concerns one who is not yet in danger but is fearful that he may die without his relatives being present. In this instance, it is permitted to hire a gentile to bring

---

6   *Shabbat* 128b, see *Tosafot.*

7   *Hilchot Shabbat* 2:2, and also *Maggid Mishneh.*

8   *Orach Chayim* 328:4, and also the *Magen Avraham.*

them, but they should not set out to come until after Shabbat. However, for a critically ill patient there is no doubt that relatives may violate Biblical prohibitions by coming to his bedside on Shabbat.[9] Thus, it would similarly be permissible to accompany a patient to the hospital on Shabbat when the patient requests it for his or her peace of mind.

However, the *Mishnah Berurah* notes[10] that many authorities rule that, for a Jew to override the restrictions of Shabbat for a patient in danger, the proscribed action must be one which is needed to prevent aggravation of the illness. But something which, though required and usually done for the patient, would not endanger him were it not done, is permitted only by a non-Jew. In a similar vein, Ha-Gaon Rabbi Moshe Feinstein suggests that a woman traveling to the hospital to deliver a baby should not be accompanied by her husband or mother merely for the purpose of allaying her fears of traveling alone, since this fear is unwarranted and foolish.[11]

Other authorities are more lenient,[12] depending upon the estimation of the patient's yearning to see the individual to be called and the extent to which it will disturb the patient if the relative is not at the bedside. If possible, one should calm the patient while reminding him of the Shabbat violations that may be involved in bringing the relatives. But even Rabbi Feinstein, in the above-cited responsum, concludes that when the woman remains fearful after it is explained that accompanying her is unnecessary, her husband or mother must travel with her, lest her mental anguish place her in danger. The *Chazon Ish*[13] offers a broader dispensa-

---

9 See *Yaskil Avdi* VII, *Orach Chayim* 22:3. Also *Aruch ha-Shulchan* 306:20.

10 *Orach Chayim* 328, *Mishnah Berurah* 14 and *Biur Halachah: Kol she-regelim.*

11 *Iggrot Moshe, Orach Chayim* 132. Rabbi Feinstein contrasts this fear with the realistic concern of giving birth in the dark, when the midwife says she can perform her tasks even in the absence of light. In the latter case, it is surely permitted to light a lamp for the sake of the woman in labor.

12 See *Teshuvot Maharsham* IV, 54; *Teshuvot Sho'el u'Meshiv*, 3rd series, II, 180; and *Chemdat ha-Nefesh* 1.

tion, maintaining that it is permissible for anyone who has the patient's confidence to accompany him to the hospital for the patient's peace of mind, even when the patient does not request it.

---

13 See Rabbi Y. Neuwirth, *Shemirat Shabbat k'Hilchatah* 2nd ed. (Jerusalem, 5739), 40:70, which cites the *Chazon Ish* (*Iggrot* I, 141).

Treatment of a non-Shabbat observer on Shabbat

Translated and adapted from the articles in *Halachah U'Refuah* I
by RABBI OVADIA YOSEF (pp. 147-50) and
by RABBI MOSHE FEINSTEIN (p.127)

As a consequence of the gravity attached to the violation of Shabbat, it was necessary for the Sages to substantiate the basis for setting aside its laws when life is in jeopardy.[1] Among the reasons cited in the Talmud is that of R. Shimon ben Menassia, who deduces from the verse "And the Children of Israel shall keep the Shabbat"[2] that the Torah permits a Jew to profane Shabbat for the sake of one who is critically ill, in order that the patient may recover and have the opportunity to observe many Shabbatot in the future.

This principle, that permission to violate Shabbat should apply only to individuals who may potentially observer future Shabbatot, is stated clearly in the Talmud in reference to the question of whether a Jewish midwife may see to the delivery of an idol worshiper on Shabbat.[3] R. Yosef (the *Amora*) held that a Jewish midwife may attend to the idol worshiper to avoid generating ill will, since the heathen woman knows that this service is rendered to Jewish women on Shabbat. Abaya, however, maintained that the midwife should explain that Jews are permitted to violate Shabbat only for people who will keep Shabbat in the future, but for those who do not observe Shabbat, we may not waive its restrictions. Yet, even according to Abaya, where it is unlikely that the explanation would be accepted, one would be permitted to attend to a heathen on

---

1 *Yoma* 85a.

2 *Shemot* 31:16.

3 *Avodah Zarah* 26a.

Shabbat to avoid ill will.[4]

Tosafot posits that permission to desecrate Shabbat to avoid enmity applies only to Rabbinical precepts. Indeed, the *Mishnah Berurah*[5] inveighs against the Torah observant physicians who violate even Biblical precepts in treating those who would surely not observe Shabbat in the future. But Rabbi Ovadia Yosef notes that the *Divrei Chayim*[6] states that the Council of Four Lands[7] promulgated an edict that Jewish doctors be allowed to violate even Biblical precepts in treating non-Jews. Rabbi Moshe Feinstein is also astounded at the *Mishnah Berurah*'s position, citing the *Chatam Sofer*, who clearly states that where there may be threat to Jewish life as a result of enmity, even Biblical precepts may be violated.[8]

Yet, how could the Council of Four Lands and the *Chatam Sofer* rule contrary to the Talmud and *Rishonim*? Rabbi Ovadia Yosef points out that according to Rabbi Yosef Colon[9] when one violates a Biblical precept in order to escape bodily harm and death, the act is considered as not being intended for its defined purpose but, rather, for an incidental benefit (*melachah she-einah tzrichah l'gufah*) and, according to most authorities, it is, therefore, forbidden only by Rabbinical edict.[10] Thus, Rabbi Colon maintains that when a Jew

---

4 Ibid., *Tosafot*; *Sovar Rav Yosef*.

5 *Mishnah Berurah* 330:8.

6 *Divrei Chayim* II, *Orach Chayim* 25.

7 Great Poland, Little Poland, Podolia with Galicia, and Volhynia. This central organization of the Jewish communities was active in the seventeenth and the first half of the eighteenth century.

8 *Yoreh De'ah* 131.

9 *Teshuvot Maharik* 137. The *Penei Yehoshua* (Novellae, *Shabbat* 72b) takes a similar position (see "Regarding a Physician Traveling to a Sick Person on Shabbat," in this volume).

10 Most authorities rule according to R. Shimon, who holds that one is not culpable for an action which is intended not for its defined purpose but, rather, for an incidental benefit (Rashba, *Shabbat* 84; Ravad, comments on the Rambam, *Hilchot Shabbat* 1:7; Ramban, end of *Shabbat*; *Tosafot* and the Rosh,

is threatened with death for refusing to cook a dish for a heathen on Shabbat,[11] the labor of cooking is no longer forbidden by Biblical law, because the Jew does not intend to prepare a dish for eating, but only to satisfy his intimidator. Rabbi Ovadia Yosef suggests that the edict of the Council of Four Lands followed the same reasoning. Since a Shabbat-observant physician is required by secular law to treat everyone equally, without regard to creed, the procedures involved in the treatment can be viewed as intended for the incidental benefit of avoiding governmental censure for withholding services, and not for the defined purpose of the work categories involved. Any Shabbat transgressions which come about as a result of the treatment would no longer be prohibited by Biblical law, and where it is possible that his refusal to provide services may provoke life-threatening hostility, the provision of services on Shabbat would surely be permitted.[12]

Rabbi Moshe Feinstein takes this reasoning one step further and suggests that the very intent of the promulgation of the Council of Four Lands was, in fact, to permit Shabbat-observant physicians to be lenient with Biblical transgressions, even in a locality where there would be no menace to life as a result of animosity. For there is concern that in their anxiousness not to violate Biblical law, the physicians may err in being more stringent, even in situations where enmity may lead to physical danger.

Shabbat 135a; and Shulchan Aruch, Orach Chayim 330). The Rambam, however, decides in favor of R. Yehudah, that one is liable by Biblical decree even for an action which is not intended for its defined purpose (Hilchot Shabbat 1). The Mishnah Berurah is also uncertain as to whether the Shulchan Aruch follows R. Shimon (Biur Halachah 317), but Rabbi Ovadia Yosef maintains that the evidence is overwhelmingly in favor of this conclusion.

11 Yevamot 121b.

12 Authorities who follow the reasoning of Rabbi Yosef Colon include the Maharam Shik (IV, 20), Rabbi Meshulam Rath (Kol Mevasser 79), Rabbi Shlomo Kluger (Chemdat Shlomo 332), Rabbi Amram Blum (Beit She'arim), and others.

Performing Shabbat-prohibited acts by means of a non-Jew

Translated and adapted from the article
by RABBI YEHOSHUA NEUWIRTH in *Halachah U'Refuah* II, 199-204

Our Sages have established that it is an obligation to violate the laws of Shabbat for one who is dangerously ill.[1] It is further stressed that necessary violations are not to be performed by "gentiles and minors, but by prominent Jews; nor do we say that we perform these actions on the advice of women or the advice of Cutheans, but their opinions are combined with those of others."[2]

Rashi explains the latter statement to mean that when two knowledgeable people say it is necessary to profane Shabbat and three say it is not, if a woman or Cuthean also says it is necessary, that opinion is added to the two affirmative decisions to become three against three, at which point the more lenient view is adopted, because of the possible life-threatening peril. However, we do not rely upon the sole affirmative opinion of a woman or Cuthean, even in the absence of a dissenting view. The *Tosafot ha-Rosh* is puzzled by Rashi's explanation, for the Talmud (and Rashi) declares earlier[3] that, in a case where there is risk to human life, two in the affirmative are sufficient to negate even one hundred contrary opinions. The *Tosafot ha-Rosh*, therefore, slightly alters Rashi's explanation, in the following manner: If three or four say Shabbat violation is not necessary and one says

---

1 *Yoma* 85b (from the verse "and he shall live by them [the mitzvot]" [*Vayikra* 18:5] and not die by them, following Rabba, who maintains that this is the principal derivation of the dispensation). *Shulchan Aruch, Orach Chayim* 328:2; Rambam, *Hilchot Shabbat* 2:3.

2 *Yoma* 84b. See the commentaries of Rashi, *Tosafot ha-Rosh*, the Ramban, the Rosh, the Rif, and the Ran.

3 *Yoma* 83a, Rashi: *D'amar R. Safra.*

it is, the opinion of a woman or Cuthean in the affirmative can join with the other affirmative view, and since there would then be two affirmative opinions, we do not follow those who take the opposing viewpoint, even though they are more numerous.

The Ramban and the Rosh are troubled by a more basic question. Why should we not follow the sole opinion of a woman who is expert in matters concerning endangerment of life, just as we violate Shabbat for a woman in childbirth on the opinion of a midwife? The Rosh[4] therefore, prefers the text of the Rif: "Nor do we say that we should perform these acts through the agency of women or Cutheans, because they may adhere to another [fallacious] opinion."[5] The *Beit Yosef*[6] explains that women and Cutheans, being generally unlearned, will conclude that Shabbat cannot be violated in order to save a life, and the tasks are asked of them because no one cares if they violate Shabbat. They may, therefore, tarry in their duties, thereby endangering the life of the patient. The *Beit Yosef* further notes that concern lest the patient be placed in danger by tarrying is the reason *Tosafot*[7] offers for also not using gentiles or minors. However, the Rosh explains that if we use gentiles or minors when they are available, we might conclude that it is preferable to seek them out even when they are not present, thereby delaying the treatment of the endangered patient.

The Rambam cites this ruling in a somewhat different fashion: "These [Shabbat violations] are not performed by

---

4 *Yoma* 84, note 14.

5 The Talmud's original "on the advice of (*al pi*)" is rendered as "through the agency of (*al yedei*)," and the original "but their opinions are combined (*aval mitzarfin*)" is put as "because they may adhere to (*mipnei she-mitzarfin*)" in the Rif's text. The Rosh also records a variant text of the Riva: "Nor do we *not* rely on the opinions of women and Cutheans, but they *can even* link their opinions to that of another to negate opposing views of men."

6 *Tur, Orach Chayim* 328, *Beit Yosef: V'ein osin.*

7 *Yoma* 84b, *Tosafot: Ella bigedolei.* See also *Shulchan Aruch, Orach Chayim* 328:12.

gentiles and minors, who are not obligated to uphold Shabbat, nor by slaves or women, so that Shabbat shall not be treated lightly by them."[8] With regard to employing gentiles and minors, we are concerned that bystanders might deduce that, for those obligated to keep Shabbat, it is not permissible to violate it at the outset, even to save a life, so that they may be reluctant to violate Shabbat even when gentiles or minors may not be found. But with regard to women, we are concerned that they may extend the leniency to violate Shabbat even where no danger to life exists.

According to the Rambam, the necessary violations of Shabbat should always be performed by adult Jews and learned individuals, to demonstrate that desecration of Shabbat is permissible only to save a life. But following the *Beit Yosef*'s explanation of the Rosh, that the reason for not employing women is that they may delay as a result of their reluctance to perform services they suspect are not really permitted on Shabbat, Rabbi Neuwirth argues that when an adult male Jew works side by side with them, their services should be employed, because it will be clear to them that it is permissible for everyone to violate Shabbat to save a life.[9] Rabbi Neuwirth further stresses that nurses in a hospital, who have specifically obligated themselves to save lives, should surely be under no suspicion of tarrying in performing their duties on Shabbat.[10]

If the reason for not employing gentiles and minors is concern lest at another time treatment would be delayed to seek them out, this rationale may not apply to services which are necessary but not immediately urgent.[11] Indeed, Rabbi Neuwirth maintains that, even for a critically ill patient, it

---

8 *Hilchot Shabbat* 2:3. See the *Maggid Mishneh* and *Kesef Mishneh*.

9 This point is, in fact, suggested by the Ran in his commentary on the Rif.

10 See the *Ketzot ha-Shulchan* 135, and the *Badei ha-Shulchan* 9.

11 See the *Aruch ha-Shulchan* 328:28; *Mishnah Berurah* 330:21, 328:14; and B*iur Halachah* 328: *Kol she-regelim*.

is preferable for a non-Jew to perform routine duties which are not very pressing, such as recording the patient's temperature. He recommends that, in a hospital which operates according to halachah, a non-Jew should be available to perform such duties, even in the intensive-care unit, where only critically ill patients are found.

The *Shiltei Giborim*,[12] however, does not differentiate between very urgent services and duties which are necessary but less immediately required. He states as a general principle, "If gentiles or minors are available, the services must be performed by them, and Shabbat should not be violated through the actions of adult Jews. Since it is possible to perform the services in a permissible manner, we must not do them in a prohibited fashion." On this authority the Rama rules[13] that, whenever possible, the services should be performed in an indirect manner or by a gentile, if there is no danger of tarrying.

---

12 On *Yoma*, the Rif 4b:2, citing the Riaz. See also Me'iri, *Yoma* 84b.

13 *Shulchan Aruch, Orach Chayim* 328:12. With regard to performing procedures in an indirect manner (*shinui*), see *Shabbat* 133a and b, and *Tosafot: Lo'es*.

On a physician's obligation to consider the patient's own assessment of the seriousness of his illness on Shabbat

Translated and adapted from the article
by RABBI ISAAC SILBERSTEIN in *Halachah U'Refuah* I, 182-83

Rabbi Isaac Silberstein deals with the halachic responsibility of a physician to concern himself with the suspicions of a patient regarding the gravity of his or her illness. He posits two situations: one, where the doctor has thoroughly examined the patient and finds nothing serious, yet the patient is adamant that there is something amiss internally; the other, where the doctor has no opportunity to examine the patient who is telephoning, yet the doctor, who is familiar with the patient's medical history, is certain that the symptoms are related to a previous complaint and the patient is in no present danger, despite the patient's claim that the current symptoms are markedly different. In both cases he presumes that the patient is demanding that the physician violate Shabbat to provide a house call.

With respect to Yom Kippur, the Talmud[1] states that we follow the demands of a sick person to eat on the holiday even though the urgency is negated by a physician, because the one who is ill is best able to appreciate his "grief." The *Shiltei Giborim*[2] is uncertain whether this principle applies only to eating or to other necessities as well. But the *Biur Halachah*[3] rules that when a person complains of malfunction of a particular organ and demands a particular treatment, we adhere to his request even when a physician maintains that no treatment is needed. However, when it is a clear-cut,

---

1 *Yoma* 83b.

2 Ibid.

3 *Biur Halachah, Orach Chayim* 328.

well-recognized illness, and the physician claims that the therapy demanded by the patient will not avail, then we defer to the greater expertise of the physician. On the other hand, if the patient is certain that he will be helped by a specific therapeutic regimen, due to a particular variation in his nature which differs from other individuals, then perhaps we should follow the directions of the patient even when they are contradicted by a physician.

Rabbi Silberstein suggests that the *Biur Halachah* must be referring to a situation where the patient is complaining about pains arising from an internal organ, yet the examining physician finds nothing amiss. In this instance, it is possible that the physician was unsuccessful in probing the organ system involved so as to discern the illness. However, when the physician is able to examine the organs involved thoroughly, and by the symptoms and signs it is *clear* to him that the patient is in no danger, then the physician is not obligated to concern himself with the persisting doubts of the patient.

With regard to the second circumstance, where there is no opportunity for the physician to examine the patient who is telephoning, we may be inclined to apply the comments of the Ramban concerning a woman who is more than seven days after delivery. The Ramban[4] explains that the Talmud rules that after the seventh day we do not heed the woman's request to heat water on Shabbat, because she is not claiming that she is now suffering from another illness other than the normal consequence of delivery, and for postpartum management our Sages have established that she would be in no danger if she were not able to have heated water after the seventh day. But he adds, "Were I not afraid of expressing so daring an idea before my masters, I would comment [that this is the case when she says] I need to wash [with hot water], but if she specifically ordered that Shabbat be violated for her, then even on the thirtieth postnatal day [when

---

4 *Chiddushei ha-Ramban, Shabbat* 128b.

she is in a lesser degree of danger] we would desecrate Shabbat on her behalf."

Perhaps, Rabbi Silberstein suggests, a physician similarly might be required to violate Shabbat in traveling to see a patient who specifically demands the visit, even though the physician is certain that it is not necessary. On the other hand, a woman who maintains she is still in danger on the thirtieth day after delivery is not comparable to the patient who telephones on Shabbat. In the former case there is no doctor who contradicts her assessment, but if a doctor were present and negated the woman's contention, the Ramban would surely be unwilling to gainsay "his masters" by maintaining that we should heed her wishes. Thus, Rabbi Silberstein concludes, when the doctor is *certain* that the patient's complaints derive from no new illness or complication, there is no halachic obligation for him to violate Shabbat on the patient's behalf.

The patient's feelings as a basis for halachic decisions on Shabbat

Translated and adapted from the article
by DR. DOV EHRLICH in *Halachah U'Refuah* I, 195-98

In the practice of medicine, much importance is attached to the words and feelings of the patient. Physicians in training are urged over and over again to pay heed to what the patient is saying — with regard to both establishing the correct diagnosis and evaluating the patient's condition in order to select the optimal treatment. Indeed, with regard to eating on Yom Kippur, the Talmud states, "If the patient says, 'I require food' and a physician says he does not, we heed the patient."[1]

Yet Dr. Dov Ehrlich cautions against attaching too much importance to the patient's comments and feelings. A good clinician cannot rely totally upon the information proffered. He must extract the pertinent features and discard the irrelevant and inadvertently twisted details. It is not unusual for the history or symptoms offered by the patient to be embellished with knowledge gathered from the media.

Pain is one of the symptoms for which there is no alternative but to accept the words of the patient. Yet pain is one of the most subjective of symptoms. It is impossible to measure objectively the quality and intensity of pain, and its perception and tolerance depend on the psychological makeup of the individual. No physician can determine accurately how much pain another individual feels. Thus, in deciding whether to override halachic restrictions on Shabbat because of severe pain, we must turn to the patient and not the doctor. In some situations, such as an attack of chest pains, the doctor must presume on the basis of the patient's

---

1 *Yoma* 83a.

complaint that there exists a danger to life, until the possibility of a heart attack is excluded by further examination and laboratory tests.

Hunger and extreme anxiety (possibly what our Sages referred to as *tiruf da'at*[2]) are also subjective perceptions. Yet it is recognized that these feelings may engender markedly adverse psychological and physiological reactions in an individual, surely in one who already is ill. We have mentioned above that on Yom Kippur we feed a patient on the basis of his own opinion as to the severity of his illness. With respect to Shabbat, the Rambam[3] rules that to calm a patient in danger it is permitted to mutter incantations over a snake bite or a scorpion sting, although the procedure is of no therapeutic value. Interestingly, there are circumstances where a patient requests a particular treatment and, although it is not appropriate logically or medically, the therapy proves beneficial. Dr. Ehrlich has observed this not infrequently in patients with asthma attacks, which are well known to have a significant psychosomatic component.

Dr. Ehrlich's comments on subjective criteria amplify the difficulties Rabbi Silberstein considers regarding the physician's obligation to take into account the patient's own assessment of his illness. These observations strengthen the conviction that the patient must be given the benefit of the doubt unless the physician is *certain* that the patient is in no danger.

---

2 *Avot d'Rabbi Natan* 25:2.

3 *Hilchot Avodat Kochavim* 11:1.

Taking blood and giving injections on Shabbat

Translated and adapted from the article
by AARON BUCHMAN in *Halachah U'Refuah* I, 219-30

The origin of the prohibition against making a wound on Shabbat lies in the Mishnah: "With regard to the eight *sheratzim*[1] which are mentioned in the Torah, one who captures them or wounds them [on Shabbat] is culpable...."[2] The *Rishonim* disagree as to the reason for the prohibition against wounding. Most hold that by causing blood to escape, injuring is equated with the taking of life, which is subsumed under the major work category of slaughtering.[3] In these animals the skin covering is tougher than the underlying flesh and in order for one to be culpable the blood need not ooze from the body, for as soon as a bruise is evident, blood has congealed beneath the skin and is irreversibly removed from the circulation.[4] Others suggest that, by causing the congealed blood to color the overlying skin, the perpetrator has transgressed the prohibition against dyeing, a different major category of forbidden work.[5] The Me'iri suggests that the link between dyeing and wounding is not meant to negate the underlying culpability for taking a life but,

---

1 These *sheratzim* are small animals which convey *tumah*-contamination when they are dead (*Vayikra* 11:29 30).

2 *Shabbat* 107a.

3 Ramban, Rashba, Me'iri, Ritva, *Tosafot ha-Rosh*, and the *Chiddushei ha-Ran* on the Talmud. See also *Ketubbot* 5b, *Tosafot: Mifkad,* and *Shabbat* 75a, *Tosafot: Ki heichi.* This follows the Biblical principle that life resides in the blood of an animal. One is culpable even if only one drop escapes as a result of the injury, for this is equated with the taking of part of a life.

4 *Shabbat* 107. See *Tosafot* and other *Rishonim.*

5 *Shabbat* 107, Rashi. See also the discussion in the Talmud as to whether a ritual slaughterer would be culpable on Shabbat for dyeing as well as for taking of life, since he also intends to induce a bright red color in the region of the knife wound, indicative of a freshly slaughtered animal (*Shabbat* 75a).

rather, to indicate that in some instances one may be culpable for both work categories.

The Rambam holds that wounding separates (*mefarek*) the blood from the flesh, an act which is a species of threshing, yet another major category of forbidden work.[6] According to the Rambam one could argue that the offender would be liable for *mefarek* not only by wounding a living person but even when blood was withdrawn from a corpse, since the prohibition of *mefarek* does not require life to be taken.[7] On the other hand, the Rambam would posit that culpability for the taking of life on Shabbat may be charged only when the injured party dies as a result of the wound, or when a living person's limb is severed and a portion of both his flesh and blood is removed. But it may be argued that if the limb was detached in a manner which avoided bleeding, one might not have transgressed the prohibition against wounding if the reason is based upon the act of *mefarek*. It is also possible that when the injured party is a *tereifah*, i.e., afflicted with a fatal organic disease, one could not be liable for inflicting a wound by reason of taking a life, since the injured party is already considered nonviable,[8] but as to the prohibition of separating blood from flesh, there would be no difference.

Now, with regard to prohibited work on Shabbat, the Mishnah establishes a principle that for one to be guilty the action must produce an improvement or benefit, but a deed which merely causes damage would not be punishable.[9]

---

6 *Hilchot Shabbat* 8:6. The blood need not ooze from the body. As long as it was removed from its usual place, even if only congealed beneath the skin, it would be similar to *mefarek* (see *Teshuvot R. Avraham ben ha-Rambam* in *Birchat Avraham* 18). Although threshing applies only to plants which grow from the earth, the Rambam posits that the subcategory of *mefarek* would apply to animals and humans, for they also derive their sustenance from the earth, albeit indirectly (see *Minchat Chinnuch*, commandment 32).

7 *Peri Megadim, Eshel Avraham, Orach Chayim* 317:15.

8 *Minchat Chinnuch*, commandment 32, *Melechet Shochet*.

9 Mishnah, *Shabbat* 105b.

There is a disagreement in the Talmud[10] as to whether this principle applies to wounding, i.e., is wounding a special case for which one is culpable merely for damaging another, or is it necessary that some benefit be derived from the act? Most *Rishonim* rule that one is culpable for wounding even without the element of benefit.[11] The Rambam, on the other hand, maintains that it is, in fact, necessary to derive some benefit even from the act of wounding in order to be liable.[12] Despite this position, the Rambam does not limit culpability in wounding to a circumstance where there was an intent to use the blood which separated from the flesh (conforming to *mefarek*), for although the one who inflicts the wound merely aims to do damage, there is nevertheless an implicit benefit in his action since he thereby assuages his rage.[13]

When analyzed within this framework, many medical procedures which appear merely destructive or damaging in nature are, in fact, beneficial or reparative when they are performed for therapeutic or diagnostic purposes, and they should not be performed on a patient who is not in life-threatening danger.[14] This is particularly true when it would be impossible to produce an improvement without the initial damaging action, e.g., incising an abscess for drainage.[15] Furthermore, it is not necessary that the forbidden act be

---

10 *Shabbat* 106a.

11 Following the opinion of R. Shimon, who infers this from the necessity for the Torah to allow circumcision on Shabbat. See Rashi, *Tosafot, Terumat ha-Deshen* 265, and *Tur, Choshen Mishpat* 424.

12 The Rambam follows R. Yehudah rather than R. Shimon in ruling that one is liable for work which is not intended for its defined purpose (*melachah she-einah tzerichah l'gufah*) but merely to produce an extraneous result, e.g., extinguishing a lamp to spare the oil (*Hilchot Shabbat* 1:7). The Rambam, therefore, also follows R. Yehudah in ruling that one who merely causes damage (*mekalkel*) is not liable where there is no benefit.

13 *Hilchot Shabbat* 8:6.

14 *Shabbat* 105b. The Mishnah states that one who damages in order to repair is liable.

15 See the Me'iri, *Shabbat* 105a.

intrinsically medically related, for any action which facilitates medical treatment would be considered beneficial. Thus the Talmud states that one is culpable for transporting an undesirable malodorous substance from a private domain into the public domain, even though the bearer has no need for the material and merely wishes to clear his premises, because the substance may later be used to prepare incense for sick people.[16]

On the other hand, medical benefit is not sufficient to prohibit an act on behalf of one who is not seriously ill when the proscribed outcome was not intended. One may, therefore, use a needle to remove a thorn on Shabbat, although it may inadvertently cause bleeding.[17] More recently, others have ruled that lancing a blister[18] or administering subcutaneous or intramuscular injections[19] should not be prohibited merely because of possible bleeding, since the presence of blood is an undesired consequence.[20]

With intravenous injections, a small amount of blood is frequently drawn back into the syringe or tubing, to verify the position of the needle or the catheter. This cannot be considered an entirely undesirable occurrence. Indeed, blood which is withdrawn for laboratory testing is surely needed for "itself," i.e., as material for analysis. Since withdrawing

---

16 *Shabbat* 90a. See the Me'iri, *Shabbat*, ch.10, mishnah 6. The general rule is that one is not punished for transporting objects from one domain to another merely to get rid of an unwanted object. It should also be noted that one is culpable only in a case where there is no danger to life which would warrant the violation of a Biblical precept.

17 *Sanhedrin* 84b.

18 *Teshuvah me-Ahavah* I, 135; *Zecher Yehosaf* 104.

19 *Minchat Yitzchak* I, 27-28; *Avnei Zikkaron* III, 40. However, in *Teshuvot Shemen ha-Maor* 34 a contrary opinion is expressed. The author maintains that it is impossible to inject without causing bleeding, so that bleeding is an intrinsic part of injecting, even though it is not desired.

20 Aside from the issue of wounding, there are other halachic considerations regarding the permissibility of injections for medical treatment (see "Medicines and Remedies on Shabbat," in this volume.)

blood in these instances impacts on Biblical prohibitions, the procedures should be permitted only where there is danger to life.[21] But when blood is passively removed through the use of a vacuum tube rather than manually withdrawn with a syringe, it is possible that the ruling might be more lenient. Rabbi Hershler refers to the Mishnah which rules that a *kohen* may wrap an injured finger on Shabbat to allow him to perform the Temple service, but not for the purpose of extracting blood from the wound.[22] Rashi explains that it is not permitted to wrap the wound tightly so as to force out blood. The *Magen Avraham*[23] infers that, in an instance where no physical act of tight wrapping is performed, placing an absorbent material on the wound to draw out the blood would not be proscribed Biblically.

As a practical measure, the site of an injection should be prepared by pouring the antiseptic over the area or by using plastic fiber pledgets rather than natural material, so as to avoid the question of squeezing out liquid (*sechitah*). Antiseptics which temporarily discolor the skin, such as Betadine solutions, may also be used without concern for violating the prohibition against dyeing.

---

21 If we follow the opinion of most *Rishonim* that the prohibition of withdrawing blood relates to the taking of life, removal of even a drop of blood would be forbidden. But according to the Rambam it would be necessary to remove a volume of blood equal to that of a dried fig (the measure required for *mefarek*) to incur culpability according to Biblical law. It is also possible that blood which is temporarily withdrawn to verify the position of the needle and then returned to the vein might be considered a momentary, reversible wound which is not proscribed as the taking of life.

22 *Eruvin* 103b.

23 *Shulchan Aruch, Orach Chayim, Magen Avraham* 328:53.

Blood tests on Shabbat for neonatal jaundice

Translated and adapted from the article by RABBI ELIEZER JUDAH
WALDENBERG in *Halachah U'Refuah* I, 281-82

Rabbi Waldenberg responds to a query posed by Dr. Meir
Issacson as to whether determination of the bilirubin blood
level is permitted on Shabbat, even in full-term infants who
are not obviously ill. Dr. Issacson pointed out that, while
jaundice occurs earlier and is more prolonged and dangerous
in premature infants, in full-term babies it is more frequently a passing phenomenon without deleterious future
consequences. Yet it may be important to quantitate the
bilirubin blood level of a full-term infant, and delaying the
determination until the conclusion of Shabbat, at times up
to twenty-four hours, may allow the bilirubin to rise to
critical levels.

Rabbi Waldenberg takes the position that visible jaundice, irrespective of the blood level of bilirubin, was recognized by our Sages as a sign of illness, since we are required
to defer circumcision on its account. It makes no difference
whether the infant is not otherwise ill, or whether it is full
term or premature.[1] If, in addition, there is concern that the
jaundice is severe enough to raise the possibility of brain
damage, it is surely imperative to draw blood for an accurate
determination of the bilirubin level, even though the act of
drawing blood is Biblically proscribed.[2]

The *Chazon Ish*[3] rules that one may ask a non-Jew to
cook food on Shabbat for a child who cannot eat anything

---

1 *Teshuvot Tzitz Eliezer* XIII, 81.

2 Rabbi Waldenberg notes that according to the Rambam who subsumes wounding under the work category of separating (*mefarek*), the few drops of blood
necessary for the determination would be less than the measure required for
Biblical culpability, which is equal to the volume of a dried fig.

3 *Chazon Ish, Mo'ed* 59, note 4.

else, even though the length of time the child will be without food is not long enough to raise the possibility of starvation. Mere discomfort, associated with abdominal pains, or which may cause constipation, diarrhea, or fever, is sufficient to raise a doubt of possible danger because of the age of the child. Now, if such a relatively minor problem can be treated so seriously, how much more so should we regard a jaundiced infant, who is already considered ill.

Rabbi Waldenberg concludes by noting that, if possible, the drawing of the blood, the determination, and the recording of the results should be performed by a non-Jew. But where there is not alternative, a Shabbat observer should not hesitate to do them.

Attaching medical equipment to patients on Shabbat

Translated and adapted from the article by
RABBI LEVI YITZCHAK HALPERIN in *Halachah U'Refuah* II, 224-38

Rabbi Halperin questions whether the record trace produced by an electrocardiogram or cardiac monitor is, in fact, an outcome of the action of the individual who attached the electrical leads to the patient or if the result is ascribed to the patient, whose physiological processes control the movement of the recording pen or the aiming of the optical trace.

From the Talmud it is apparent that an action which is effected by one's weight, with no active participation otherwise, is considered a deed for which an individual is responsible.[1] Thus, a person blown off a roof by an unexpected wind of extraordinary force would be liable for damages [caused by his body falling upon another individual].[2] Similarly, with regard to the laws of ritual purity, the Mishnah[3] states that a man who crosses a field in which a grave was plowed over[4] by walking on stones which will not shift under his weight or by being borne by a strong man or animal with a steady gait remains clean [because he does not directly move any

---

1 See Rabbi L. Y. Halperin, *Ma'aseh u'Gerama b'Halachah* (Jerusalem: Institute for Science and Halachah 5738, part VIII.

2 A person is required to pay for damages caused by him, even when he was not negligent and had no intention of performing the action, e.g., when he was asleep. He is, however, exempt from the additional four items of compensation; for pain, medical expenses, loss of time from work, and disgrace (e.g., if he shamed a woman by falling on her). Liability for these four items is incurred only where there is intent to do harm. Since he was thrust by a wind of unusual occurrence, we assume it was without his intention. See *Bava Kamma* 27a.

3 *Oholot*, ch. 18, mishnah 6.

4 Such a field, which may contain bone splinters the size of a barley corn, conveys uncleanliness by contact (*magga*) or by carrying (*massa*) its earth, but not by overshadowing (*ohel*).

fragments of uncleanliness which are mixed within the soil];
but, if he steps on stones that can be shifted easily or is
carried by a weak man or beast who is not sure-footed, he
becomes unclean [because he shares in moving the uncleanliness within the soil by his weight].

Moreover, it would appear that an act which is effected
merely through the presence of an individual is also considered an action ascribable to that person. The Mishnah[5] rules
that when an individual carrying a barrel in a thoroughfare
collides with another person who is carrying a beam and the
barrel is ruptured by the beam, the owner of the beam is not
liable for damages, for both are entitled to walk there.
However, if the one carrying the beam was in front and he
unexpectedly stopped short [so that the one with the barrel
did not notice and the barrel crashed into the beam], the
carrier of the beam is liable [as though he shattered the barrel
with his own hands].[6] This is also evident from the discussion
regarding the previous mishnah as to whether stumbling is
considered negligence, so that if one fell and another who
was following stumbled over the first and also fell, the first
would be liable for damages.[7] The Talmud assumes that one
who is lying in a public domain and did not rise or at least
caution others as to his presence is liable for damages.

It would thus appear that the recording of physiological
parameters on a tracing, which is effected merely by the
presence of an individual, should be considered an action of
the person connected to the apparatus. True, it may be
argued that an individual is liable for actions effected
through his weight or mere presence only when he has
performed a preceding positive act which created the conditions for the mishap to occur (e.g., he walked up to the roof,

---

5 *Bava Kamma* 31b.

6 Ibid. The *Nimmukei Yosef* points out that, although the barrel was broken in
a passive manner, since the one carrying the beam is standing and in full
control of himself, it is considered as though he committed the damage.

7 *Bava Kamma* 31a.

or climbed upon an animal to ride, or stumbled as he walked, or lay down upon the ground in a public domain). But if a wind swept him off his feet while he was on the ground and after he was lifted high in the air he crashed down on someone, he would not be liable for damages. Similarly, in the case at hand, a patient may also be completely passive in being connected to the recording device. Furthermore, since another individual brought the machine and placed the leads on the patient, perhaps the situation would be comparable to that of one who pushes another, causing the second individual to stumble over a man lying in the public domain. Surely, in this case, the one who does the pushing would be liable for damages.

However, from *Tosafot*[8] it would appear that even when one is completely passive, not even performing an otherwise permissible action which facilitated the misdeed, he is still considered the executor of the deed. For with regard to the requirement than an individual allows himself to be killed when given the choice of saving himself by killing another, *Tosafot* observes that this principle applies only when he "will execute the murder with his hands. But where he does not act, as when others will throw him onto an infant who will be crushed, it is logical to assume that he is not required to sacrifice himself. Since he performs no action, he can say, on the contrary, why propose that my friend's blood is dearer, perhaps my blood is dearer."From these last words it would seem that, although the individual would not be required to sacrifice himself in such a circumstance, *Tosafot* still ascribes the resultant murder to him, as passive murder, because otherwise *Tosafot* could simply have said, "Since he performs no action, he is not a murderer."

But this way of interpreting *Tosafot*'s words is not followed by *Chazon Ish*.[9] For, regarding the case cited by *Tosafot*, the *Chazon Ish* asks how one could go toward the

---

8 *Sanhedrin* 74b, *Tosafot: V'ha Esther.*

9 *Gilyonot Chazon Ish al Ha-Gaon Rav Chayim Halevi*, chapter "*Yesodei ha-Torah.*"

infant or move closer to those who wished to cast him onto the infant. Since it is certain that their intention is to throw him on the infant, the matter is similar to one who positions himself on a roof so that an ordinary gust of wind would cause him to topple over, thereby crushing an infant. Although he may not be liable for the death penalty, since he did not actively murder the infant, the deed would still be prohibited as an act of murder. The *Chazon Ish*'s elucidation of *Tosafot* is surprising, for there is no clear indication in the words of *Tosafot* that it is referring to a situation where the individual was asked to walk over to the site from which he will be thrown. We must, therefore, conclude that the *Chazon Ish* maintains that in a situation where one was entirely passive, standing in one spot without any movement, there would be nothing novel in this point of *Tosafot* not requiring him to sacrifice his life, for then the individual who is thrown performs no action which can be linked to the murder by facilitating his being thrown onto the infant.[10]

From the *Chazon Ish*'s understanding of *Tosafot*, Rabbi Halperin concludes that, in order to relate an act which is effected merely through the presence of an individual to that person, it is necessary for him to perform some action, even a prior, permissible act. But if he did nothing at all, the resultant action could not be ascribed to him. Thus, when a patient walks over to the treatment room for the specific purpose of being connected to an electrocardiogram or other recording device, the resultant production of the tracing could be ascribed to him, even though walking by itself is permissible. However, when a patient already lying in bed offers no assistance to the person connecting him to the machine, (e.g., raising his arm or leg to facilitate the attachment of the straps), he cannot be held responsible for the resultant physiologic trace.

---

10 Rabbi Halperin enters into a lengthy digression concerning direct and indirect acts of murder, and the application of the rule requiring one to sacrifice himself rather than murder another. For the sake of brevity, we have omitted this section, which adds no further insight to his conclusion.

Non-permanent writing on Shabbat

Translated and adapted from the articles in *Halachah U'Refuah* I by
RABBI YITZCHAK YAAKOV WEISS (233-35),
RABBI SHLOMO ZALMAN AUERBACH (235-35),
RABBI LEVI YITZCHAK HALPERIN (237-49, 249-55)

The necessity of recording medical information in a hospital on Shabbat and *Yom Tov* raises the problem of violating the major work category of writing (*kotev*). Although one may desecrate Shabbat for a patient who is in danger, this applies only to manipulations and procedures which are part of the treatment and for the patient's direct benefit. Data which is routinely recorded is often not necessary for the immediate treatment of the patient. Furthermore, in recording histories and results in a hospital, no differentiation is made between patients who are dangerously ill and those less critical.

Rabbi Levi Yitzchak Halperin suggests that by writing in a non-permanent manner, either by using a non-permanent writing medium or a non-permanent writing surface, it is possible to avoid a clear-cut Biblical prohibition. For the work category of writing implies a degree of permanence, and when the written material persists for only a transitory period, there would be a deficiency in the *melechet machshevet*[1] of this major work category. This principle is derived from the Mishnah: "...if one writes with a fluid, with fruit juice,...or with anything that cannot endure, he is not culpable."[2] The *Tosefta* adds, "...if one writes on the leaves of vegetables or on anything which cannot endure, he is not culpable. This is the rule: [if one writes with] a substance that endures on a material that does not endure, or [if one

---

1 *Melechet Machshevet* is an essential principle which applies to Biblically proscribed acts on Shabbat. It requires the intention to perform the action and a certain degree of creative design, both in its objective and in its manner of performance.

2 *Shabbat* 104b.

writes with] a substance that cannot endure on a material that endures, one is not culpable."[3] The Rambam combines the Mishnah and the *Tosefta* in ruling that only when both the writing substance and the material written upon endure does one violate the Biblical precept.[4]

But how long must the writing persist for it to be proscribed according to Biblical law? The Mishnah (discussing the work category of building) establishes that "whoever does work and his work lasts through Shabbat is culpable."[5] The Rambam also states (with regard to dyeing) that "any work which does not last through Shabbat is not culpable."[6] The wording of the Mishnah and the Rambam seems to indicate that there is no requirement for the result to last beyond the end of Shabbat. Indeed, Rabbi Yitzchak Yaakov Weiss adopts this point of view, citing the *Mishnah Berurah*[7] and Rabbi Meir Dan Plotzki[8] in support. Rabbi Weiss notes that, according to the *Mishnah Berurah*, writing on food[9] or on one's skin[10] is considered permanent, even though the inscription is bound to disintegrate in a relatively short period of time.

Yet Rabbi Halperin protests that if the Rambam meant

---

3 Ibid., ch. 12:8.

4 *Hilchot Shabbat* 12:8. See also *Shulchan Aruch, Choshen Mishpat* 34:4, 5.

5 *Shabbat* 102b.

6 *Hilchot Shabbat* 9:13.

7 Ibid., *Mishnah Berurah* 22.

8 *Hilchot Shabbat* 303, *Sha'ar ha-Tziyun* 68. Rabbi Halperin suggests that, while the *Mishnah Berurah* interprets the Rambam in this manner, he does not follow this ruling later (see n.9).

9 *Chemdat Yisrael, Kuntras Ner Mitzvah*, Laws of Shabbat 21. Rabbi Halperin points out that, according to the *Chemdat Yisrael*, the rule of lasting through Shabbat might be sufficient for dyeing and some other work categories but not for writing, since writing with fluid which is not permanent is not considered writing. (That is why it is not valid for a bill of divorce [see Rambam, *Hilchot Gerushin* 5:1).

10 *Hilchot Shabbat* 340, *Biur Halachah: B'mashkin*.

to say that to incur punishment the writing need last only to the conclusion of Shabbat, there would be no fixed minimum length of time that it must remain! Writing executed on Friday night which persisted until shortly before the termination of Shabbat would apparently not incur culpability, while such work performed late on Shabbat day which lasted only a mere hour or two, until after the close of Shabbat, would be considered halachically as work of an enduring nature. Perhaps this is why Rashi stresses that the word "on Shabbat" in the Mishnah cited above should be repositioned so that the Mishnah reads "whoever does work on Shabbat and his work endures is culpable."[11] Furthermore, Ha-Gaon Rabbi Shlomo Zalman Auerbach points out that the Rambam himself rules that ink written on vegetable leaves does not incur culpability, because the material written upon does not endure, even though such writing would surely last two or more days, well beyond the period of Shabbat. Similarly, in reference to writing on foodstuffs, the *Peri Megadim*[12] also considers cake a material which does not endure, although it is common knowledge that baked goods may last many days before disintegrating.

Rabbi Auerbach also reasons that since the work categories that are Biblical prohibited are derived from the kinds of work used in the construction of the Mishkan, we may also deduce that writing which fades after two or three days is not permanent enough to qualify as Biblically proscribed. In the Mishkan, writing was used to number the boards of the walls so that they could be placed in appropriate sequence when the Mishkan was assembled. The procedure of assembling and taking apart the Mishkan was performed many times during the sojourn of the Children of Israel in the desert, so the numbers inscribed had to last a relatively long time.

---

11 *Shabbat* 102b, Rashi: *B'Shabbat*; and see the Ran, *Chiddushei ha-Me'iri*, and the *Tosafot Yom Tov.*

12 *Peri Megadim, Shulchan Aruch, Orach Chayim* 340:2.

That writing must persist more than a day or two, in order to be considered of a lasting nature and for one to be culpable Biblically, is also apparent from the Rashba's interpretation of a query in the Talmud. This discusses the permissibility of rescuing Holy Scriptures from a conflagration on Shabbat if they are not written in ink, but rather with substances such as dye, red paint, or gum ink, which are not permanent.[13] The Rashba was initially puzzled by the Talmud's uncertainty, since we note from the earlier Mishnah that writing on Shabbat with dye, red paint, or gum ink does incur culpability, so perforce they must endure. The Rashba, therefore, differentiates between the two situations. With regard to rescuing Holy Scriptures from a conflagration, the text must be written in ink which lasts for many generations. But to be considered a work of sufficient creative and productive nature so as to incur culpability for writing on Shabbat, it is enough that the writing last for a relatively short time period, as in the case of notes, memoranda, or diaries, which are not expected to last forever. From the text of the Rashba it is clear that to be Biblically proscribed the writing must endure longer than a day, or even several days. In keeping with the Rashba, the *Mishnah Berurah*[14] notes that nowadays writing with a pencil also would incur culpability on Shabbat, since merchants are accustomed to using it to record their accounts (surely for longer than a day or two).

Rabbi Halperin cites a great many proofs to support his contention that writing which lasts through Shabbat but no longer than several days may be considered writing which does not endure and that such writing, although Rabbinically prohibited, is not proscribed Biblically. Therefore, it may be employed when one is caring for bedridden, sick individuals, even if they are not dangerously ill. Rabbi Auer-

---

13 *Shabbat* 115b, *Chiddushei ha-Rashba.*

14 See *Ketzot ha-Shulchan* 146, *Shulchan Atzei Shittim,* Work category of writing.

bach adds that when the text is not in Hebrew we may be even more lenient, particularly when script is used.[15]

Yet Rabbi Weiss rejects Rabbi Halperin's proposal to use non-permanent ink to record medical histories on Shabbat, preferring the present system of employing a non-Jew. He contends that even if Rabbi Halperin's proposal were acceptable in theory, it is objectionable for practical reasons, since permitting Jews to write on Shabbat in a non-permanent manner would ultimately lead to increased violations of Shabbat. For those who do not appreciate the fine halachic distinction may conclude that all writing is permissible for all kinds of patients.

---

15 See *Magen Avraham, Orach Chayim* 140:10 and 545:21.

Issues regarding the use of a microphone and a tape recorder on Shabbat

Translated and adapted from the article by
RABBI CHAIM DAVID REGENSBERG in *Halachah U'Refuah* I, 3-11

The halachic considerations regarding the use of a tape recorder on Shabbat, although initially written by the author in a different context, should be included in this volume, because of the possibility that observant physicians might avoid Biblical prohibitions by recording histories and data, rather than writing them.

Rabbi Chaim David Regensberg initially reviews the prohibitions associated with turning on an electric circuit on Shabbat. Most authorities consider the completion of an electric circuit as an act of kindling, because it creates a glowing metal filament.[1] There is some discussion as to whether the person closing the circuit is only indirectly responsible, since he merely allows the current to flow to the filament, but since the effect is instantaneous, it is as though the person directly causes the metal to glow.[2] Moreover, argues Rabbi Regensberg, even though one may not be considered totally responsible for an action in civil or criminal law, with regard to Shabbat, any work activity which is performed in its usual manner would still be prohibited. Thus, one who winnows with the aid of the wind has committed a Shabbat offense, although he would not be culpable for damages if a fire he had previously set was further fanned

---

1 *Teshuvot Beit Yitzchak, Yoreh De'ah* 31; *Achi'ezer* III, 60.

2 *Achi'ezer* III, 60. See *Sanhedrin* 77b (regarding one who commits murder by binding an individual below a dam and then directing a channel of water to drown him), and the commentary of the *Yad Ramah*, pertaining to direct and indirect actions. (A discussion of this topic is found in "Use of an Electric Oven for Cooking and Baking on *Yom Tov*," in this volume.)

by the wind, resulting in a conflagration.[3]

With solid-state circuits, however, there should be no prohibition arising from the work category of kindling, since no glowing filament is produced. Yet the *Chazon Ish*[4] maintains that completing an electric circuit would be forbidden as an act of building, because 1) the individual units of the circuit become interconnected as a complete device; 2) with the initiation of current flow, the typical characteristics of a functioning electric circuit are first acquired; and 3) motion is imparted to the electric particles which previously had been inert. Rabbi Regensberg wonders whether the work category of building should apply to a non-permanent "structure" which will totally collapse at one stroke, returning the components to their initial state, as when a circuit is opened. The difference between closing a circuit and setting up a collapsible chair is also not clear, for both acquire their characteristics, i.e., of a functioning circuit or of a chair, with the completion of the reversible action. Yet setting up a folding chair on Shabbat is clearly permissible, so why should an electric circuit be different?[5] Moreover, the *Peri Megadim* establishes the rule that utensils which cannot be used without being disassembled and put together [6] are not considered as being constructed or given the finishing stroke (*makkeh ba-pattish*) when they are utilized in this manner, but are treated as items fabricated initially so as to be pieced together each time they are used.[7]

---

3 *Rabbenu Chananel, Shabbat* 120b (regarding a candle behind a door being opened). See also *Bava Kamma* 60a.

4 *Chazon Ish, Orach Chayim, Hilchot Shabbat* 50.

5 *Shabbat* 135a. See also *Shulchan Aruch, Orach Chayim* 315:5.

6 Such as a glass in which the cup portion which is initially inverted over the stem is removed and turned upright, and then the stem is inserted into its base.

7 *Orach Chayim* 313:6; *Turei Zahav* 7; *Peri Megadim* 7. Of course the utensil must be fastened together loosely and must be able to be secured by an unskilled person. For, if the pieces were joined snugly or if an artisan were required to put them together, it would surely be an act of construction (see

Rabbi Regensberg thus concludes that there should be no more than a Rabbinic prohibition against using solid-state circuits, where no filament is heated. He also notes that an additional Rabbinic prohibition derives from a concern that the user might repair the device if it should break down.[8] Since we are concerned only with Rabbinic prohibitions, an additional point of leniency could be based on the Rashba's ruling concerning an action which has simultaneous permitted and proscribed consequences. The Rashba[9] decides that, although trapping is a Biblically forbidden work category, a door may be closed behind a deer which found its way into a house, because the owner's intention in shutting the door is to protect the contents of the house, and not just to trap the deer. We may reason similarly with regard to using a microphone, as the speaker's goal is to communicate with those sitting close by without electronic amplification at the same time that he is reaching out to those further away through the loudspeaker.

Aside from the halachic issues related to the electronics of these devices, Rabbi Regensberg is concerned that recording speech on a tape may invoke the Biblically proscribed work category of applying the finishing stroke (*makkeh ba-pattish*). For unlike a microphone, which undergoes no permanent change as it is being used, the tape is altered by the act of recording, even though the change is not apparent to the eye. According to the *Chazon Ish*, cited above, this should surely be in the nature of a forbidden construction, as the originally "silent" tape becomes "live" as a result of the recording. Rabbi Regensberg wonders whether a tape recorder could be considered a device in the category of things that are routinely disassembled and put together in order to use them, because the sequential orientation of the

---

commentaries of the Ramban, Rashba, Ran, and Ritva on the subject, at the beginning of *Shabbat*, ch. 12).

8 *Beitzah* 36b.

9 *Chiddushei ha-Rashba*, *Shabbat* ch.8.

magnetic particles on the tape is rearranged[10] — and thus the leniency that applies to such devices should pertain also to recording on magnetic tape.

---

10 Others have argued that there is no Biblical prohibition precisely for this reason (according to Ha-Gaon Rabbi S. Z. Auerbach, Rabbi L. Y. Halperin, and Prof. A. Halpern [see "Non-Permanent Writing on Shabbat," in this volume]). Perhaps one could reason that the particles which become magnetized are already present on the tape at the outset, and they are merely repositioned by the recording into a temporary orientation which can readily revert to the original random state with the momentary passage of a magnet.

Use of a voice-controlled diagnostic computer on Shabbat

Translated and adapted from the article
by PROF. ZEEV LOW in *Halachah U'Refuah* II, 205-23

A number of halachic issues pertain to the use of a device which is activated by the voice of the physician. We may avoid the question of initiating operation of the device during Shabbat, by assuming that it has been turned on before Shabbat. To activate the computer, the physician speaks into a microphone, producing a continuum of electric pulses which, after searching its memory, are matched by the computer to preexisting electronic fingerprints of words. The words are then converted by the computer into electronic signals which control the computer's operation, directing it to solve the problem with the data presented. The requested solution or answer is transmitted to the doctor on a video screen, on printed paper, or by means of spoken words through a loudspeaker.

The question of using a microphone on Shabbat has been dealt with previously.[1] Technologically, it is now possible to overcome many of the halachic considerations prohibiting the use of microphones when solid state circuits are employed and no glowing filament is activated.[2] When the circuit is constantly closed, there would also be no concern

---

1 Rabbi E. Weisfish, *Electricity in Halachah* I, (Jerusalem: Institute for Science and Halachah, 5738), section on Communication. See also Rabbi Chaim David Regensberg, "Issues Regarding the Use of a Microphone and a Tape Recorder on Shabbat," in this volume; and Rabbi L. Y. Halperin, "Use of Microphone in the Synagogue on Shabbat and Weekdays," *Torah u'Maddah* 9 (Adar 5740).

2 A prohibition under the work category of kindling, because of sparks which may be generated, should not be raised since sparks do not usually arise in solid-state circuits. Furthermore, sparks are an undesirable by-product which cause interference in the circuit, and any which may be propagated would be so small as to be barely seen by the naked eye. See Prof. Z. Low, "*Molid Zerem*," in *T'chumim*, vol. II (5741).

for the *Chazon Ish*'s stringent ruling that completing an electric circuit is a type of constructing (*boneh*).[3]

Similarly, when the machine's results are transmitted by loudspeaker there is no question of Biblical transgression, merely the potential of the Rabbinic prohibition of disgracing Shabbat by an activity which detracts from the aura of Shabbat (*uvada d'chol*). But this would not apply in a hospital setting, where the information is needed for patient care, and surely not when the volume of the loudspeaker is turned low or when earphones are used, so that no attention is called to the machines operation.

A critical issue is whether printed results (which may, in fact, be Biblically proscribed as the work category of writing) are considered a direct consequence of the doctor's speech or if they are to be considered indirect actions, not forbidden on Shabbat. Furthermore, even if we were to assume that the printing is a direct consequence of the doctor's speech, is a result which comes about through one's voice tantamount to performance of the deed for Shabbat restrictions?

There is a dispute in the Talmud as to whether causing an animal to interrupt its feeding on the threshing floor by shouting at it is punishable by lashes under the rubric of muzzling a working animal.[4] Normally, one does not receive lashes for a transgression which involves no action. In this case, R. Yochanan maintains that the movement of one's lips is an action, while Reish Lakish rules that the exercise of one's voice is not an action. Various reasons have been offered to explain why speech may be considered an action with regard to muzzling. Some reason that it is because the shout causes the animal to perform the action of continuing to thresh without eating.[5] Others hold that, since muzzling is a negative act in which the animal is withheld from eating,

---

3 *Chazon Ish, Orach Chayim* 50.

4 *Bava Metzia* 90b. See *Devarim* 25:4.

5 *Tosafot, Bava Metzia*, 90b.

anything that holds back the animal from eating is included in the prohibition.[6] The *Avnei Nezer*[7] explains that, to be punishable by lashes, two requirements must be met: the transgression should result from a wrongful act, and the individual responsible must perform an action. In muzzling an animal with one's voice, the transgression is linked to the action of the animal turning away from the grain and beginning to thresh, while the human action is effected through the movement of the individual's lips. However, Rabbi L. Y. Halperin[8] notes that only with regard to punishment by lashes is it necessary to combine the actions of the human being with that of the animal, but to violate the prohibition of muzzling, movement of one's lips is sufficient.

On the face of it, the question of operating an electronic device by moving one's lips should be similar to verbally muzzling an animal, for in both instances the resulting action is an outcome of the individual's speech. However, Prof. Low suggests that there may be a difference between the prohibition of muzzling and performing work on Shabbat. With regard to muzzling, it is the outcome of not permitting the animal to eat that the Torah banned. Thus, any act, no matter how slight, which effects this result is prohibited. But with respect to work prohibited on Shabbat, the individual is only forbidden to intentionally and directly perform work specified as one of the thirty-nine categories, in the manner in which it is usually accomplished (*melechet machshevet*).[9] Even with regard to other prohibitions not related

---

6 *Me'iri, Bava Metzia* 90b.

7 *Avnei Nezer, Orach Chayim* 57 and 58.

8 Rabbi L.Y. Halperin, *Ma'aseh u'Gerama b'Halachah*, (Jerusalem: Institute for Science and Halachah, 5738), p.232.

9 True, a person's action combined with another force may also be prohibited on Shabbat, just as one's voice combines with the action of the animal being verbally muzzled, but that is only when it is the usual manner of performing that category of work, e.g., winnowing with the assistance of the wind (*Bava Kamma* 61; see also Rabbi L. Y. Halperin, *Ma'aseh u'Gerama b'Halachah* p.293, and Prof. Z. Low, *Birur Mussagim: Ko'ach Kocho v'Ko'ach Sheni b'Ha-*

to Shabbat, R. Yochanan, who rules that verbal muzzling is a punishable action, holds that speech is not necessarily a punishable action.[10] As to Reish Lakish, he never considers speech-related sin a punishable action.

On closer inspection, the conclusion, that speech-induced violations of Shabbat may not be interdicted, might apply only when the proscribed action results from an utterance which is heard and acted upon. But when vocalization or shouting produces a series of pressure waves which directly operate a device or set an object in motion on Shabbat, a punishable action should be imputed. With regard to civil damages this is the case, for the Talmud states that if a cock put its head into a glass utensil and crowed, causing the glass to break, the owner must pay.[11] Clearly, the damage caused by the sound waves of the cock is considered a direct action of the animal. Similarly, the vibration of the microphone membrane by the pressure of the sound waves arising from the physician's vocal cords should be considered his direct action.

Let us now analyze whether the electrical pulses arising from the vibration of the microphone membrane should be Rabbinically restricted from being used, as new currents which first became available on Shabbat (*nolad*).[12] In an

---

lachah [Jerusalem: Mosad ha-Rav Kook, 1978], p. 214), and trapping, which necessitates an act on the part of the animal as well (Mishnah *Shabbat* 17b; concerning the prohibition against spreading snares, see *Tosafot, Chiddushei ha-Ritva*, and *Chiddushei ha-Rashba*, see also *Minchat Chinnuch*, commandment 32, and Prof. Z. Low, *Birur Mussagim*, p.83).

10 See the discussion about blasphemy, where the transgression depends on the intention of one's heart, and about witnesses who are proven false by others who testify that they were not present at the alleged time and place the crime was committed (*edim zomemin*). Where it is not mandatory to move one's lips in order to testify falsely, as the companion of the witness who testifies first need only grunt his assent to indicate his concurrence with the testimony (*Sanhedrin* 65a and b). Verbally exchanging a consecrated animal is punishable by lashes according to R. Yochanan, because the whole act causing an unconsecrated animal to become consecrated is a verbal one (*Temurah* 3b).

11 *Bava Kamma* 118b. See Rambam, *Hilchot Nizkei Mamon* 2:9.

already-completed circuit, which has been turned on before Shabbat, vibrations of a microphone membrane merely transmute the existing current and voltage into an alternating current. Prof. Low reasons that there is no new creation of current in this circumstance, just as there would be no creation of fragrance when the lid of an already-opened box of aromatics is waved to and fro in a closet, thereby varying the output of fragrance into the air and onto the garments.[13] There is, in fact, no restriction against producing a wave of fragrance on *Yom Tov*. One is merely enjoined from transferring fragrance from one body to another which had no fragrance initially. Indeed, not only is it permissible to increase the fragrance by rubbing or chipping off the edge of an already-present piece of aromatic wood, but one may also bring new pieces of the same species of scent to place among the garments.[14] Now, just as boosting the intensity of fragrance and adding new fragrant-producing chips are not prohibited under *nolad*, so too varying a preexisting electrical current or converting a direct current to an alternating current (producing alternate phases of upswings and downswings of current) also should be counted as *nolad*.

Prof. Low raises an additional issue. From the discussion of the Talmud regarding a winepress which operates by turning a wheel to lower a heavy beam onto the grapes,[15] it is clear that although the mechanical pieces in this apparatus are interconnected, the pressing of the grapes is considered only an indirect action of the idolater. An apparatus which encompasses several electronic steps should also be considered halachically an array of components and transmissions rather than one unit, and one could argue that its

---

12 *Beit Yitzchak, Yoreh De'ah* II, 31, and in the addenda at the end of the volume.

13 *Beitzah* 23a. See also Rabbi S. Z. Auerbach, *Collected Papers on the Subject of Electricity on Shabbat*, (Jerusalem: Institute for Science and Halachah), p.35.

14 *Shulchan Aruch, Orach Chayim* 512:2.

15 *Avodah Zarah* 60a, see *Tosafot: Hava uvda.*

use should be permitted on Shabbat, since the proscribed printed output of the computer is linked to the operator's voice in only a very indirect manner. But with regard to Shabbat, an action which is indirect is not automatically permissible. The deciding factor is whether the sequence of events comprising the action is in the nature of the proscribed work category.

Thus, R. Papa considers one who throws a clod of earth at a palm tree, causing a cluster of dates to be dislodged, to be liable for two penalties: one for detaching [that which is attached to the ground] (*tolesh*) and another for separating [the dates from their outer skin or twigs] (*mefarek*).[16] The clearest explanation is offered by the Ran and the Ramban, who note that the separating is done indirectly in the following manner: the clod strikes a bunch of dates, causing it to be detached, and when the bunch strikes the ground the blow causes individual dates to be separated from the twigs. R. Ashi disagrees with R. Papa's ruling, not because it is an indirect action but, rather, because this is neither the method of detaching nor of separating. Prof. Low concludes that, as long as the interdicted work is performed on Shabbat in a manner forbidden by the Torah, it does not matter whether the individual uses an apparatus designed to operate by transmitting various forces in sequence or even in conjunction with an external force. This principle is derived from the comments of the Rabbenu Chananel regarding opening a door in front of a flame: "Since it is a rule that even a usual gust of wind will fan the flame higher and [the perpetrator] took it into account, [opening the door and generating a breeze] is forbidden on Shabbat as an act performed in its usual manner."[17]

Yet one could contend that, for culpability on Shabbat,

---

16 *Shabbat* 73b, and see the commentaries of the Ran and the Ramban.

17 Rabbenu Chananel, *Shabbat* 120b. Rashi also says, "His intention was fulfilled, since he is content with the wind helping him" (*Bava Kamma* 60, Rashi: *Melechet machshevet*).

the printed output from the machine is viewed as linked to the initial action of speaking only when the machine prints exactly what is spoken, but not when the printed results are generated by the calculations and memory banks within the computer, which were programmed before Shabbat. For, as Prof. Low reasons, when the contents of the output are not determined by the speaker, the resultant action may be considered defective with regard to the degree of *melechet machshevet* which is necessary for culpability for writing on Shabbat. Thus the printed output should surely be considered a permissible indirect action.[18]

We must also reckon whether operating a typewriter by means of speech is considered a manner of writing. For if it is not, the prohibition of performing an act in an unusual manner is merely of Rabbinic decree and since it is indirect action (as noted above), we should be lenient in permitting the use of such an apparatus for one who is ill, even though not at life-threatening risk. Moreover, Prof. Low suggests, such a radical departure from the usual mode of writing may not even be prohibited Rabbinically. He explains that our Sages enacted prohibitions to prevent an individual from performing work in an unusual manner only when the human act is modified but the manner of effecting the result remains unchanged. For example, one may write in an indirect manner, but recording the written words is still effected by means of a writing implement and ink. However, when the means of effecting the result is itself unusual, as with cooking by means of solar heat,[19] there should not even be Rabbinic prohibition.

As a corollary, we may query whether the manner of

---

18 See Rabbi L. Y. Halperin, *Ma'aseh u'Gerama b'Halachah* and Prof. Z. Low, *Birur Mussagim.*

19 *Shabbat* 39a, see Rashi: *D'shari.* The *Eglei Tal* differentiates between a modification in the means of doing the work and an alteration in the end products. He maintains that food cooked by solar energy actually differs from food cooked on a fire (*Eglei Tal,* Work category of baking [*ofeh*] 44.)

performing a specific type of work forbidden on Shabbat should be allowed to vary with the technology of the age, or whether its mode is fixed eternally to conform with its description in the Talmud. Ha-Gaon R. Elchanan Wasserman writes, "All the laws of the Torah were meant to apply in a usual manner...it is clear that this depends on the time and place. For example, with regard to Shabbat, one who carries from one domain to another on his elbow is not liable, because this is not the manner of carrying on weekdays. However, if the custom would change, so that on weekdays everyone would carry on their elbows, one would surely be culpable for doing it on Shabbat."[20] Thus, if in the future the technology to control the written output of a computer by the spoken voice will become widely used, perhaps even a Biblical prohibition against performing such work on Shabbat might then apply.

Turning to the storage of data, Prof. Low wonders whether entering data into the computer is a kind of writing. In reality, no "words" as such are stored in the computer, merely an array of tiny elements which are in one of two states (on or off, positive or negative, present or absent), which are controlled electrically. The states are neither visible nor permanent. There is also no essential change in the substrate upon which the data is recorded. That there is no Biblical prohibition of writing in putting this kind of data into computer memory is clear from the Rambam, who requires permanent writing on permanent substrate.[21] Since no letters are formed, the issue is also not similar to writing numbers as a series of letters,[22] nor to chiseling out letters

---

20 *Kovetz Shiurim, Ketubbot* 23. See also *Kovetz Iggrot ha-Chazon Ish,* letter 3, from Rabbi Chaim Ozer, p. 182, regarding milking a cow in an unusual manner on Shabbat.

21 *Hilchot Shabbat* 11:9, 17.

22 This is culpable. Rambam, *Hilchot Shabbat* 11:14; and see the additional notes in *Tzofnat Pa'ne'ach.* Also see the *Tosafot Yom Tov* on *Shabbat,* ch. 12, mishnah 3.

in relief (*chak tuchos*).[23] Computer storage is also different from storage of voice patterns on a paraffin-coated surface using a panograph, which was forbidden by the *Beit Yitzchak*,[24] because the recording produces scratches on the surface which are permanent and visible to the naked eye. Prof. Low concludes that entering data into a computer is, therefore, not a form of writing, nor should the data be considered as components of a human language.[25]

---

23 *Mordechai, Gittin,* ch. II.

24 *Beit Yitzchak, Yoreh De'ah,* additional notes 31.

25 Even according to those who maintain that writing in any language script, not just Hebrew, is forbidden. The *Avnei Nezer* also requires that to be proscribed the author must recognize and understand the language being written (*Avnei Nezer, Orach Chayim* 200). But magnetic bits of storage cannot be read directly without an interpretation device.

On the use of fax machines on Shabbat and Yom Tov in hospitals

by PROF. ZEEV LOW

Information technology is changing rapidly and is becoming very sophisticated. The introduction in the near future of information highways of multimedia may change the technology underlying the operation of fax machines, to some extent. Hence, new halachic problems may emerge, on the one hand, and, on the other hand, former questions may become irrelevant. One of the major problems of modern responsa is that many Rabbis tend to generalize from one particular gadget to alternate, but different, instruments, although some serve similar purposes. Hence, many of these responsa are flawed or, at best, incomplete, because of a lack of basic knowledge of the construction and operation of such instruments. There is real danger of permitting prohibitions (*issurim*), as well as the opposite risk of prohibiting what is permitted. Small changes in technology could have a profound halachic consequence, which may change many considerations of such a responsum. One should keep in mind the profound remark of the *Chazon Ish, zt"l*, that, for each mistake that a Rabbi may make in halachic reasoning, there is a hundredfold probability that he may not understand the factuality (*metziut*) and, hence, may come to the wrong conclusion. We, therefore, open our discussion on the use of fax machines on Shabbat and *Yom Tov* with a description of the technology.

Elementary Description of a Fax Machine[1]

Fax machines are used to transmit copies of typed or handwritten documents from the sender to the addressee, who

---

1 This description is for conventional fax models used in 5753.

also has a fax machine. The transmission of the copy is done, at present, through the telephone communication system, using simple pulse digital techniques. The fax machine passes the document across an optical reader. The reader translates each black dot encountered in a given line into an electrical pulse that is transmitted, in the sequence of the scan, through the telephone, to the fax machine of the addressee.[2] On the receiving end, the electrical pulses are translated back into black dots which appear as printed lines on paper, producing a clear copy of the transmitted document.[3] The sending and receiving fax machines actually do

---

2 Some optical readers register only the white spaces around the letters and transmit these in proper time sequence to the receiver's fax machine. This kind of a reader is sort of a negative of the usual fax machine. There might be a difference between the two machines in the halachic considerations.

3 The letters on a computer or fax screen are formed from dots, but no continuous letters. This is true also for many printers. There is a question as to whether letters consisting of dots fall under the prohibition of proscribed writing on Shabbat. The *Talmud Yerushalmi* discusses this in tractates *Shabbat* (12:4) and *Gittin* (2:3): "[Concerning a *get*, it is written in the Torah] 'and he shall write,' but not engrave; 'and he shall write,' [but] not drip dots of ink; 'and he shall write, [but] not pour ink [to make previously invisible letters visible]. [With regard to dripping dots of ink] R. Yudan ben R. Shalom and R. Mattanyah [differ]: one says it is referring to [a case] when he did not commingle the dots, and the other says that, even if he commingled the dots [the letters would be invalid]." The *Korban ha-Edah* comments on "dripping dots of ink" that he made dots like letters; and on "he did not commingle the dots" that the did not retrace the quill over the dots and make [the dots] into an intact letter, but if he did commingle the dots it is valid. The *Penei Moshe* explains: "and they differ, for one says [that the expression] 'when he did not commingle the dots,' [is speaking of a situation where] afterwards he did not extend [the ink] from dot to dot to commingle [the dots] and make them into a complete letter, but if he did commingle them it is valid; and the other says that even if he commingled [the dots] afterwards it is invalid, because he did not write the form of an actual letter initially. Alternately, [the expression] 'when he did not commingle the dots' [is speaking of a situation where] he did not adjoin [the dots], but if he made them contiguous he is permitted to make them into a letter; and the other says that even if he made [the dots] contiguous to one another and numerous in distribution it is not a form of writing, and it is of no avail afterwards to make [the dots] into a complete letter."

It is clear, therefore, that a letter that consists of disconnected points or lines is not a letter as far as a *get* is concerned, and the *get* is not valid. The difference of opinion arises only if one thereafter completes the letter by filling

not "read" or "print" individual letters. The reader, which is the length of one document line, scans the document lines vertically down and not horizontally. Similarly, the printer of the receiving machine does not print letters but a vertical spray of black marks, corresponding to the pulses received.[4]

Fax machines are connected like any electrical instrument to an electrical outlet, and they can usually be operated around the clock, seven days a week. Communication by fax is cheaper than a telephone conversation, because a large amount of data can be transmitted in a short period of time. In the future, fax transmission will be a standard item in every home computer, permitting transmission between computers. This has halachic implications, since the transmitted document, which is stored in the memory of the transmitting computer, is only reproduced on the screen or as a written document when a specific command is given. If the receiving fax machine is a computer, the transmitted signals are also stored in the memory, and, here too, a special command will be needed to have the message appear on the screen or to operate the printer. This command can be given after Shabbat.

Manual Actions Necessary to Operate the Fax Machine

If we assume that the machine is connected all the time to the electrical outlet, no one has to switch on the fax machine.

On the digital screen, usually a liquid crystal display or LED screen, there is a message that the machine is ready

---

in the empty spaces between the dots. There are many proofs that these considerations regarding the kashrut of a *get* apply also to Biblically proscribed writing on Shabbat.

4 This may not make too much difference halachically. Rabbi Moshe Hershler, *zt"l*, pointed out to the author a proof from the Talmud *Yoma* and from the Yerushalmi, *Yoma* (3:9), where it is mentioned that Ben Kamtzar refused to teach his style of writing to others. He was able to write the four letters of Hashem's Name simultaneously (not one letter after the other) with four pens held with his five fingers. Hence, writing a whole line at once is a valid way of writing.

for operation. One must place the document in the appropriate slot of the fax machine (usually by hand, unless the system has been preprogrammed for special operation). In most fax machines this closes a microswitch. In others, a key tab command moves the document automatically into the right position. In more modern machines, no electrical switch will be closed, but a sensing element will take over.

On the screen, a number of questions then appear in sequence, e.g., how many pages are to be transmitted, what budget number should be billed, and what is the telephone number of the addressee. Each query has to be answered by touching one of the many tabs. In most machines, touching the tabs activates a microswitch and transmits a signal to the microprocessor.

All queries and the "typed" answers appear on the screen, one after the other, including the telephone number to which the message is to be sent. (Some machines store frequently used telephone numbers that the sender does not have to "type." One touches a telephone selection tab to select the number and activate the dialer.) However, the screen is not essential for the operation of the fax machine. The main purpose of the messages on the screen is to enable the sender to view what he has done and to decide whether he has given the right instructions in the proper sequence. Hence, the screen can be blanked out on Shabbat.

Touching the command "start" tab activates the process. The machine automatically dials the telephone number that has been previously "typed." Should the telephone of the addressee be busy or disconnected, the fax machine will automatically try the same number several times in intervals of several minutes, without any additional command from the sender. After several cycles, should it be impossible to make the connection, the machine will desist from further calling, so that the fax machine can receive incoming calls. It is possible to program the machine so that the document will be transmitted at a later time, for example, when the telephone rates are cheaper.[5]

Once the connection has been made, the optical reader will read and translate the letters into electrical pulses and transmit these to the fax machine of the addressee, which in turn will convert them back into letters. These then will be printed on the paper inside the fax machine. The person who receives the document does not have to do anything at all. The received document falls into a basket or is stored in the computer memory.

Hence, the manual operations can be classified as follows:

1. Insertion of the document in the appropriate slot with the resultant closing of a microswitch.

2. Touching various keyboard tabs and therefore, closing miniature circuits. Some of these circuits activate the screen, where various letters appear.

3. Touching the start button activating the whole process, including the "printing" of the transmitted document at the receiving end.

Possible Prohibitions Against Using the Fax on Shabbat

1. Closing microcircuits by touching different tabs is not permitted, either as a Biblical or Rabbinic prohibition.[6]

---

5 We discriminate between primary and secondary causation (*ko'ach rishon* and *ko'ach sheni*). The main difference between the two is in the length of time it takes for the result to occur after an action has been taken. If the result of the human action is delayed, then this is considered an indirect causation. Hence, if the document is transmitted later, one could consider the resultant "writing" of the document as not directly connected with touching the command start key. The prohibition in this case may be Rabbinic and not Biblical. It is usually difficult to determine what is considered immediate and what is a delayed result. A fairly good rule is that a delayed action is one which can still be reversed or obviated by human intervention before the action takes place. For further discussion see the author's book *Bi'ur Mussagim: Ko'ach Kocho v'Ko'ach Sheni b'Halachah* (Jerusalem: Mosad ha-Rav Kook, 1978).

6 The Rabbinical prohibition is that of *molid* (an object which was not prepared before Shabbat, but became available for use on Shabbat). See, for example, *Teshuvot Beit Yitzchak, Yoreh De'ah*, addenda to sect. 39. The *Chazon Ish* considers that this is prohibited under the Biblical work category of building (*boneh*) (*Chazon Ish, Orach Chayim*, sect. 50, and *Teshuvot Minchat Shelomo*,

2. Various messages or commands appear on the screen. Most of these are preprogrammed — that is to say, the person does not type them when sending the fax, but presses a prompt tab to make them appear on the screen. However, some of these messages, such as the telephone number, are "typed" in by the sender.

There is a question whether the writing that appears on the screen is prohibited as a Biblical work category or a Rabbinic prohibition. Firstly, the writing on a liquid crystal has no permanency (*davar she-eino mitkayeim*). Secondly, there is no actual writing, but the generated electrical field (and not currents of electricity) orders the orientation of the crystallites, so that a contrast is formed in the shape of letters. Reordering elements is usually not considered a Biblical prohibition, only a Rabbinic one. Thirdly, the so-called letters are not formed as contiguous forms. Each letter consists of many small lines, which the eye integrates and perceives as a letter. A letter composed in this manner would invalidate both a *Sefer Torah* and a *get*. It is true that the laws of writing on Shabbat are not to be compared completely with writing a *get*, in part because of the general rule which requires the fulfillment of *melechet machshevet* for work to be proscribed Biblically on Shabbat, but does not require this principle when one is writing a *get*. But the purposeful intention of the person pressing the various tabs to achieve the desired goal of making up these letter forms is not sufficient. What is also required is a certain degree of creative design, both in the objective and the manner of performance. We have never found that intention alone can transform an act that is not considered writing into writing, or transform an action that is not one of the Biblical work

---

sect. 12). If the circuit is closed inductively or capacitatively, with no creation of a metallic circuit connection, according to the *Chazon Ish* it would be permitted, but for the *Beit Yitzchak* there remains the prohibition of *molid*. For further discussion, see chapter 3 in the author's forthcoming book *Chikrei Lev*.

categories into a Biblical work category.[7] Hence, it is unlikely that there is any Biblical prohibition in producing this kind of writing.

3. As a result of activating the microcircuits, the electrical pulses are transformed into binary language, and the manuscript or other messages are stored in microcircuits in the memory of the microprocessor.

Storing of data in the microprocessor also is not a Biblical prohibition. Most of the *Acharonim* have written that storing information on tape recorders is not writing (*kotev*) or making an impression (*roshem*).[8] The same considerations apply here. Firstly, the small changes in the elementary magnets or the microcircuits, which constitute the letters, cannot be seen by the eye, not even with a strong magnifying glass. Secondly, they do not resemble letters or commonly used signs. Thirdly, binary computer language is not a language in a halachic sense. Finally, the rearrangements of elementary magnets in these microprocessors are not changes which last (*davar shel kayama*). From these considerations and many others, there is no doubt that information storage in microprocessors is not to be considered *kotev* or *roshem*.

4. The main problem of writing is encountered when the copy of the transmitted document is printed on paper at the receiver's fax machine. (Storage of the transmitted messages in the memory of the addressee's computer is included in item 3 above.) The question is whether this is considered *kotev* or *roshem*, or neither of these two *issurim*.

---

7 The Talmud in *Bava Kamma* (60a) does note, in the name of R. Ashi: "When do we say winnowing with the assistance of the wind [is liable]? Only with regard to Shabbat, where the Torah prohibited *melechet machshevet*." The Biblical work category of winnowing is normally performed with the help of an external force, the wind, and hence, according to R. Ashi, it is proscribed on Shabbat, but when damages are incurred when the wind fans a flame initially set by the perpetrator, the act of the wind would be considered a secondary cause. However, the case we are discussing is very different.

8 We shall not discuss here the various opinions regarding the differences between *kotev* and *roshem*. For a full discussion, see my book *Chikrei Lev*.

On the one hand, one could reason that the process is complicated and goes through several intermediate steps — as briefly described above — before the copy is printed. Moreover, the printing is carried out in a very different location from that of the transmitter. The sender does not directly print the document. He is not even aware of the receiver's fax machine. Hence, the final result of printing could be an indirect action.

Against these points one could argue that, in a sense, the two fax machines are coupled together by means of the telephone. The sender directly activates the receiver's device by sending the message. It is true that, most of the time, two separate fax machines are involved, but once the telephone link has been established, they are connected as a functioning unit, like two gears that are engaged in a single machine. The logic follows the well-known approach of the *Chazon Ish*,[9] who discusses the use of a tractor or plowing machine on Shabbat. One could divide the action being performed into two components. The operator only moves the machine, while the engine independently runs the plow. At first glance one could claim that the man is not plowing; the machine is doing all the work. But, the *Chazon Ish* writes, we have to look at the gasoline-operated plowing machine as the man's direct tool, despite the many diverse operative steps that occur within the mechanism of the plowing machine. There is no difference, from the halachic viewpoint, whether the operator uses a manual plow or a sophisticated plowing machine. In the final analysis, the man plows on Shabbat.

Similarly, in our case, we can view the two fax machines as one integrated unit. Thus, in the final analysis, by pressing the command "start," the transmitter writes the message at the other end of the line. However, when the telephone line is disconnected at the receiver's end and the message is transmitted at a later time, the situation might be different. In this case, considerations such as secondary or indirect

---

9 *Chazon Ish, Orach Chayim* 36.

causation (*ko'ach sheni*) are relevant.[10]

Even if we were to posit that the writing at the other end is directly executed, there are other considerations which cast doubt on whether this is the kind of writing which is Biblically disallowed. If the transmitted document is not written in Hebrew but, for example, in English — there are half a dozen *Rishonim* who decide that this is not writing enjoined by the Torah.[11]

5. In many fax machines, after completion of the transmission, a note is printed on the transmitting end containing information such as the time when the transmission was completed, the duration of the transmission, the telephone number dialed, etc. This service can be easily dispensed with and, hence, should not create a problem on Shabbat.

Conclusions

A person using a fax machine on Shabbat is transgressing several Rabbinic prohibitions and possibly a Biblical interdiction. Some of these prohibitions can be obviated by clever changes in the fax machine. Nevertheless, some of the prohibitions remain. If a doctor has to transmit a message to a nurse or to another department in the hospital or to a pharmacy, and his choice is to write or to send a fax, it seems

---

10 One might be tempted to use the following analogy: According to most authorities, a person cannot fulfill the mitzvah of listening to the reading of the Megillah via the radio. What he hears is not the voice of the reader but an electronic rendition — a copy — that resembles the reader's voice. (The *Chazon Ish* disagrees and thinks that he does fulfill his obligation in this manner.) Here, too, the transmitted document is not the original printed document, but only a copy — and not even a carbon copy. Nevertheless, the main consideration is that a document was printed, and it may not be relevant that only a copy was printed.

11 The *Noda bi-Yehudah* writes that this position of the *Or Zarua* is the opinion of only one *Rishon* (*Teshuvot Noda bi-Yehudah*, 1st ed., 36).However, this is also the opinion of the Ra'avya, the *Agudah*, the *Hagahot Maymuniyot*, the *Leket Yosher*, and possibly the *Mordechai*, as well as several others. The conclusion is that this opinion was held by a school of scholars over a period of 150 years. Further details are found in the forthcoming book *Chikrei Lev*.

to me that it is preferable to send a fax, even if he has to type out his message on a word processor that has been connected to the electrical outlet before Shabbat.

Halachic problems in diagnosing and preventing infection on Shabbat

Translated and adapted from the article
by DR. MEIR ISSACSON in *Halachah U'Refuah* II, 252-54

The determination of the presence of an infection or of a communicable disease relies upon the laboratory examination of various specimens, e.g., blood, urine, and spinal fluid. Dr. Issacson summarizes the halachic issues in handling these specimens.

Drawing blood is a form of wounding, *chovel*, which is forbidden on Shabbat.[1] But when the patient is in danger, it is imperative to obtain blood cultures even on Shabbat. The blood is incubated at body temperature for twelve hours or longer, and then a portion of the broth or plate is spread on a slide stained with dyes, to facilitate microscopic identification of the growth. At times, it may be necessary to stain specimens on Shabbat which initially were seeded on a weekday. Urine, spinal fluid, and other secretions may be examined similarly.

Dr. Issacson notes that most urgent examinations relate to bacterial infections. He maintains that diagnostic workups for viral infections usually can be deferred until after Shabbat since, by and large, no specific therapy is available. In the event of a potentially fatal virulent infection which can be treated (e.g., meningitis due to herpes virus), examination of the blood and spinal fluid is imperative to establish the correct diagnosis. Antibody-deficient patients (e.g., individuals undergoing cancer chemotherapy) who develop viral eruptions should also be evaluated quickly, since they are very susceptible to infection. On the other hand, the diagnosis of serious fungal infections is a long process of

---

1 This topic is more fully discussed by A. Buchman in *Halachah U'Refuah* I, 219-30.

several days and sometimes weeks, so that, for the most part, the specimens may be gathered after Shabbat.[2]

In treating infections, it is clear that for a patient in danger we may of course violate Shabbat. Fever is a common manifestation of infectious disease, and its presence is sufficient to transform a patient not otherwise critically ill into one who is halachically considered to be in danger. The symptomatic treatment of fever usually involves sponge bathing or immersion in a cool tub, as well as medication. When wet compresses need to be applied, halachic issues may be raised regarding wringing the water from the towels and the concern that the towels may be washed clean by the water they have absorbed. It is possible, in some instances, to reduce the problem by adding water to the towel while it is applied to the patient, thereby avoiding the problem of wringing water from the towel, but this method usually is not effective in lowering the temperature adequately.

With many lower respiratory infections it may be necessary to heat water in a vaporizer to provide a warm-mist atmosphere for the patient. Since this involves the Biblical prohibition of cooking, it is permissible only where the patient is in danger. Where possible, the vaporizer should be plugged in before Shabbat, and a pot of water should be prepared and kept hot over Shabbat to replenish the vaporizer's reservoir.[3] In some situations (e.g., hoarseness), a cold-mist vaporizer may suffice but, here too, the vaporizer should be plugged in before Shabbat.[4]

---

2 One may, however, argue that despite the long incubation time needed to grow a fungal specimen, one day's lead may be significant in later treatment and, therefore, the procedure should be initiated immediately.

3 *Shulchan Aruch, Orach Chayim* 74:15; see the Rama's gloss on the text. See also *Assia* 6 (24), 637. Perhaps one may use this method even in less serious circumstances. Others have, however, maintained that even if the water was heated previously it is forbidden to add it to the vaporizer while it is turned on (*Otzrot Yerushalayim* 227:115).

4 The possibility that dispersal of cold mist may be forbidden as a species of winnowing (*zoreh*) has also been raised. However, this work category applies

With contagious diseases, urgent precautions may be required to prevent the development of illness in an exposed individual and to halt its spread within the population. Subcutaneous or intramuscular injections may be permitted to administer necessary antisera, since there is no Biblical violation in their administration, as there is no intention to draw blood. Of course, in exceptional circumstances, such as animal bites about the face or with deep infected wounds, we should treat the patient as critically ill.

---

only to plants (*Teshuvot Akiva Eiger* 20).

Medicines and remedies on Shabbat

Translated and adapted from the article
by RABBI MOSHE HERSHLER in *Halachah U'Refuah* I, 67-112

The Rabbis forbade preparing and taking medicines on Shabbat in the absence of significant illness,[1] for fear that in error one might think it permissible to grind together ingredients to compound the medicine, which is a violation of a Biblical precept (*tochen*).[2] The Rif explains that, if one were permitted to take medicines previously prepared, in a situation of urgency one might, in error, think that it is also permissible to grind together medical components on Shabbat, even though there is no life-threatening peril.[3] Rashi further adds that the major concern is that an uneducated bystander who observes the treatment might make an incorrect inference, expanding the leniency to include the preparation of medicaments.[4]

The restriction against taking medicine still applies today, even though a majority of people and health-care providers are unfamiliar with the procedures of compounding medicines and pharmaceuticals, for medicines are still prepared in factories and pharmacies by pulverizing ingredients and mixing them together. Indeed, since compounded medicines are a mainstay of therapy, the Rabbis extended

---

1 The explanation of this term, as it applies to medical therapy on Shabbat, will be analyzed later in this chapter.

2 *Shabbat* 53b, Rashi: *Gezerah mishum.* (See also *Shabbat* 64b, 40b, 108, and 109).

3 *Shabbat* 53b, Rif. The Rif notes that since it is unlikely that an individual would become so agitated as to lose his bearings over the illness of an animal, the Rabbis did not restrict an owner from giving medication to an animal (see also *Mo'ed Katan* 10b, *Tosafot: V'ein*). But Rashi and others maintain that leniency in treating one's animal is restricted to situations where significant financial loss may be incurred (Ibid., Rashi: *U'mi gazrinon*).

4 Rashi: *Ein mekar lib'heima.*

their restriction to include all therapeutic procedures, even where there is, in fact, no possibility of grinding and mixing ingredients.[5] But a procedure which is merely protective in nature and not therapeutic per se, such as placing a bandage over a wound which has healed, would be allowed.[6]

Since the basis of the Rabbinic prohibition against taking medicines is concern lest observers err, concluding that preparing mixtures and potions also is permitted on Shabbat, the restriction would not apply in a case where the procedure is not recognizably therapeutic. If another individual could infer that the treatment or potion was in fact administered for one's pleasure or to satisfy one's hunger or thirst, then, even if the intent was therapeutic, the regimen would still be permitted. Thus the Talmud reasons that it may be permissible to immerse a person in cool water as therapy for an attack of congestion, since it appears as though he is cooling himself for his enjoyment.[7] Similarly, one may doctor the eye on Shabbat by administering wine to the closed lid, since it seems as though it is merely being washed.[8] But dripping wine into the eye would be forbidden as an obvious treatment.

While it is true that in these instances observers could not definitely conclude that it is permitted to use medicines on Shabbat and wrongly infer that medicines may also be compounded, should there be concern that the user himself might wrongfully err in extending the leniency? The *Tosafot ha-Rid*[9] reasons that a learned patient would surely know the law, while an uneducated individual who would question the permissibility of putting wine on a closed eyelid could be

---

5 *Shabbat* 53b. See also *Eglei Tal, Melechet Tochen* 17:5.

6 *Shulchan Aruch, Orach Chayim* 328:27. The *Magen Avraham* explains that since the wound has already healed, there is no urgency in the treatment.

7 *Shabbat* 53b.

8 Ibid. 108b, Rashi: *Al gav ha-ayin.*

9 Ibid. Similarly in the *Eglei Tal, Tochen* 22:46(2).

instructed not to infer from the leniency in sanctioning such a procedure that medicines may generally be used on Shabbat. Our concern in only with regard to unlearned spectator who would not question what he has seen.

Leniency in permitting remedies which are not clearly therapeutic applies only when the procedure or agent is not inherently therapeutic, such as foodstuffs or washes. However, an item which can be used for one's pleasure but is mainly employed medicinally may not be permissible as a remedy unless it is prepared or used in a special manner. Rashi[10] explains that, although bystanders would infer that a patient using collyrium salve on Shabbat was merely washing his eye, the user, whose actual intent is therapeutic, must prepare the wash by steeping it in water before Shabbat. Since the collyrium salve is mainly used as a remedy, the user himself must prepare it in this unique manner so that he also clearly understands that it is generally not permissible to take or to prepare medicines on Shabbat. Where special preparation is not possible, the therapeutic agent may be used only for nonmedicinal purposes. Thus, natural purgative waters may be imbibed on Shabbat to quench one's thirst only if one is not ill, since they are not primarily a beverage.[11]

Foodstuffs and Beverages as Remedies

The Talmud establishes the principle that all foodstuffs and beverages may be ingested or imbibed on Shabbat, even if intended as a remedy.[12] However, if the food is eaten or used in a manner which clearly indicates to a spectator that it is being used medicinally, the Rabbinic restriction against remedies for one not significantly ill remains in force. One

---

10 *Shabbat* 108b, Rashi: *V'noten al gav einav.*

11 *Shabbat* 109b.

12 Ibid.: Mishnah, *Shabbat* 111a; and *Berachot* 38a. See also Rambam, *Hilchot Shabbat* 21;22.

may, therefore, sip vinegar for a toothache only when the vinegar is swallowed, but not if it is subsequently spit out.[13] Also, one may swallow oil for a sore throat, but not gargle even if he will subsequently swallow it, since the gargling demonstrates the therapeutic intention.[14]

Rabbi Hershler raises the question whether the underlying reason for permitting foodstuffs as remedies is that when they are ingested it is not apparent to an observer that the intent is therapeutic, or if foodstuffs by their very nature were excluded from the Rabbinic restriction against taking medicines. He suggests that the difference of opinion between the *Amora'im* Abaya and Rava concerning the use of vinegar for a toothache[15] might hinge upon this question. According to Abaya, if one eats a food in a normal manner, the Rabbinic restriction does not apply. But, as Rashi notes, Rava holds that even if it is ingested in a normal fashion, it may yet be proscribed if it is taken at a time when one does not usually sip it, thereby allowing a bystander to surmise a therapeutic intention.

One may similarly comprehend *Tosafot*'s explanation of the difference between R. Yosef and Abaya concerning the use of a mixture of unripe barley flour and honey as a remedy on Shabbat.[16] According to R. Yosef, the remedy would be proscribed, even though the components are merely foodstuffs which are fit to be eaten, because the mixture is prepared only as a remedy, and it would thus be obvious that the purpose is therapeutic. But Abaya maintains that as bona fide foodstuff ingested in a usual manner, the mixture cannot be proscribed, even if one could surmise that it is for a remedy. The *Rishonim* also do not agree whether foodstuffs are authorized merely when therapeutic intent is not obvi-

---

13 *Shabbat* 111a.

14 *Berachot* 36a, Rashi.

15 *Shabbat* 111a.

16 *Berachot* 38a, *Tosafot: V'salka da'atech*, and *V'ha tenan kol ha-ochlin.*

ous[17] or if they are entirely removed from the domain of the restriction against medicines on Shabbat.[18]

Universal acceptance as a food is not necessary in order for an edible to be sanctioned as a remedy on Shabbat. Even if a significant minority of people avoid the food because it is injurious to their health, as long as it is considered foodstuff it may be used as a remedy on Shabbat.[19] Furthermore, preparations of fruits or herbs which are not ingested to satisfy one's hunger, yet are eaten by healthy individuals to prevent the occurrence of certain ailments, may also be used as remedies on Shabbat.[20] But herbal concoctions which are never ingested as food prior to the onset of an illness may not be used on Shabbat, even if one developed an idiosyncratic desire to eat the leaves for one's enjoyment or to satisfy one's hunger.[21] On the other hand, something that is not a food but is widely used by healthy individuals as a precaution (in addition to any therapeutic value it may have) cannot be permitted as a foodstuff on Shabbat. Thus Rabbi Hershler brushes aside the position of some who permit aspirin for discomfort since it is used by many medically unknowledgeable individuals to avoid "catching a cold."[22]

---

17 *Piskei Tosafot ha-Rid* regarding Mishnah, *Shabbat* 109b; *Sefer ha-Terumah*, and *Ra'avan* 356.

18 Rashba in Novellae, *Berachot* 38a (see note 14); Rashi, *Shabbat* 140a, regarding drinking *chiltit*, a plant used for spice as a remedy for "heaviness of heart" (possibly asthma or heartburn).

19 Rashi, *Shabbat* 110a, regarding the permissibility of eating spleen and a species of bean, both of which were not widely eaten in Talmudic times when their therapeutic effect was not needed, because the former was considered injurious to the teeth and the latter to the gastrointestinal tract. See also *Tur, Orach Chayim* 328, and Me'iri.

20 *Shabbat* 109b, the Mishnah concerning *abuv ro'eh* and *yo'ezer*. Rashi explains that some healthy individuals ingest them for their pleasure. But from the *Piskei ha-Rid* it is apparent that they are used prior to exposure in order to ward off certain illnesses.

21 *Shabbat* 109b, the Mishnah concerning *izbion* (Greek hyssop).

22 (Aspirin, in low dose, is also widely used today to prevent coronary thrombosis.) Rabbi Hershler also excludes vitamins as a foodstuff, but it may be argued

With regard to fluid extracts and potions which are essentially used medicinally, but on occasion may be imbibed for pleasure or to quench one's thirst, the *Rishonim* differ as to the circumstances in which they may be consumed on Shabbat. The Mishnah states, "All beverages may be imbibed, except for waters of *dekalim* because they are basically used for jaundice, but one may drink the waters to quench one's thirst."[23] Rashi[24] explains that one may drink them only if he is not ill. Since the waters are not regarded as a beverage, their use by one who is ill would always be interpreted by observers as medicinal, even when the intent was to quench one's thirst.[25] Others hold that if the intent in drinking them was to quench one's thirst, their use as a beverage cannot be proscribed even if one were acting ill.[26]

---

that, unlike aspirin, which is a drug, vitamins are merely concentrates of nutrients which are found in food. They are widely used as part of the normal diet and not as a drug to prevent illness. It is true that, in some instances, large doses of vitamins have been used to treat specific ailments, but this may be similar to drinking concentrated orange juice when someone has a cold because of its vitamin C content. However, perhaps vitamins should not be permitted in the form of a pill. (See also below, the section "Medicine Not Intended as a Remedy.")

23 *Shabbat* 109b. Waters of *dekalim* (possibly an extract of the palm tree) were used in Talmudic times as a purgative for jaundice. (The Talmud [*Shabbat* 110a] also offers a variant reading: waters of *dekarim*.)

24 Rashi. The *Tur* rules similarly (*Orach Chayim* 328).

25 Rabbi Hershler explains that the Mishnah is more lenient with waters of *dekalim* than with *izbion*, because *izbion* is never considered food, and even when it is ingested with the intention to satisfy one's hunger, the behavior is unusual and peculiar. On the other hand, waters of *dekalim*, although not inherently a beverage, may be considered so if one were to imbibe them for pleasure, since they are used occasionally by healthy individuals as well. One may also speculate that the ruling regarding waters of *dekalim* is unique, since they were prescribed for jaundice, a very obvious affliction. Drinking other beverages for other illnesses may not be as apparent, particularly when the patient does not act as though he is taking a medicine. But jaundice is always obvious, even when the patient does not act ill. Thus, there is no way for one who is jaundiced to appear to be drinking the purgative waters merely as a beverage to quench his thirst. Perhaps this is the reason that the Mishnah specifies the illness for which waters of *dekalim* are used.

26 The Ran and *Piskei ha-Rid*, cited in the *Biur Halachah* 328:37.

On the other hand, fluid extracts and syrups which are not
at all within the category of beverages may not be ingested
by one who ails but is not significantly ill, even if his intent
is to savor their sweetness.

Oils, Creams, and Lotions

In Mishnaic and Talmudic times, various oils and aromatic
extracts were smeared over the body for pleasure, as well as
therapeutically for a variety of ailments. As with foods and
beverages, anointing oneself in the usual manner with a
substance which is not clearly medicinal would be permitted
Thus, the Mishnah declares, "If one's loins ache, he must not
rub them with wine or vinegar, but he may anoint them with
oil, but not rose oil. Royalty may rub rose oil on their wounds,
since it is their practice to use it on weekdays. R. Shimon
says all Israel are considered royal children."[27] Rashi[28] explains that wine and vinegar are rubbed on the body only as
a remedy, but anointing oneself with common oil is not
prohibited, even when it is intended therapeutically, since it
is used by the average person for pleasure as well as medicinally. However, rose oil, which is expensive and not generally available, could be used therapeutically on Shabbat only
by royalty, not by commoners. But Rashi does not clearly
indicate whether a commoner who had no intention to treat
an ailment would be permitted to use rose oil on Shabbat for
his pleasure. Rabbi Hershler suggests that its use would be
allowed by inference from the case of waters of *dekalim* cited
previously.[29]

---

27 Mishnah, *Shabbat* 111a.

28 Ibid., Rashi: also Novellae of the Ramban and Rashba, and *Piskei ha-Rid*.

29 *Tosafot (Shabbat* 111a: *L'memra d'Rav), Rabbenu Chananel,* and *Halachot
    Gedolot* (cited in the Rashba) posit that R. Shimon's disagreement with the
    first opinion of the Mishnah follows his own position that an action which is
    planned for an authorized purpose is always permitted on Shabbat, even
    though it might lead to a recognized, but unintended, proscribed consequence.
    According to the first opinion, which maintains that such an act would be

Currently, the halachic ruling regarding the use of oils should follow that of rose oil, since it is not the custom to anoint ones body as in previous times. Thus, if the intent in smearing on oil or lotion were therapeutic, it would be forbidden on Shabbat. But for one's pleasure, and to protect the skin from injury, it would be permissible. Sunscreen lotions for people with sensitive skin, insect repellents, and creams to prevent chapping of the skin could be used on Shabbat. However, Rabbi Hershler cautions that smearing the body for the purpose of sunbathing might be considered a weekday activity (*uvdah d'chol*),[30] not appropriate for Shabbat.

Manipulations Not Involving Medicines

The Rambam[31] rules that it is permissible to invert a heated cup over an infant's navel on Shabbat to elevate it, to manipulate a displaced cervical vertebra by squeezing the neck, to swaddle an infant, to reset displaced ears manually or with an instrument, and to elevate the sternal cartilage which may produce nausea by pressing on the stomach, "because in all these procedures and in similar cases no medicaments are used which would cause concern lest one grind up compounds, and the person is in distress." But pressing on a child's abdomen to induce defecation is forbidden, lest it lead to the administration of purgatives. The *Kesef Mishneh*[32] explains that treatments which cannot be

---

forbidden, an average person could not use rose oil even when he intends no remedy, since medical benefit may be derived incidentally. But the halachic ruling follows the opinion of R. Shimon in this regard. Therefore, where one's goal is merely pleasure, even rose oil could be used.

30 Such an activity is prohibited Rabbinically because it detracts from the atmosphere of Shabbat, or it resembles Biblically forbidden work, or it may lead to Biblically forbidden work because a person engaged in such a pursuit would be more likely to forget that it is Shabbat.

31 *Hilchot Shabbat* 21:31. See also *Shabbat* 66b, 129b, and 147b, and *Avodah Zarah* 28b.

32 *Hilchot Shabbat* 21:31. He offers a similar explanation in the *Beit Yosef* (*Tur*

effected with pharmaceuticals, but only by manipulation, do not come under the Rabbinic restriction against taking medicines. But, where medicines could be used, even manipulation would be prohibited.

However, with regard to inducing vomiting on Shabbat, the Rambam rules that it is permitted by inserting the hand into the mouth, but not through the use of an emetic, lest one prepare a compounded pharmaceutical.[33] But, since vomiting can also be induced by a pharmaceutical preparation, should it not be prohibited manually? Furthermore, there are other remedies not involving medicines which were included in the Rabbinic restriction against the use of medicinals.[34]

Rabbi Hershler, therefore, suggests that the Rambam differentiates between manipulations which are, in fact, therapeutic in nature and other procedures which merely appear to embellish and improve the individual. While the latter are not normally included in the Rabbinic restriction,[35] where the procedure is therapeutic the Rabbinic stricture applies, even if no pharmaceuticals are used. For if it is apparent that the individual is being treated, one should be concerned that an observer might conclude that medicines may be compounded on Shabbat.

We must also assume that the Rambam did not regard the induction of vomiting and the use of emetics as purely therapeutic in nature. Ingestion of an emetic to empty the stomach before eating was commonly practiced in the Mish-

Orach Chayim 328). The Taz (*Orach Chayim* 328) and the *Mishnah Berurah* (328:13) reason similarly.

33 *Hilchot Shabbat* 21;31. See also *Shabbat* 147b.

34 Such as immersing oneself in water as a remedy for congestion (see *Shabbat* 53b.)

35 Although procedures which improve an individual's physique may not be therapeutic, they may be prohibited for other reasons. Thus, aligning the vertebra of an infant, which was not considered urgent, is forbidden because of its similarity to building (placing one vertebral "block" upon another) (*Shabbat* 147b).

naic and Talmudic period. It was not unusual for gourmands to induce vomiting several times during the course of festivities so that they might partake of all the varieties of edibles. Thus, manual induction of vomiting would not be prohibited as a clear-cut therapy. It would be permitted despite its similarity to vomiting induced by an emetic, since ingestion of the emetic itself could be viewed by an observer as preparatory to eating, rather than therapeutic. Yet, the emetic itself could not be used, because it is not a food but rather a preparation that is similar to pharmaceuticals, which are proscribed on Shabbat.[36]

Medicine Not Intended as a Remedy

From the Talmud's conclusion that vomiting may be induced manually but not with an emetic, which is similar to a medicinal remedy, we infer that all kinds of pills and drops should be similarly proscribed, even though they are not used therapeutically, but only to maintain the individual's

---

36 Rashi also did not view the use of an emetic as a therapeutic procedure (*Shabbat* 123b, Rashi: *Apiktvizin*). Nevertheless, he explains that emesis induced by a drug would not be permitted because it is "similar to a remedy and there is concern that one may come to compound pharmaceuticals" on Shabbat (*Shabbat* 147b, Rashi: *Ella b'sam*). However, the commentaries are puzzled by an apparent contradiction, for in the first citation Rashi continues, "Even though there is in the case of an emetic no restrictive concern lest one may compound pharmaceuticals because it is not used for a remedy, it is still prohibited because it improves and embellishes the individual." But this statement was merely an explanation of R. Nachman's use of the ruling concerning *apiktvizin* to support his contention that it is forbidden to manipulate and straighten a newborn's limbs on Shabbat (see *Shabbat* 123a, Rashi: *Asubei yenuka*). R. Nachman must have understood the issue in both instances to be a question of permitting a procedure on Shabbat which will better the individual. For if the prohibition against using an emetic was based on its similarity to a medicinal remedy, one could argue that it has no bearing on his ruling. Since the final halachic ruling is not in accordance with R. Nachman, we may combine both citations of Rashi in explaining that although it is not "used as a remedy, but only to empty his stomach so that he may eat and drink much more" (*Shabbat* 123b), an emetic is still forbidden because it is "similar to a remedy" (ibid. 147b). (See also below, the section "Medicine Not Intended as a Remedy.")

well-being. Items such as sleeping pills, appetite stimulants or depressants, and even vitamins which appear in the form of a medicine should not be used.

Similarly, with regard to carrying in a public domain, the Mishnah rules that a woman may go out on Shabbat "with peppercorn or a globule of salt, or any other substance that was placed in her mouth before Shabbat, but she must not initially put it in her mouth on Shabbat."[37] Although the Talmud notes that peppercorn was used to counteract bad breath, [38] R. Yosef Poras[39] explains that in both instances the reason for not allowing the woman to put them in her mouth on Shabbat was the restriction against taking medicines. However, the *Tosefta* specifically permits chewing mastic or rinsing with mouthwash on Shabbat when the intent is not medicinal but only to improve one's breath.

In explaining this discrepancy, R. Chayim *Or Zarua*[40] maintains that mouthwash is permissible because it is not a remedy for bad breath but merely conceals the foul odor so that it is not recognizable. Peppercorn, on the other hand, was actually thought to be a remedy for bad breath, if only for a short time. With regard to chewing spices on Shabbat to make one's voice pleasant (the issue of the responsum), R. Chayim suggests that this is actually a remedy for dryness of the throat and raspiness, which impair the voice. Although this condition is not an illness per se, it can be considered an ailment which troubles the sufferer. In a parallel fashion, although an emetic is not intended to treat an illness, R. Chayim contends that it improves the condition of the stomach, reducing the troubling sensation of heaviness.

The *Beit Yosef* takes a more lenient position. To the *Tur*'s

---

37 Mishnah, *Shabbat* 84b.

38 *Shabbat* 85a. Salt was thought to be a remedy for toothaches (Rashi) or gum inflammation (Jastrow).

39 *Shabbat* 84b, *Tosafot: U'bilvad she-lo titen.*

40 *Teshuvot* 57.

ruling — "Anything which is not a usual foodstuff or beverage for healthy people is forbidden to be ingested or imbibed
as a remedy, but if one eats or drinks it to satisfy his hunger
or thirst and he has no illness, it is permitted."[41]*Beit Yosef*
adds, "Since he is not ill, no restriction can be enacted;
therefore, even if he is not hungry or thirsty, it is permissible
to eat or drink them."[42] Now, if he is not hungry or thirsty
and intends no remedy, he must, undoubtedly, derive another general benefit from ingesting the substance, i.e., a
sense of improved well-being. We may thus deduce that
according to the *Beit Yosef* it is permissible to ingest substances and pharmaceuticals which are precautionary and
increase one's resistance to illness. In the *Shulchan Aruch*
he specifies, "It is permitted to eat sweet resinous substances
and to sip a raw egg in order to improve one's voice."[43] The
Mordechai, the original source of this ruling, adds that this
is because "it is only to make the voice pleasant and not a
remedy, for he has no affliction in his throat."[44]

In his comments on the *Shulchan Aruch*, the *Magen
Avraham*[45] demurs. He stresses that the *Tur* specifically
limits allowable ingestion for the purpose of satisfying one's
hunger or quenching one's thirst; but if it is intended for a
treatment, it is forbidden, "even if he is well." The *Peri
Megadim* adds that although he is well and he takes the
substance merely "to maintain his health and temperament
so that he not become weakened, it is forbidden."[46]

The disagreement between the *Beit Yosef* and the*Magen
Avraham* is of practical significance. For according to the
Peri Megadim, pills and medicinal extracts which are used

---

41 *Orach Chayim* 328.

42 Ibid., *Beit Yosef.* See also the *Shulchan Aruch, Orach Chayim* 328:37.

43 Ibid., 328:38.

44 *Shabbat* 111a, the *Mordechai* 384.

45 *Orach Chayim* 328, *Magen Avraham* 43.

46 Ibid., *Eshel Avraham* 49.

prophylactically, such as vitamins, would be permitted by the former, but not by the latter authority. Other authorities have suggested that aspirin also may be permitted prophylactically, particularly since it is widely used by relatively healthy people.[47] But Rabbi Hershler correctly rejects this position, stressing that aspirin and similar medicines are taken for pains and other afflictions of variable severity. Tranquilizers, sedatives, and sleeping pills also are not used merely in a precautionary manner, for these medicinals actually exert a calming effect, reducing the state of anxiety and wakefulness.

Treatment of Wounds and Hemorrhage

With regard to wounds, prevention of hemorrhage is considered a form of therapy. The *Shulchan Aruch* rules that blood may be rinsed off with water or wine.[48] But one may not administer a strong astringent, such as vinegar, which will contract the flesh and prevent further hemorrhage.[49]

Yet it is possible to treat the wound indirectly by pouring the medicine outside the injured area and allowing it to run into the wound. The Talmud records that Rav and Shemuel differ regarding the permissibility of placing a mixture of hot water and oil on a wound on Shabbat.[50] Rav says that it may be placed on the wound directly, but Shemuel maintains it should be poured outside the perimeter of the wound and be allowed to run into the affected area.

The *Rishonim* differ as to the basis of Shemuel's sugges-

---

47 *Be'er Moshe* 33.

48 *Orach Chayim* 328:48.

49 *Shabbat* 109a. According to Rashi, wine assuages bleeding for most people. But for the sensitive inhabitants of Machoza, it is a relatively strong astringent, similar to vinegar, causing the flesh to contract, with cessation of hemorrhage. Immersing the wound in a fluid which does not halt the bleeding is similar to washing with water (*Piskei ha-Rid*).

50 *Shabbat* 134b. The mixture was undoubtedly therapeutic (see *Tosafot: V'ein monin*).

tion. The Ramban[51] explains that when the medicine is not placed directly in the wound the treatment is indirect. But the Rashba[52] suggests that causing the liquid to flow into the wound from an uninjured area is similar to rinsing, and is not a clear-cut therapeutic action. The Rashba restricts Shemuel's technique to mixtures which may be used occasionally for washing or anointing oneself when one has no injury. The difference in explanation is not merely theoretical. For washing the wound with a substance that is clearly medicinal, such as hydrogen peroxide, iodine, Betadine, or alcohol, would be permitted only if Shemuel's procedure were meant as an indirect action. But if it is supposed to be similar to rinsing with water, any substance that is clearly medicinal to a spectator could not be allowed.

Treatment of a Patient Who Is Ill But Not in Danger

As we have indicated at the outset of our discussion, the Rabbinic restriction against using medicines and remedies on Shabbat applies to individuals who are not significantly ill. One who is indisposed from an ailment or an ache but otherwise is in reasonable general health would thus be constrained from employing therapeutic interventions within the guidelines discussed above. At the other extreme, the requirements of a patient who is dangerously ill clearly may be attended to on Shabbat even if Biblical work categories are violated. But to what extent are Shabbat restrictions relaxed for the benefit of a patient who is ill but not dangerously so? It is clear that in this circumstance Biblical prohibitions remain intact. Yet, what are the criteria for determining the degree of leniency in removing Rabbinic restrictions?

It is generally accepted that for a patient who is ill but not in danger the Rabbinic restriction against having a

---

51 Novellae, *Avodah Zarah* 28a.

52 *Teshuvot* V, 223. Rashi appears to offer a similar explanation.

non-Jew perform procedures which are forbidden to a Jew
on Shabbat is removed. In requesting the non-Jew's assistance, the patient or those caring for him do not actively
perform a proscribed action.[53] Thus, the Talmud permits a
non-Jew, but not a Jew, to attend to the needs of a woman
who is thirty days postdelivery, because she is considered to
be in no danger.[54] Similarly, in a case where there was no
danger, Amemar, the *Amora*, allowed a non-Jew to dab an
ailing eye with medicine on Shabbat.[55] However, there is a
controversy among the *Rishonim* whether a Shabbat observer may himself actively violate a Rabbinic restriction for
the sake of one who is not dangerously ill.

The Talmud rules that an individual who is sighing
deeply from cardiac pains (possibly angina pectoris or heartburn) may suck milk directly from a goat's udders for a
remedy on Shabbat.[56] Although milking is included in the
Biblical prohibition against threshing (because food which is
not initially available is extracted and separated from its
enclosure), by sucking it out directly the patient extracts the
milk in an unusual manner, which is restricted only Rabbinically. But the Rabbis did not intend their enactment to
apply to an individual in pain. *Tosafot* explains that, according to the opinion which maintains that the Biblical work
category of threshing applies only to plants, it would not be
necessary to milk the goat indirectly, since milking in the
usual fashion is itself proscribed merely by Rabbinic restriction.[57] It follows from this explanation that *Tosafot* would
hold that a Shabbat observer may himself violate Rabbinic
restrictions in caring for a patient who is significantly ill,

---

53 *Eruvin* 68a.

54 *Shabbat* 129a.

55 *Beitzah* 22a.

56 *Ketubbot* 60a. See Rashi's explanation.

57 Ibid., *Tosafot: Mefarek*. See also *Shabbat* 73b, *Tosafot: Mefarek*, which negates
the possibility that one would require an indirect, unusual action according to
this opinion.

although not in danger. However, it is not clear whether *Tosafot*'s leniency applies only when one is in much pain, and not to other instances of nondangerous illness.

On the other hand, from the Talmud's leniency in allowing a patient with cardiac pains to suck milk directly from an animal's udders, and from the rule that a fracture may be set on Shabbat,[58] the Ra'avad explicitly concludes that a Shabbat observer may himself actively violate Rabbinic restrictions for one who is partially ill (but not for one merely indisposed).[59]

The Rashba further specifies that for a patient with generalized illness involving his whole body, a Shabbat observer may ignore Rabbinic restrictions, while a non-Jew may even be asked to carry out procedures which are prohibited Biblically.[60] The Rashba derives this position from the presumption of the Talmud that one may not transgress a Biblical prohibition in treating an inflamed eye, because it poses no danger to life. Yet, because of the danger to the organ, it may be dabbed with medicine on Shabbat, despite the Rabbinic restriction regarding the use of remedies.[61] He considers peril to an organ halachically equivalent to a generalized, noncritical illness involving the whole body and to a patient whose ailment forces him to bed.[62]

---

58 *Shabbat* 148a.

59 Comments on Rambam, *Hilchot Shabbat* 6:9.

60 *Teshuvot* VII, 272. But in his Novellae (*Shabbat* 129a) the Rashba adopts a position similar to that of the Ramban (see below).

61 *Avodah Zarah* 28b. The Taz (*Orach Chayim* 328:7) objects to the Rashba's conclusion because of Amemar's need to employ a non-Jew to dab the eye with medicine (see n. 55 above). However, in Amemar's case, the inflammation may have been in the last stages of the illness, when there was no longer a danger of losing the organ (see Avodah Zarah 28b).

62 However, the Rosh is not convinced that one may extrapolate from the case of an endangered organ or limb to permit active violation of Rabbinic restrictions by Shabbat observers for the benefit of a patient who is bedridden, but in no danger of losing life or limb (*Avodah Zarah*, ch. 2, note 10).

Of the *Acharonim*, the Rama does permit active violation
of a Rabbinic restriction by a Shabbat observer who is
attending a bedridden, noncritical patient. Yet, in his notes
on the *Shulchan Aruch*, he chose to comment on this merely
with regard to the ingestion of medicine.[63] The Rama does
not gainsay R. Yosef Karo's earlier declaration that he is
inclined to require that the procedure be performed in an
unusual manner when a Rabbinic restriction is actively
violated by a Shabbat observer for the benefit of a patient
who is ill but in no danger of losing an organ.[64] The *Mishnah
Berurah*[65] infers that the Rama is more lenient than R. Karo
only with regard to medical therapy, for when medicines are
used no work whatsoever is actually performed and they are
only forbidden lest another individual conclude from his
actions that pharmaceuticals may also be compounded on
Shabbat.

However, in his commentary on the *Tur*,[66] the Rama
clearly states that he is inclined toward the more lenient
position of the Rashba, on the principle that doubts concerning Rabbinic laws are always adjudicated leniently.

At the other extreme, some authorities maintain that
according to some *Rishonim* active violations of Rabbinic
restrictions by Shabbat observers are never permitted for
patients who are not dangerously ill. The *Eglei Tal*[67] notes
that Rashi specifically states that all remedies are forbidden
on Shabbat "where there is no danger."[68] Rashi's statement
implies that Shabbat illnesses are lumped into only two
categories — those which pose a danger to life and those
which do not. In the former instance, all Shabbat violations

---

63 *Orach Chayim* 328:37.

64 Ibid. 328:17.

65 Ibid., *Mishnah Berurah* 121, and *Biur Halachah: V'chen im nafal.*

66 *Tur, Ohr Chayim, Darchei Moshe* 328:8.

67 Work category of grinding (*tochen*), 38:2.

68 *Avodah Zarah* 28a, Rashi: *Lo yigma b'Shabbat.*

are permitted, while in the latter case even Rabbinic restrictions remain intact. The *Mishnah Berurah*[69] suggests that this view may be inferred from the Talmud[70] itself. For in response to Ravina's remonstrations about R. Ashi's soaking his swollen foot in vinegar, R. Ashi did not respond that he was in great pain from the blow but, rather, that an injury on the back of the hand or foot is like an internal wound with respect to the danger involved.

Yet, even according to this opinion, it is necessary to differentiate between a patient who is significantly ill and one who is merely indisposed. For in the former instance, all authorities agree that Rabbinic restrictions which involve no direct action on the part of a Shabbat observer, i.e., asking a non-Jew to perform the procedure, may be disregarded. Furthermore, in the presence of significant pain, the Talmud permits the patient himself to violate the Rabbinic restriction against using remedies.[71]

The Ramban[72] adopts an intermediate position. He subdivides nondangerous illness into three categories: a patient who is indisposed but otherwise not generally ill, one who has taken to bed as a result of his illness, and one who is in danger of losing a limb but not his life. In the first instance, no Rabbinic restrictions may be violated, even where there is no direct action on the part of a Shabbat observer, i.e., he asks a non-Jew to perform the procedure. However, once the patient has taken to bed, we may ask a non-Jew to perform procedures which violate Rabbinic restrictions for his bene-

---

69 *Orach Chayim* 328:37, *Biur Halachah: V'chen im nafal.*

70 *Shabbat* 109a.

71 *Ketubbot* 60a, in the case of one sighing deeply from cardiac pain. See also *Shabbat* 107a (where *Tosafot* explains that an abscess may be lanced because of pain), 94b, (where the Talmud allows a partially severed nail to be removed by hand if it is very painful), and 135a (where *Tosafot* explains that a woman may milk herself to relieve the pain of an engorged breast).

72 *Torah ha-Adam* (*Kitvei ha-Ramban*, edited by Rabbi Chayim David Chavel [Jerusalem: Mosad ha-Rav Kook, 5724], *Sha'ar ha-Meichush*, p.21.

fit.[73] Yet, a Shabbat observer may himself not directly violate
Rabbinic restrictions for the patient, as evidenced by the
Talmud's statement that even according to R. Shimon — who
holds that one is not culpable for performing a Biblically
forbidden act which is not intended for its defined purpose
but, rather, for an incidental benefit (*melachah she-einah
tzerichah l'gufah*)[74] — one must not extinguish a lamp on
Shabbat for a patient who is not at risk, even though the goal
of letting the patient sleep is incidental to the proscribed
action of extinguishing.[75] But, if the Rabbinically restricted
procedure can be performed in an unusual manner (*shinui*),
such as sucking milk directly from an animals udder, then
the services of a non-Jew are not necessary.[76]

The Ramban views danger to a limb as more serious in
nature. Although no Biblical prohibitions may be violated,

---

73 *Shabbat* 129a.

74 There is a disagreement as to the meaning of "its defined purpose." It may
    refer to the purpose for which the task was performed in the *Mishkan* (*Shabbat*
    94a, *Tosafot: Rabbi Shimon potair*) or to any creative purpose intrinsic to the
    activity (*Shabbat* 93b, Rashi *v'Rabbi Shimon potair*).

75 *Shabbat* 30a. According to R. Shimon, extinguishing a lamp for this purpose
    would only be proscribed Rabbinically. But it is possible that the Rabbinic ban
    against performing a Biblically forbidden act which is intended not for its
    defined purpose but, rather, for an incidental benefit is more serious than other
    Rabbinic constraints. However, the Me'iri comments that the reason for
    stringency in this instance is that a) extinguishing the lamp is not a remedy,
    but is merely to calm the patient, and b) it is not absolutely necessary to
    extinguish the lamp, for the room could be darkened by obstructing the light
    or by removing the lamp.

76 In *Torah ha-Adam*, the Ramban does not specify whether a *shinui* is sufficient
    to permit even a Biblically proscribed treatment. The *Shulchan Aruch* (*Orach
    Chayim* 328:17) and the *Mishnah Berurah* (ibid. 54) hold that only Rabbinic
    restrictions can be overridden by using a *shinui*. However, the *Shulchan Aruch
    ha-Rav* (ibid.) and the *Eglei Tal* (*Tochen* 38:10) maintain that, although the
    Ramban does not permit direct violation of a Rabbinic restriction without a
    shinui, a *shinui* in and of itself is sufficient to permit even Biblically proscribed
    actions. But the latter position is difficult to sustain, for the Ramban derives
    his rule of *shinui* from the permission given to a patient to suck milk directly
    from a goat's udder, in the case of cardiac pain, and the Ramban clearly holds
    that milking is only Rabbinically prohibited (Novellae, *Shabbat* 144a).

all Rabbinic restrictions may be ignored, even without using a *shinui*. He derives this from the Talmud's dispensation to treat an inflamed eye[77] and to set a fracture on Shabbat,[78] undoubtedly because of the possibility that the eye would be blinded or the limb irreversibly damaged.

The Ran accepts the classification of the Ramban.[79] He agrees that for an individual merely indisposed with an ache or an ailment, but suffering no significant illness, no Shabbat violations are permitted. On the other hand, an illness which endangers a limb may be ministered to by a Jew as well as a non-Jew. However, he specifies that whereas a Jew may violate only Rabbinic interdictions for the patient, a non-Jew may perform even Biblically proscribed procedures. Yet, with regard to one who is bedridden or generally ill but not in danger, the Ran is apparently more stringent, maintaining that only a non-Jew may violate Shabbat for the sake of the patient, whereas a Jew is not permitted to brush aside even a Rabbinic ban.

However, the Ran's a priori distinction is, in practice, qualified where it is not possible to employ the services of a non-Jew. Thus the Ran posits that the individual with cardiac pains cannot have a non-Jew obtain goat's milk for him, because direct ingestion of warm milk at body temperature from the animal is part of the therapeutic regimen.[80] *Biur ha-Gra*[81] and the *Mishnah Berurah*[82] qualify that where a non-Jew cannot be used, the Ran would follow the ruling of

---

77 *Avodah Zarah* 28b. According to the Ramban, Amemar (*Beitzah* 22a) required the services of a non-Jew because the illness carried no risk of blindness at that point. But one must presume that Amemar still suffered significantly from the affliction and was not merely indisposed.

78 *Shabbat* 148a.

79 Commentary on *Shabbat*, Rif 39b, and Novellae, *Avodah Zarah* 28 (both with regard to the case of treating an inflamed eye on Shabbat).

80 Commentary on *Shabbat*, Rif 61a.

81 *Orach Chayim* 328:17.

82 Ibid. 328:53.

the Ramban, allowing a Jew to violate Rabbinic restrictions only with a *shinui*. This may be inferred from the fact that the Ran cites the Ramban at the conclusion of his discussion of the unusual procedure of sucking milk directly from an animal.

The *Eglei Tal*,[83] however, uses the Ran's citing of the Ramban as evidence that the positions of these two *Rishonim* are identical. Moreover, he suggests that, according to the Ran, doing the procedure with a *shinui* may not be inferior to having a non-Jew perform it in its usual manner. The Ran[84] in fact offers the suggestion that a *shinui* may be preferable to using a non-Jew, in his attempt to resolve the apparent contradiction in the Talmud's ruling, on the one hand, that on Shabbat one should not urge a non-Jew to extinguish a conflagration where there is no personal risk[85] and, on the other hand, that one may discreetly crush rubbish with one's foot to unclog a gutter so as to prevent the overflowing water from damaging the house.[86] The Ran reasons that, in the case of the clogged gutter, freeing the blockage with one's foot is an unusual manner of repair and, although work performed on Shabbat with a *shinui* is Rabbinically restricted, the Rabbis did not intend their enactment to apply where there is significant financial loss. On the other hand, one may not ask a non-Jew to put out a fire, even though extinguishing the flame to save one's home may be forbidden only Rabbinically (because the action is not intended for its defined purpose, i.e., to produce charcoal, which is the direct product of the act of extinguishing).[87]

Most authorities find it difficult to accept the concept that a *shinui* is preferable to asking a non-Jew, for the latter

---

83 *Tochen* 39:10.

84 Commentary on *Shabbat*, the Rif 61a.

85 *Shabbat* 121a.

86 *Ketubbot* 60a.

87 But see n. 75 above.

involves no action on the part of a Shabbat observer.[88] The consensus is that the case of the gutter is unique,[89] undoubtedly, because the process of relieving the obstruction is hardly noticeable when it is done with one's foot.

Rabbi Akiva Eiger,[90] on the other hand, assumes that the Ran cites the Ramban as an opposing opinion. He maintains that the Ran himself does not reckon with the concept of *shinui*. According to him, the Ran would be more lenient for a patient who is bedridden only when it was not possible to use a non-Jew, for then a Shabbat observer would be permitted to violate Rabbinic restrictions without the need to seek an indirect measure.

There is also broad controversy as to the details of the Rambam's position. The Rambam rules: "If a person is ill, but not in danger, all his needs may be attended to by a non-Jew. The non-Jew may be told to do all things for him, such as cooking, baking, and bringing medicines from one domain to the other, etc. Similarly, he may allow a non-Jew to dab his eyes [with medicine] even though there is no danger [as a result of the illness]. If the patient needs treatments which require no prohibited work, they may be administered even by a Jew. Thus, it is permissible to reset the ears and the sternal cartilage, to set a fracture, and to carry out procedures of a similar nature."[91]

The *Tur*[92] interprets the phrase "treatments which require no prohibited work" as treatments which involve no Biblically prohibited work. But procedures which are Rabbinically proscribed may be actively performed even by a Jew. The difficulty with the *Tur*'s position is the Rambam's apparent gratuitous grouping of the treatment of dabbing

---

88 See *Eruvin* 68a.

89 *Orach Chayim* 307, *Magen Avraham* 7, and the *Chazon Ish, Shabbat* 56:4.

90 Novellae, *Ketubbot* 60a and *Teshuvot* 5.

91 *Hilchot Shabbat* 2:10.

92 *Orach Chayim* 328.

the eyes with other necessities that only a non-Jew may provide. For dabbing the eyes is only Rabbinically restricted as a remedy, and even a Shabbat observer should have been permitted to administer this therapy.[93]

In a lengthy discussion, the *Maggid Mishneh* concludes that the Rambam differentiates between an illness which is general and one which affects only one organ. In the former situation, one may use either the services of a non-Jew or, if only a Rabbinic restriction is involved, the active participation of a Shabbat observer. But for a nondangerous affliction which is limited to one organ, such as the eye, treatment could not be administered by a Shabbat observer, even if the procedure violated only a Rabbinic prohibition.[94]

But the clarification of the *Maggid Mishneh* has itself generated controversy. For the *Maggid Mishneh* does not specify whether "a nondangerous affliction which is limited to one organ" refers only to an affliction that is not life-threatening or if it also includes the absence of irrevocable, permanent injury to the organ itself. The *Beit Yosef*[95] assumes that it makes no difference whether or not the organ is in danger. In both instances, Shabbat observers could not violate Rabbinic restrictions in ministering to the patient. But the *Magen Avraham*[96] is astounded at this assumption, for according to most *Rishonim*, one is more lenient in attending to a patient with an endangered limb, at the very least on a par with one who is generally ill. Indeed, the *Maggid Mishnah* himself seems to imply that there is more leniency for an endangered limb when he states, "but full-

---

93 Perhaps the Rambam refers to the recovery phase of the illness, at which time the patient is slightly ill. In this instance, the Rambam would require the services of a non-Jew (*Hilchot Shabbat* 6:9). But its inclusion in the halachic ruling concerning one who is actually ill is puzzling.

94 The Rambam refers to the recovery phase of the illness, when the danger has passed. See also *Beitzah* 22a.

95 *Orach Chayim* 328. See also *Kesef Mishneh, Hilchot Shabbat* 2:10.

96 *Orach Chayim* 328, *Magen Avraham* 12.

fledged work [Biblically prohibited] is not permitted by a Jew even for an endangered limb, only where one's life is threatened." One may infer that work which is only Rabbinically proscribed may be performed by a Jew attending to a patient with a limb at risk.[97]

The *Magen Avraham*, therefore, proposes that the Rambam considers three categories of illness which pose no danger to life: a) generalized illness involving the whole body, or danger to a limb or organ; b) slight illness or an affliction involving a limb or organ which is not endangered; c) indisposition due to an ache or ailment in one who is not otherwise ill. For a patient whose illness is generalized or whose limb is at risk, a non-Jew may perform all procedures, while a Shabbat observer may waive only Rabbinic restrictions.[98] The *Magen Avraham* derives this rule from the Talmudic discussion concerning the treatment of an inflamed eye. According to the *Magen Avraham*, the presumption of the Talmud is that the eye is endangered, but not the patient's life. Thus, a Jew may treat the eye, but not violate Biblical prohibitions to prepare the remedy or to bring it through a public domain. Similarly, according to the Talmud, one who is bedridden from cardiac pains may obtain goat's milk by the Rabbinically restricted, unusual procedure of sucking milk directly from the animal.

The halachic ruling for an affliction which does not endanger a limb is derived from Amemar's employment of a non-Jew to treat the recovery phase of an eye inflamma-

---

97 The comments of the *Maggid Mishneh* on *Hilchot Shabbat* 6:9 also indicate that he viewed an endangered limb as halachically equivalent to a generalized illness involving the whole body.

98 Although the *Magen Avraham* indicates that most authorities follow the third opinion cited by the *Shulchan Aruch*, which is that of the Ramban (328:7), his intent is only to negate the conclusions of the Bach. But in the final halachic ruling, he apparently follows his interpretation of the *Maggid Mishneh*'s explanations of the Rambam, for when he mentions that wood ash could be placed on an open wound to draw out an infection which has caused illness throughout the body, he does not indicate the necessity of applying the treatment in an unusual manner (328:30).

tion.[99] Since applying a remedy is restricted only by Rabbinic
ordinance, the *Magen Avraham* concludes that in the case of
an affliction which does not imperil the limb, not only must
a non-Jew's services be employed but the non-Jew may not
perform Biblically forbidden work. This is one example of
"slight illness" for which a non-Jew may be asked to do only
"those acts which do not constitute [Biblically] prohibited
work and are forbidden only because they are [Rabbinically]
contrary to the spirit of Shabbat rest."[100] With regard to an
individual who is merely indisposed, the Halachah is even
more stringent and, according to the *Magen Avraham*, even
a non-Jew may not intervene, even though the measure he
would use merely violates a Rabbinic restriction.[101]

The Status of an Imperiled Organ

In the preceding discussion we have seen that, according to
most authorities, endangerment of an organ is not considered halachically equivalent to risking one's life. However,
Tosafot[102] explicitly states, "Danger to an organ is like danger to one's life, even [with respect] to violating the Shabbat
with [Biblically prohibited work], as evidenced from the
Talmud concerning an inflamed eye."[103] The Talmud's conclusion is based upon an incident concerning Mar Shemuel's
maid, who developed an eye inflammation on Shabbat that

---

99 *Beitzah* 22a.

100 Rambam, *Hilchot Shabbat* 6:9. See also the *Shulchan Aruch* 307:5, *Magen
Avraham* 7; and 328:25, *Magen Avraham* 28.

101 However, the *Lechem Mishneh* (*Hilchot Shabbat* 2:10) is reluctant to accept
this stringency. He maintains that despite the *Maggid Mishneh*'s statement,
"for one who is merely indisposed, even Rabbinic restrictions are not permitted,
and even by a non-Jew," the *Maggid Mishneh*'s intent is not to forbid Rabbinic
restrictions which are performed by a non-Jew. The *Lechem Mishneh* con-
strains the text to offer an entirely different meaning: "Even Rabbinic restrictions are not permitted [by a Jew] and even [Biblical prohibitions] by a
non-Jew."

102 *Sukkah* 26a, *Tosafot: V'ilu chash b'einav.*

103 *Avodah Zarah* 28b.

was not thought to be serious enough to violate Shabbat. When Mar Shemuel saw that her eye had "dropped" (apparently ceasing to function) as a result of her neglect, he propounded the rule that it is permissible to treat such a disorder on Shabbat. *Tosafot* apparently reasons that, since the text does not indicate a clear endangerment of the maid's life,[104] the risk of being blinded is in itself sufficient to warrant violation of Biblical prohibitions on Shabbat. But when there is only a minor affliction, with no risk of irrevocable injury to the eye, as in the instance of Amemar,[105] even Rabbinic restrictions could not be ignored by a Shabbat observer and the services of a non-Jew would be required.

The *Or Zarua*[106] explains that *Tosafot* presumes an implicit danger to life in every situation where an organ is imperiled, despite the fact that only a minority of individuals actually succumb. According to this view, it is possible that *Tosafot* would permit Biblical violations of Shabbat in a situation where there clearly is no danger to life, even though a limb or organ is at risk. However, the Me'iri,[107] who follows *Tosafot*'s position, disagrees.

In practice, the Shach[108] rules that in an emergency one could rely on the minority opinion, which halachically equates an imperiled organ to a life-threatening illness. The *Peri Megadim*[109] maintains that the Shach intended this leniency only with regard to other restrictions, but not for the more serious prohibitions of Shabbat. Since there is a difference of opinion, Rabbi Hershler notes that whenever a

---

104 However, in the Munich manuscript of the Talmud and in the version cited in the Rif, the text concludes: "The eye dropped and she died." Undoubtedly, the more stringent ruling of the Ramban, the Rosh, the Ran, and Rashi is based on this reading.

105 *Beitzah* 22a.

106 *Hilchot Yom ha-Kippurim* 280:65(3).

107 Commentary on *Avodah Zarah* 28b.

108 *Shulchan Aruch, Yoreh De'ah* 157, *Shach* 3.

109 *Shulchan Aruch, Orach Chayim* 328:17, *Mishbetzot Zahav* 7.

limb or organ is imperiled, a halachic doubt as to possible
danger to life is engendered. It is, therefore, difficult in
practice to be stringent with such concerns. Furthermore,
the *Tzitz Eliezer*[110] points out that, according to current
medical opinion, there is always concern that a serious
illness which is confined to one organ may spread throughout
the body, endangering the patient's life as well.

The Rationale for Leniency for Individuals in Pain

We must consider whether the leniency extended to a patient
in significant pain to disregard Rabbinic restrictions is related to the rules of treating patients who are significantly
ill, or if it is halachically a special case which has no bearing
on the use of remedies. This question is especially relevant
to the Ramban and other *Rishonim* who require Shabbat
observers to use a *shinui* when Rabbinic restrictions are
waived for the sake of a patient who is in no danger. For in
permitting one to lance a painful abscess in order to evacuate
the pus, the Talmud[111] makes no mention of the necessity for
draining it in an unusual manner. Rashi and *Tosafot* explain
that, although it is Biblically forbidden to create a portal on
Shabbat under the work category of building, opening a boil
to remove the pus would be restricted only Rabbinically,
since the procedure is not intended for the constructive
purpose of providing a permanent hole, and the Rabbis did
not intend their ban to apply where an individual suffers
considerable pain.[112]

But if direct violation of Rabbinic restrictions by a Jew
is not allowed in treating a patient who is in no danger,
should this not all the more apply to lancing an abscess? Has

---

110 Vol. VIII, 15:10, 11.

111 *Shabbat* 107a.

112 Ibid., Rashi: *Patur*, and *Tosafot: U'mimai d'patur. Tosafot* offers a similar
     explanation for allowing a woman to milk herself manually on Shabbat to
     relieve the pain of an engorged breast (*Shabbat* 135a: *Mipnei ha-sakkanah*).

it not been suggested above that the Rabbinic ban against performing a Biblically forbidden act which is not intended for its defined purpose but, rather, for an incidental benefit (*melachah she-einah tzerichah l'gufah*) may be more stringent than other Rabbinic constraints?[113] Moreover, from Mar Shemuel's behavior toward his maid it is evident that, despite her pain, he did not think her illness serious enough to allow her eye to be treated.

In an effort to resolve this apparent contradiction, some authorities maintain that a *shinui* would also be necessary in treating an abscess, since the pus may be evacuated only by hand, not with an instrument.[114] In their commentaries on the Mishnah,[115] the Rambam and the Me'iri also indicate that the boil is squeezed by hand, but it is not clear whether their intention is to prohibit the use of an instrument in draining the fluid from the abscess. Indeed, in his authoritative halachic work, the Rambam is entirely silent on this matter.[116]

Rabbi Hershler suggests that the evacuation of pus is not to be viewed as a remedy but, rather, as the removal of a noxious irritant. For the Sages and authorities similarly allowed a variety of actions usually forbidden on Shabbat in order to eliminate pests and harmful substances. Thus, a needle may be used to remove a thorn embedded in the flesh,[117] a partially torn-off fingernail which is painful may be wholly removed by hand,[118] a woman may express milk

---

113 See also *Eglei Tal, Tochen* 35:31.

114 *Orach Chayim* 328:28, *Peri Megadim, Mishbetzot Zahav* 21, and *Biur Halachah: K'dai leharchiv.*

115 *Ediot* 2:5.

116 *Hilchot Shabbat* 10:17.

117 *Shabbat* 107a and 122b.

118 Ibid. 94b. See Rashi: *Kelappei ma'alah*; Rambam, *Hilchot Shabbat* 9:9; and the *Shulchan Aruch, Orach Chayim* 328:31. An instrument is not permitted because that would involve two Rabbinic restrictions: tearing off the fingernail and using an instrument for cutting.

from her breast to relieve the pain of engorgement,[119] a
stinging insect may be caught and removed from the skin,[120]
and snakes and scorpions may be captured and tied up.[121]
But procedures which are in the nature of a remedy would
not be permitted merely to alleviate an individual's pain and
discomfort. This is substantiated not only from the incident
of Mar Shemuel's maid but also from the Rambam's requirement that, as a remedy for cardiac pain, goat's milk must be
obtained through the *shinui* of sucking it directly from the
animal.

We are thus confronted by an apparent inconsistency. On
the one hand, Rabbinic restrictions are relaxed for individuals in pain, but, on the other, the restriction against using
remedies remains intact. Yet this is not surprising, for if all
remedies and treatments were permitted for pain, the restriction against using medicines would be meaningless,
since most ailments are associated with some degree of
aching and discomfort. However, when the pain is severe
enough to affect the whole body or to cause the patient to be
bedridden, then treatments are permitted as for a patient
who is significantly ill though not in life-threatening danger.
Thus with regard to the prohibition against sipping vinegar
for a toothache, the Taz comments, "Clearly this is only for
an ache, but if he suffers greatly because of the pain and, as
a result, he has become generally weakened, it is permitted
to administer all remedies."[122]

Preparation of Medicines on Shabbat

If taking medicines on Shabbat is forbidden lest one grind
together ingredients in their preparation, then the preparation of medicine itself, even through halachically permissible

---

119 *Shulchan Aruch, Orach Chayim* 330:8.

120 *Mordechai, Shabbat,* ch.1, note 233, and *Or Zarua, Hilchot Shabbat* 32.

121 *Shabbat* 107a. See the Rambam, *Hilchot Shabbat* 10:25.

122 *Orach Chayim* 328:32, Taz 24.

means, would surely be proscribed. Thus the Talmid forbids soaking *chiltit*,[123] beating wine and oil together,[124] preparing *aluntith*,[125], and balsam. and soaking collyrium[126] on Shabbat. Although the mixture or preparation could be used on Shabbat because of its similarity in appearance and application to nonmedicinals, its preparation still would not be permitted. Indeed, preparation of the substance would be proscribed even when it was intended to be used merely for pleasure, undoubtedly because the procedure is more clearly a weekday activity *(uvada d'chol)*[127] than taking medicine, which is restricted only because of the remote possibility of transgressing a Biblical prohibition.

Rabbi Hershler suggests that with regard to the preparation of mixtures and extracts on Shabbat, there is a basic halachic difference between those which are combinations of clearly identifiable foodstuffs and those which are not. An item which can be eaten or drunk for one's pleasure as well as medicinally, but which is not an obvious foodstuff, may not be prepared on Shabbat, even when it is not intended as a remedy. Thus collyrium, which is not a food, should not be soaked on Shabbat, even though the extract is to be used as an eye rinse[128] and not as a remedy. *Chiltit* also is not a food, even though the fluid extract of this plant may be imbibed by individuals who are in good health. On the other hand, the combination of several food items cannot be restricted on Shabbat, even if the concoction is not widely used by healthy individuals, unless the manner of its preparation involves

---

123 *Shabbat* 104a. Asafoetida, a plant whose resin and leaves were used for medicinal purposes.

124 Ibid. 134a. See also Ramban, *Torah ha-Adam, Sha'ar ha-Meichush*; and the Rashba, Novellae, *Shabbat* 129a.

125 *Shabbat* 140a. A mixture of old wine, water, and balsam.

126 Ibid. 108b. An eye salve. See also *Shabbat* 18a, *Tosafot: U'mitrapa'at.*

127 See *Shabbat* 140a, Rashi: *Shello ya'aseh*; 147a, Rashi: *V'lo mitgarin*; and ibid. 138a, Rashi: *Ella amar Abaya.*

128 *Shabbat* 18a, *Tosafot: U'mitrapa'at.*

procedures which are not appropriate for Shabbat. One would, therefore, not be restricted in mixing together wine and oil were it not for the fact that the ingredients are beaten together violently in preparing the emulsion.[129] Also, barley flour may be combined with honey, even though the mixture of these food items is not usually eaten by those who are well.

Now, if concocting therapeutic mixtures on Shabbat is included in the Rabbinic restriction against utilizing medicines, would the leniency in permitting remedies for patients who are ill but not in danger include their preparation as well? Specifically, according to those authorities who maintain that, although a *shinui* is required when a Jew waives Rabbinic restrictions for the sake of a patient who is ill but not endangered, the patient himself may ingest medicines without a *shinui*,[130] would the requirement of a *shinui* also be set aside for the purpose of preparing a medicine?

In resolving this question, it should be noted that only ingestion of a pharmaceutical is permitted without a *shinui*, but a therapeutic procedure which involves any manual action whatsoever would not be allowed in its usual manner. This is evident from the Talmud's requirement that a wound be treated indirectly by pouring the medicinal mixture outside the injured area and allowing it to flow into the wound.[131] The *Mishnah Berurah* also comments that, even if the patient were generally ill, a *shinui* would be required for a Shabbat observer to place wood ash on a wound,[132] to exercise the patient in order to cause him to perspire,[133] and to administer an enema.[134] Thus, preparation of the phar-

---

129 *Berachot* 38a.

130 *Orach Chayim* 328, *Mishnah Berurah* 121, and *Biur Halachah: V'chen im nafal.*

131 *Shabbat* 134b. Ramban (*Torat ha-Adam*) explains the procedure as a *shinui.*

132 *Mishnah Berurah* 328:85.

133 Ibid. 130.

134 Ibid. 150.

maceutical, a procedure which involves active participation, should similarly require a *shinui*.

One might reason that ingestion of a medicine would not need a *shinui* because it is not a direct therapeutic treatment per se. Swallowing the pharmaceutical merely brings it into the body, where, as a result of various physiological processes, it disperses to the sites of disease or symptoms and exerts its salutary effect. In the absence of significant illness, one is constrained from being healed on Shabbat, even when no direct manual treatment is involved. But where this restriction has been lifted, because illness has become generalized, it would not matter whether the medicine were ingested in its usual manner or not. For a *shinui* in the manner of ingestion changes nothing with respect to being healed by the medicine on Shabbat.

If we accept the thesis that the concept of *shinui* would not apply to ingestion of medicine, since the prohibition does not reside in the act of ingestion but rather in allowing oneself to be healed on Shabbat, then no leniency could be extended to allow one who is indisposed to take medicines with a *shinui*.[135] But, if the medicine itself were disguised or changed, so that it no longer appeared to be a pharmaceutical, perhaps one might be able to take the drug for an ailment on Shabbat.

Although collyrium many not be steeped on Shabbat to be used as an eyewash, the Talmud does allow it to be prepared before Shabbat with the intention to use it on

---

135 The Maharsham (*Orach Chayim* 532, note 3) suggested that it might be possible to permit one who is not significantly ill to ingest medicine on Shabbat by swallowing the powder or pill while it is enclosed in a paper wrapping, or to take pharmaceuticals through a tube. The *Tzitz Eliezer* (VIII, 15:15 [6]) brings support for the Maharsham's contention from the *Levush*, who reasons that one who is indisposed may induce vomiting on Shabbat by putting his fingers in his throat, because causing oneself to vomit in this manner is a *shinui* with regard to the usual method of taking an emetic. But, according to our previous explanation, the value of a *shinui* in a direct therapeutic action would prove nothing regarding its efficacy in abating the restriction of ingesting medicinals.

Shabbat.[136] Rashi explains that to a spectator it appears as though one is rinsing and not treating his eye and, as for himself, since he is required to steep it before Shabbat, he has a clear indication that he must be wary about preparing medicines on Shabbat. According to Rashi, the additional necessity of a recognizable indication that medicines must not be compounded on Shabbat would pertain only to mixtures which are basically medicinal in nature, but this would not be required for a concoction of foodstuffs. Similarly, one could argue that it would be permissible to dissolve capsules or pills or mix them with foodstuffs before Shabbat in order to take the medicine on Shabbat. For by requiring the patient to disguise or dissolve the capsules before Shabbat, there is a recognizable indication to the patient that medicines may not be compounded on Shabbat, and, as for others who observe the sipping on Shabbat, the solution would appear to be merely a beverage.[137] But on Shabbat itself, the admixture with food would not be permitted.[138]

Continuing Therapy Initiated before Shabbat

We have thus far considered the Halachah with regard to preparing medicines for initiating therapy on Shabbat. But what are the considerations for continuing a course of treatment which has commenced before Shabbat? Is the patient's improved state of health which may follow several days of therapy taken into account, or is one who has started a remedy allowed to prepare mixtures on Shabbat to finish the

---

136 *Shabbat* 108b. See Rashi: *V'noten al gav einav.*

137 Rabbi Y. Neuwirth, in *Shemirat Shabbat k'Hilchata,* 2nd ed. (Jerusalem, 5739), 34:27, maintains that an individual in the habit of dissolving medicines in beverages for use on weekdays could not use this procedure for Shabbat, because it is no longer a *shinui* for him. But Rabbi Hershler contends that it would not matter, for the issue is not that of *shinui* but whether there is a recognizable indication that medicines may not be compounded on Shabbat. This requirement would be fulfilled, since he is not permitted to prepare the solution on Shabbat itself, although he may do so every other day of the week.

138 *Iggrot Moshe, Orach Chayim* 86.

course of therapy, irrespective of whether he is still bedridden?

In expounding the Mishnaic prohibition against soaking *chiltit* on Shabbat, the Talmud[139] relates an instance when R. Acha b. Yosef was advised to drink *chiltit* on three days as a cure for "heaviness of the heart."[140] He drank the extract on Thursday and Friday, and on Shabbat he went to *beit ha-midrash* to ask whether he might continue taking the remedy. To the Rabbi's response that one may drink the extract without fear of transgressing Shabbat, R. Acha retorted, "I do not ask about drinking, but about steeping it [if it was not prepared before Shabbat]." The Talmud concludes that, even according to the opinion that forbids soaking *chiltit* in cold as well as hot water, in this instance he may put it in cold water and place it in the sun to be warmed and thereby steep it with a *shinui*, for, "since he had imbibed it on Thursday and Friday, if he would not drink it on Shabbat he would be endangered."

The *Rishonim* differ widely in their explanation of the Talmud. Rashi notes that R. Acha's question was not with regard to drinking the *chiltit* extract, since it is also a beverage which may be imbibed without intending it as a remedy. On the other hand, since it is usually steeped for its medicinal value, its preparation would normally not be allowed unless the patient were in danger. But in this case, he may prepare the extract with a *shinui*, because interrupting the course of therapy may intensify the illness.[141]

The Rambam also specifies that, although *chiltit* should not be soaked in warm or cold water on Shabbat, "if an individual drank the extract on Thursday and Friday, on Shabbat he may soak it in cold water and place it to warm in the sun, so that he should not become ill by interrupting

---

139 *Shabbat* 140a.

140 Possibly asthma.

141 The phrase "he would be endangered" cannot be accepted literally, for otherwise it should be possible to steep the *chiltit* directly in warm water.

the course of drinking."[142] But as to the rationale for allowing
the extract to be ingested, the Rambam follows Rashi in
assuming that it is considered a beverage which is enjoyed
by healthy individuals as well. Despite this, the Rambam
rules that drinking *chiltit* may not be initiated on Shabbat.
He states, "If an individual has drunk *chiltit* extract before
Shabbat and he is continuing to drink it regularly, he may
drink it on Shabbat, in localities where healthy persons
usually drink the extract."[143] However, the *Maggid Mishnah*[144] is puzzled as to why the course of drinking must be
initiated before Shabbat, if the preparation is a beverage for
people who are well. Hence he emends the text to read, "he
may drink it on Shabbat, even in localities where healthy
people do not usually drink the extract." Thus, according to
the *Maggid Mishnah*, R. Acha took it for granted that he
could continue to drink *chiltit* water on Shabbat to avoid
becoming ill by interrupting the course of therapy. He only
asked whether soaking it would not be permitted when there
was merely a possibility of becoming ill, since it could have
been prepared before Shabbat.

The Ramban[145] is reluctant to constrain the simple
meaning of the Talmud's statement that "if he would not
drink it on Shabbat he would be endangered." He agrees that
the Talmud could not have meant that he is immediately
endangered, for if so there would be no necessity for a *shinui*
in preparing the *chiltit*. Hence, he reasons that there is no
danger if the patient skips a day, but if he never completes
the course of therapy, he would eventually be in peril. The
novelty of the Talmud's ruling is that, even in this circumstance, on Shabbat the mixture may be prepared with a

---

142 *Hilchot Shabbat* 22:7.

143 Ibid. 21, 22. This text is also found in *Sefer ha-Battim.*

144 *Hilchot Shabbat* 22:21.

145 Cited in the Novellae of the Rashba, *Ketubbot* 6a. The Rashba also follows this
     view.

shinui, because the remedy is viewed as one which abates danger. It is also possible that in a situation where the patient had not initiated therapy, but which may imperil him if he were never to initiate the course of therapy, the Ramban would also view the therapy as one which abates danger, and permit him to start the remedy on Shabbat.

But what about a patient who is being treated for a generalized illness which does not place him in danger? After several days of therapy the patient may be up and about, with no overt manifestations of illness. Yet, were he to discontinue the course of treatment, he would risk a relapse. In this instance, could the therapy be continued on Shabbat, even though the patient would suffer no adverse effect by skipping one day?

According to Rashi and the original version of the Rambam, it might be necessary to discontinue the treatment if the therapeutic preparation is not also enjoyed by healthy people. The *Maggid Mishneh*'s position would be less clear, for while the patient would indeed suffer a relapse by discontinuing the therapy, omitting the treatment on the day of Shabbat would lead to no untoward consequence. However, the Ramban would rule that once a course of therapy has been initiated, it need not be interrupted on Shabbat, for even though the patient does not appear significantly ill now, the remedy is one which abates illness. This view is quoted by Rabbi Shlomo Kluger[146] as a generally accepted saying, although he expresses some uncertainty as to its source.

---

146 *Sefer ha-Chayim* 328:37.

A guide to treating eye disorders on Shabbat

Translated and adapted from the articles in *Halachah U'Refuah*I
by RABBI ELIEZER JUDAH WALDENBERG (pp.151-55),
RABBI MOSHE HERSHLER (pp.106-109), and
DR. ELCHANAN YEDVAB (pp.199-202)

The Talmud[1] relates an incident concerning Mar Shemuel's maid, who developed an eye inflammation on Shabbat which was not thought to be serious enough to violate Shabbat. When Mar Shemuel saw that her eye had "dropped" (apparently ceasing to function) as a result of her neglect, he propounded the rule that it is permissible to treat such a disorder on Shabbat. From the Talmud's discussion about treating eye ailments on Shabbat, it is clear that the Sages appreciated the potential seriousness of afflictions involving this vital organ. Negligence in caring for a diseased eye may lead to blindness or even death. In the idiom of the Talmud, "The bands [i.e., muscles] of the eye are connected with [i.e., have influence on] the mental faculties[2] [or pericardium[3]]."[4]

With respect to treatment on Shabbat, the Halachah differentiates between illnesses of varying severity. If there

---

1 *Avodah Zarah* 28b. See also the section "The Status of an Imperiled Organ" in the article "Medicines and Remedies on Shabbat" by Rabbi Moshe Hershler in this volume.

2 *Avodah Zarah* 28b, *Tosafot: Shuryanei d'aina.*

3 *Avodah Zarah* 28b, Rashi: *Afilu mischak.*

4 Dr. Yedvab cites an interesting variant text in the *Halachot Gedolot*, ed. E. Hildesheimer, (Jerusalem, 5738), *Hilchot Avot Melachot*, p.182: "The next day her eye dropped and she died, and they tore open her heart [at the autopsy] and found that the arteries of the eye connected to the heart." Dr. Yedvab suggests that Mar Shemuel's maid may have suffered an embolism to the ophthalmic artery originating from a clot in the left ventricle which was due to an underlying myocardial infarction. The latter affliction was the actual cause of her death. Alternately, the embolism may have originated from an infected cardiac valve.

is an inflammation in even one eye[5] with a discharge of pus, or if there is congestion, pain, extreme tearing, or other evidence that a serious illness is developing, the patient is considered in peril,[6] and, if necessary, it is permissible to violate even Biblical precepts to care for him on Shabbat.

As an ophthalmologist, Dr. Yedvab notes that acute inflammation may involve the conjunctiva and lids, or the cornea. Purulent discharge is frequently seen with the former, but extreme tearing with no obvious pus also may be associated with inflammation as well as with foreign body irritation. Neglecting an acute inflammation could lead to adhesions, scarring, and degenerative changes in the conjunctiva, thickening of the lid, or ptosis due to involvement of the third cranial nerve. Corneal inflammations may be due to foreign bodies, bacteria, viruses, fungi, dryness, or vitamin deficiency. These are more serious, as the cornea may ulcerate, allowing the infection to penetrate into the anterior chamber of the eye and result in glaucoma. Congestion, inflammation, and pain may also follow any eye injury, whether due to blunt or penetrating trauma, chemicals, or exposure to intense sunlight or other forms of radiant energy. Intense pain may also follow sudden elevation of intraocular pressure, whatever the underlying etiology. Clearly, one who is concerned about inflammation or significant pain related to the eye should not hesitate to telephone or travel to a physician to evaluate the severity of the affliction and undergo treatment if necessary.[7]

With regard to an ailment that is likely to cause blindness, but is otherwise not associated with features of a

---

5 Rambam, *Hilchot Shabbat* 2:4. Also *Tur* and *Shulchan Aruch, Orach Chayim* 328:9. From the Talmud's recounting of the case of Mar Shemuel's maid, it is clear that the disorder need not involve both eyes.

6 *Beitzah* 22a, and *Avodah Zarah* 28b; *Shulchan Aruch, Orach Chayim* 328:9. See also *Tzitz Eliezer* (XIII, 83:4), who maintains, on the advice of Dr. Issacson, that even if the discharge originates from an obstruction of the nasolacrimal duct, it is dangerous to allow it to remain untreated until after Shabbat.

7 *Mishnah Berurah* 328, *Biur Halachah: V'dafka*. See also *Brit Olam* 56.

potentially life-threatening danger, such as an inflammation, it would appear that, in accordance with prevailing
halachic opinion, one should not violate a Biblical precept to
save an organ.[8] Although, as noted in the review by Rabbi
Hershler, "Medicines and Remedies on Shabbat" (in this
volume), some *Rishonim* hold that an imperiled organ is
similar halachically to a life-threatening situation,[9] later
authorities do not follow this opinion.

But danger to the eye may yet be considered more serious
than that to other imperiled organs, according to Halachah.
The *Mishnah Berurah*[10] specifically declares that danger to
an eye is halachically not equivalent to peril involving another organ, because the Talmud in *Avodah Zarah* clearly
indicates that eye ailments may be associated with danger
to life. In fact, Rashi states that eyesight in general is linked
to the region of the heart. Indeed, on the basis of the Talmud,
the Rivash[11] rules that there is danger to life in any blinding
of the eye, even if inflicted by an injury and not through
illness. Some authorities limit this lenience to an instance
when there is danger of blindness to both eyes,[12] but, as noted
above, the thrust of the Talmud would suggest that imperil-
ment of one eye is sufficient.

---

8   *Tur, Orach Chayim* 328; *Shulchan Aruch* 328:17; and the Rambam, *Hilchot
    Shabbat* 5:4. These authorities specify the variety of illnesses which are listed
    in the Talmud (*Avodah Zarah* 28b) as warranting violation of Biblical prohi-
    bitions on Shabbat, but they do not include the isolated possibility of being
    blinded.

9   *Rabbenu Tam* (*Sukkah* 26a, *Tosafot: Vafilu*), *Tosafot* (*Avodah Zarah* 28b:
    Shuryanei; Tosafot ha-Rosh (*Sukkah* 26a); *Sefer ha-Agudah* (*Sukkah* ch. II);
    and Me'iri (*Avodah Zarah* 28b). *Hagahot Mordechai* (*Shabbat*, ch.13, 464) and
    Or Zarua (*Hilchot Yom ha-Kippurim* 280) explain that, according to Rabbenu
    Tam, in every instance of an imperiled organ there is a remote possibility of
    threat to life, even though statistically it is unlikely that the individual would
    actually succumb as a consequence of the loss of the organ.

10 *Hilchot Shabbat* 328:22.

11 *Teshuvot* 251.

12 *Hagahot Chochmat Shelomo* on *Orach Chayim* 328:46. Also cited in *Teshuvot
    Chatam Sofer* 34 and *Tzitz Eliezer* VIII, 15:10.

Rabbi Waldenberg further stresses that since the Sages established the rule that danger to the eye is associated with a threat to life, the dictum remains in force even for a remote possibility which may not be obvious. Hence, even if all physicians would vouchsafe the absence of danger to life, halachically we must still assume a potential threat to life and permit even Biblical violations of Shabbat on the patient's behalf[13] — and all the more so since medical opinion considers that, in general, there is a potential danger to life in every instance of peril to the eye.

Hence, the patient who suffers sudden loss of visual acuity may surely telephone or travel to a physician on Shabbat, for he lacks the expertise to ascertain the etiology of the disorder and there is concern about the possibility of a life-threatening affliction. Dr. Yedvab notes that this symptom may be encountered with acute inflammations of the cornea or internal ocular tissues, sudden elevation of intraocular pressure, intraocular hemorrhage, retinal detachment, optic neuritis, and occlusion of the retinal or choroidal artery or vein. Rabbi Hershler suggests that sudden loss of vision surely strengthens the suspicion of a life-threatening malady, and there is no reason to be stringent in such an instance. Hence, according to Rabbi Waldenberg, the physician may utilize electrical instruments and other procedures which would normally be forbidden according to Biblical precept, to evaluate the process and institute appropriate therapy.

If, however, one has a simple inflammation with nonpurulent discharge, or a disorder that has for the most part responded to therapy (though there is some residual conjunctival burning or redness), or it is still necessary to apply medicine to improve vision, or if (in the absence of other

---

13 In other instances, such as scurvy, a wound inflicted by a metallic object, and a woman within the first three days after delivery, we also maintain halachically that even if the patient or a physician declares that treatment on Shabbat is not necessary, we do not heed them (Commentary of the Bach on the *Tur, Orach Chayim* 328; *Peri Megadim, Mishbetzot Zahav* 328:2).

evidence of disorder) one's eyes ache with sufficient intensity to cause generalized malaise or to require the patient to go to bed, the patient is considered halachically as one who is not dangerously ill.[14] Hence, if it is necessary to violate Biblical work categories in treating the disorder, the services of a non-Jew should be employed. However, Rabbinic prohibitions may be desecrated by a Jew, preferably with a *shinui* but if this is not possible, then even in their usual manner of performance.

It is thus permissible to apply drops or ointments directly into the eye,[15] and to wash and cleanse it with antiseptic solutions[16] that have been prepared before Shabbat.[17] If, however, one forgot to prepare a solution on Friday, one may do so with a *shinui* on Shabbat,[18] e.g., by adding the water to the solid material, or by mixing them together in an unusual manner. Care must be exercised not to squeeze the wet cotton pledgets when washing the eye, as wringing out fluid is forbidden on Shabbat. Of course, the pledgets themselves may not be torn from a larger wad of cotton on Shabbat. Also, if the eye is to be covered, one must not smear ointment on the dressing,[19] but rather apply it to the eye directly and then cover it.

For minor ailments, such as mild irritations, dryness, mild mucus discharge, slight redness, mild weakness of the

---

14 *Beitzah* 22a, Rashi: *Sof uchla uftzuchei eina*, and the commentary of the Me'iri; *Avodah Zarah* 28b, Rashi: *Sof uchla*. See also *Eglei Tal* 17:38.

15 *Shulchan Aruch* 328:33, and *Mishnah Berurah* (in the name of the Radbaz). The *Beit Me'ir* also agrees that it is not necessary to take medicine with a *shinui* when one is ill but not in danger.

16 *Shabbat* 108b; *Shulchan Aruch* 328:69.

17 *Shulchan Aruch* 328:17, and the article "Medicines and Remedies on Shabbat," in this volume.

18 *Shabbat* 101a.

19 Rabbi Y. Neuwirth, *Shemirat Shabbat k'Hilchatah*, 2nd ed. [Jerusalem, 5739], 34:40 notes that smearing ointment on a dressing would be proscribed Biblically.

ocular muscles, and slight blurring of vision, no medical treatment would be permitted on Shabbat.[20] One may not apply drops or ointments, nor place a dressing over the eye. But if the medicines and dressing were applied before Shabbat, they may remain in place on Shabbat.[21] Moreover, daily treatments initiated during the week may, if necessary, be continued on Shabbat.[22] It is also permitted to wash one's face, including the eyes, with warm water and colorless antiseptic or medicinal solutions which have been prepared before Shabbat, since neither the fluid nor the procedure of washing is obviously therapeutic in nature to an uninformed observer.[23] But one must not use colored solutions, which are more clearly identified as medicinal in nature.[24]

---

20 *Shabbat* 108b; the Rambam 21:25; *Shulchan Aruch, Orach Chayim* 328:20.

21 *Shabbat* 18a; *Shulchan Aruch* 252:5.

22 See "Medicines and Remedies on Shabbat," in this volume.

23 *Shabbat* 108b and Rashi; *Shulchan Aruch* 328:20.

24 Ibid., *Magen Avraham.*

Medical therapy on Yom Tov

Translated and adapted from the article
by RABBI BENJAMIN HIRSCHMAN in *Halachah U'Refuah* I, 190-94

Since the prohibition against taking medicines on Shabbat derives from the concern that one may transgress the Biblical prohibition of grinding or crushing together ingredients,[1] it follows that this Rabbinic precaution should not extend to *Yom Tov*, when the prohibition against grinding is itself only Rabbinic in origin.[2] However, from the Talmudic axiom, "There is no difference between the restrictions of *Yom Tov* and Shabbat, except with regard to the matter of preparing food,"[3] which is sanctioned on *Yom Tov*, it would seem that no work categories other than those specifically related to food preparation, which are forbidden on Shabbat, would be permissible on *Yom Tov* a priori.[4] Thus, taking medicines, which is not food-related, would not be permitted on *Yom Tov*. *Tosafot*,[5] on the other hand, maintains that the gist of the text is that there is no example of a Biblically defined work activity which is forbidden on Shabbat that is not also disallowed on *Yom Tov*, except with regard to preparation of foodstuffs, but since taking medicine involves no actual work, it might be permitted on *Yom Tov*. Indeed, the Talmud[6] specifies that for Shabbat, when the prohibition against working is punishable by stoning, the Rabbis enacted preventive edicts, but for *Yom Tov*, when the interdiction is only that of a negative commandment, Rabbinic

---

1 *Shabbat* 53b, Rashi.

2 *Shulchan Aruch, Orach Chayim* 495:2.

3 *Megillah* 7b.

4 Ibid., Rashi.

5 Ibid., *Tosafot*.

6 *Yevamot* 114a.

precautions were not necessary.

Although there is no specific reference in the Talmud forbidding or permitting the taking of medicines on *Yom Tov*, the *Magen Avraham*[7] infers such a prohibition from the *Shulchan Aruch*'s ruling: "All medicines are permitted on *chol ha-mo'ed*." The origin of this ruling is in the *Tosefta*,[8] which states that, at the outset, it was maintained that certain medicinal waters and potions could not be imbibed on *chol ha-mo'ed*, until Rabbi Akiva taught that it was permissible.

Other authorities hold that the issue in the *Tosefta* is whether medicinal therapy (obviously when one is not in danger) takes precedence over the commandment to enjoy oneself on *Yom Tov* (since after taking many medicinal potions the patient may be unable to eat or drink because of nausea).[9] It is also possible that the intent of the *Tosefta* is to permit the preparation of the potion, since it may involve work normally forbidden on *chol ha-mo'ed*. But with regard to the taking of medicine already prepared, there was no reason to question its approval.[10]

The Rambam[11] maintains that all Shabbat restrictions, whether or not they are Rabbinic in origin, are applicable also to *Yom Tov*. He specifically excludes restrictions which relate to the preparation of foodstuffs. But it is not clear whether the latter ruling would apply also to the taking of medicine. It can be argued that, since the work of grinding is itself permitted in preparing food,[12] a Rabbinic restriction which is based on the concern lest one come to grind ingre-

---

7 *Orach Chayim* 532, *Magen Avraham*. See also *Teshuvot Avnei Nezer, Hilchot Yom Tov* 194- 95.

8 *Mo'ed Katan* 2:10. Also see the commentary *Chasdei David*.

9 *Keren Orah, Mo'ed Katan* 10b, and *Aruch ha-Shulchan* 532.

10 *Nachal Eshkol* on *Sefer ha-Eshkol, Hilchot Mo'ed Katan*, p.147.

11 *Hilchot Yom Tov* 1:17.

12 Ibid. 3:12.

dients is groundless.[13] On the other hand, it is possible that, since medicines are not foodstuffs, the Rabbinic edict against taking medicine on Shabbat is carried over to *Yom Tov*, irrespective of the original reason for the enactment. Indeed, the Rambam rules that all foodstuffs and drinks which are used medicinally, but not by individuals who are well, may be taken on *chol ha-mo'ed*. Since the Rambam restricts the authorization to *chol ha-mo'ed*, we may infer, as the *Magen Avraham* deduced from the specification of the *Tosefta*, that on *Yom Tov* itself ingestion of medicines would not be permitted.[14]

The Ritva, on the other hand, clearly states that on *Yom Tov* "We are not concerned lest one come to grind ingredients, since it is permissible to grind peppercorns and spices for the holiday, and taking medicines was forbidden only on Shabbat, because grinding the ingredients is banned by Biblical precepts."[15]

---

13 Ibid. 8:15.

14 Note that taking medicines can be equated to burning incense (Mishnah *Beitzah* 2:7), which is not included in the general dispensation for food preparation, as it is not usually indulged in by an ordinary person.

15 Quoted in the *Shittah Mekubetzet, Beitzah* 22a.

Therapeutic measurements on Shabbat

Translated and adapted from the article
by RABBI MOSHE HERSHLER in *Halachah U'Refuah* I, 113-15

Although it is generally forbidden to measure on Shabbat,[1] because it is a workday activity, one may take measurements for the purpose of performing a mitzvah.[2] It is similarly permissible to take measurements for the benefit of a patient,[3] even one who is merely indisposed, since healing a patient is also a mitzvah. Performing measurements cannot be proscribed under the Rabbinic restriction against taking medicine on Shabbat,[4] since the process of measuring is not therapeutic in itself.

Thus, on Shabbat, one may use a thermometer,[5] determine the blood pressure and the pulse, and use a watch to time events and intervals between feedings. The mercury level may be lowered by shaking the thermometer before using it on Shabbat,[6] but devices which are set electrically

---

1 *Shabbat* 157b and 149a; *Beitzah* 29a; Rambam, *Hilchot Shabbat* 23:13, and *Hilchot Yom Tov* 4:21; *Shulchan Aruch, Orach Chayim* 323:1 and 308:51. See also *Beitzah* 28a, Rashi: *D'asur lishkol b'litra.*

2 E.g., pacing to measure the distance one may walk from an inhabited area on Shabbat. *Shabbat* 157b; Rambam, *Hilchot Shabbat* 24:5; *Shulchan Aruch* 306:7, *Magen Avraham* 15, and 317:3. See also *Shabbat* 126b, *Tosafot*; and Ritva, *Eruvin* 46a.

3 *Shulchan Aruch, Orach Chayim; Tosafot Shabbat* on the *Magen Avraham* 37. See also the *Shulchan Aruch* 306:7; *Tashbatz* 45; *Mordechai* on *Shabbat*, 385; and *Hagahot Maymuniyot, Hilchot Shabbat* 244:4.

4 *Mishnah Berurah* 306:35. See "Medicines and Remedies on Shabbat" in this volume.

5 It is also permissible for women to measure their basal temperature on Shabbat to determine the time of ovulation, even though they are not ill (*Shevet ha-Levi, Orach Chayim* 61:2, and *Tzitz Eliezer* XI, 38).

6 *Tzitz Eliezer* XI, 38. See also *Az Nidberu* I, 62, who maintains that resetting the mercury level does not come under the category of repairing the thermometer or applying the finishing stroke before use (*makkeh ba-pattish*), since the

may not be employed. Nor should one set a mechanical stopwatch or timer, unless it is urgently needed.[7] All devices and instruments which can be used for measurements on Shabbat may also be moved freely, with no concern of *muktzeh*, since they are utensils which are employed for permitted applications (*keli she-melachto l'heter*).[8]

Temperature strips that vary in color with the temperature of the patient are also authorized on Shabbat.[9] If nonpermanent letters or symbols appear, their use is Rabbinically restricted as a form of writing, but they may be allowed in a very urgent situation.[10]

When it is necessary to weigh or measure medicines, one should not use weights or a ruler, but gauge the amount by comparing it to a similar-sized object.[11] However, when an exact measure of medicine is needed for a bedridden patient, one may weigh it in the usual manner, since many authorities maintain that one may actively violate a Rabbinic restriction for such an individual. Infants may also be weighed after eating to determine how much they have ingested, since they are considered like individuals who are ill, although not in danger.

---

mercury level is constantly moved up and down during normal use. However, the *Shevet ha-Levi, Orach Chayim* 61:2, does insist that the thermometer be reset before Shabbat.

7   *Mishnah Berurah* 338:15, and *Chayei Adam* 59:9.

8   *Chelkat Yaakov* III, 24, and Ha-Gaon Rabbi Shlomo Z. Auerbach in *Shemirat Shabbat K'Hilchatah*, 2nd ed. (Jerusalem, 5739), 40:2.

9   Ha-Gaon Rabbi Moshe Feinstein similarly permits the use of sunglasses whose optical density varies with the intensity of light (*Iggrot Moshe, Orach Chayim* III, 45). See also *Mishnah Berurah* 340:17, and *Shemirat Shabbat k'Hilchatah* 40:8. (However, with regard to sunglasses, specifically, there may be a problem with carrying from one domain to another.)

10   Ha-Gaon Rabbi Shlomo Z. Auerbach cited in *Shemirat Shabbat k'Hilchatah* 40:8. See also *Minchat Yitzchak* VII, 22.

11   *Pesach ha-Devir* 306:15; *Kaf ha-Chayim* 306:63. See also *Mishnah Berurah* 306:35, and *Peri Megadim* 306:1.

Dental care on Shabbat

Translated and adapted from the article
by RABBI MOSHE HERSHLER in *Halachah U'Refuah* I, 117-24

Dental treatment generally involves many procedures associated with Biblically forbidden work categories. These include routine diagnostic and therapeutic techniques such as
illumination of the mouth by electrical means, obtaining
X-ray images, drilling holes, cutting and tearing tissues,
extractions, preparing and placing permanent fillings, and
smearing ointments. Rabbinically forbidden activities are
encountered in placing temporary fillings, draining ab-
scesses manually, using topical or subcutaneous anesthesia
or applications, ingesting medicaments, and using hot or
cold soaks (taking care not to squeeze out fluid).

Dental conditions which raise the possibility of danger to
the patient, necessitating urgent attention, include: severe
toothache with signs of abscess, swelling and gum inflammation, abscess with systemic signs of fever and toxicity,
inflammation of the tooth pulp, and unceasing hemorrhage
due to poor clotting, related to previous extraction or infection or arising spontaneously. Pain is the most frequent
symptom which causes an individual to seek dental attention. In general, dental pain arises from pressure within the
tooth canal or direct irritation of the nerve. Since pain cannot
be evaluated objectively, one must rely upon the sensitivity
and tolerance of the patient in estimating its intensity. But
the ultimate determination of risk to the patient depends
upon the dentist's overall assessment of the clinical state. In
the absence of pain, localized swelling may, on occasion, also
provide evidence of underlying inflammation which must be
treated promptly to avoid further complications.

Halachically, intense pain or inflammation involving the
teeth or gums is considered an internal affliction,[1] and hence
a potentially life-threatening malady. As a rule, in treating

an internal affliction one may violate Biblical precepts if
necessary, unless the patient or physician affirms that the
illness will not be aggravated by delaying until after Shabbat.[2]

However, with regard to dental problems, the treatment
of infection and pain is nowadays more advanced, so that
serious life-threatening complications that were more common previously are rarely seen. Even if one has an intense
toothache or swelling and infection in the gums or root canal,
one can usually get through Shabbat without complications
by taking antibiotics and pain medication. Hence, most
individuals who suffer from acute dental problems should be
classified, halachically, as patients with a generalized illness[3] which is not life-endangering.[4] It would, therefore, not
be permissible for a Shabbat observer to violate Biblical
restrictions on the patient's behalf, but the Rabbinic restric-

---

1 *Avodah Zarah* 28a. Although the issue is not resolved in the Talmud, the Rosh
and other *Rishonim* rule leniently. *Shulchan Aruch, Orach Chayim* 328:3,
Mishnah Berurah 7, and *Sha'ar ha-Tziyun* 2. According to the *Mishnah
Berurah* (8), it is not necessary for the tooth to be inflamed. Intense pain which
causes a generalized feeling of illness is sufficient. However, the *Magen
Avraham* (2) appears to require an actual inflammation of the teeth, as is the
case with gum disease.

2 *Shulchan Aruch* 328:4; *Mishnah Berurah* 8, 15 and 16. In the case of scurvy
(*tzapidna* or *tzafdina*), which causes hemorrhage of the gums, the opinion of
the patient or the physician is of no consequence, for it was accepted by the
Sages that the illness is generalized and life-threatening. Rabbi Hershler adds
that urgency, warranting Biblical violations, may also be present in very
severe infections, in diabetes, and in patients with blood-clotting disorders.
See *Mishnah Berurah* 100.

3 *Magen Avraham* 328:3; see also *Mishnah Berurah* 9, and *Biur Halachah:
U'mitzta'er*. The *Acharonim* apparently felt that intense pain of dental origin
is similar to a generalized illness affecting the whole body. It should be noted
that as a result of dental infection, pain may in fact spread over a large area,
being referred to the region of the temple, the ear, the angle of the jaw, etc.

4 Rabbi Y. Neuwirth, *Shemirat Shabbat k'Hilchatah*, ch. 34, also concurs that,
as a consequence of current expertise in antisepsis and antibiotics, there
usually is no concern of peril in instances of dental problems. It should be noted
that with respect to procuring the required antibiotics, the patient should be
regarded as one who is in life-threatening peril.

tion against asking a non-Jew to perform Biblically forbidden procedures would be removed.[5] The patient may also take pain medication in any form, including tablets, capsules, syrups, suppositories, topical sprays, and subcutaneous or intramuscular injections.

Dental Extractions

Therapeutic tooth extraction has limited application in modern dentistry, as in most instances it is possible to save the tooth through drainage procedures and fillings. Moreover, even where extraction is indicated, it is sometimes preferable to delay the procedure while initiating antibiotic therapy to prevent systemic dissemination of infection.

Regarding dental extraction, the *Magen Avraham* rules that it is Biblically prohibited on Shabbat, because a hemorrhagic wound is produced for therapeutic benefit.[6] The *Biur Halachah* doubts the veracity of this decision, for when

---

5 See "Medicines and Remedies on Shabbat," in this volume.

6 *Shulchan Aruch* 328, *Magen Avraham* 3, and 317, 15. There is no punishment for committing an action on Shabbat which is purely damaging in nature (Mishnah *Shabbat* 105b), for by juxtaposing the section which speaks of the craftsmanship required for the *Mishkan* (*Shemot* 31:4-5) with the section dealing with the prohibition of work on Shabbat (*Shemot* 31:14-15), the Torah indicates that work forbidden on Shabbat must be intended and directed toward some creative process or design, with respect to its objective as well as its manner of performance (*melechet machshevet*), similar to the craftsmanship of the *Mishkan* (*Beitzah* 13b, Rashi: *Ella mai it lach l'meimar*; and *Chagigah* 10b, Rashi: *Melechet machshevet*). But if an improvement or benefit is intended along with the damaging action, as when one rends his garment to fulfill his obligation with respect to a deceased relative over whom one is required to mourn (*Shabbat* 105b), then the perpetrator is culpable. However, R. Shimon maintains that one who wounds another so as to cause bleeding (and one who sets a fire) is also culpable, even though his intention is merely to damage (*Shabbat* 106a; *Sanhedrin* 84b), for otherwise it would not be necessary for the Torah to specifically permit circumcision on Shabbat. R. Yehudah disagrees, contending that circumcision had to be specifically permitted on Shabbat because it also confers a benefit, for it is the means by which the infant enters into the covenant of Avraham. But for wounding which is purely damaging in nature, R. Yehudah holds that there is no culpability, unless some benefit is derived, even one extraneous to the destructive act itself, e.g., using the blood from the wound to feed an animal.

extraction is performed, the therapeutic intention "is only to remove the tooth, and the blood comes of itself. Even if hemorrhage is inevitable, yet [he does not need the blood and] it makes no difference to him."[7] Thus, according to the opinion that wounding which merely damages does not incur Biblical liability, the prohibition should be less stringent, as it is only Rabbinic in origin. But, the *Biur Halachah* adds, according to the opinion which considers wounding which is entirely destructive also accountable Biblically, Biblical interdiction would depend upon the certainty (*pesik reisheih*) of the resulting hemorrhage. This is noted by the Gra regarding liability for performance of an improper circumcision on Shabbat. The *Biur ha-Gra*[8] cites the *Terumat ha-Deshen*, who disagrees with the *Tur* and asserts that another *mohel* who performed an improper circumcision would be no less culpable for creating an unauthorized hemorrhagic wound than the infant's father, despite his lack of intention to benefit the infant. For, in the instance of wounding, *melechet machshevet* is not necessary.

The *Biur Halachah*'s comments concerning lack of intention to cause hemorrhage apparently derive from the Talmud's ruling that a thorn embedded in the skin may be extracted on Shabbat, even though a hemorrhagic wound might be created in the process.[9] The Talmud reasons that, although at first glance it appears that this ruling follows the view which removes culpability from an act of wounding

---

7 *Mishnah Berurah* 328, *Biur Halachah: U'mitzta'er. Ma'amar Mordechai* and *Shulchan Aruch ha-Rav* are also of the opinion that the prohibition is only Rabbinic.

8 *Shulchan Aruch, Orach Chayim* 331:10. The *Tur* (*Yoreh De'ah* 266) ruled that, if another *mohel* is available, it is best that a father not circumcise his son on Shabbat, for if the father performs the procedure improperly, he would violate Shabbat, because he has created a hemorrhagic wound with the intention of benefiting his son. Another *mohel* would not be culpable in the same circumstance, for it makes no difference to him, as he is not obliged by Biblical commandment to benefit the infant through circumcision.

9 *Sanhedrin* 84b. See also Rashi: *Mekalkel hu*.

which is of no benefit, even R. Shimon, who maintains that one is liable for inflicting any wound, would concur in this case. For R. Shimon presumes that, to be punishable, the intention in performing the work must be to accomplish the forbidden defined purpose (*melachah she-tzerichah l'gufah*), and in this instance the intention is to extract the thorn and not to wound. Hence, even if bleeding were inevitable following removal of the thorn, R. Shimon would agree that the action does not make one culpable by Biblical law.[10]

But, according to R. Shimon, why is it necessary to perform the procedure for the express purpose of accomplishing the forbidden action? The requirement of *melachah she-tzerichah l'gufah* is to assure that the action is planned and creative (*melechet machshevet*) and if, in the case of wounding, an action which is only destructive would make one culpable, the principle of *melechet machshevet* could not apply. Hence, one should be liable as long as wounding accompanied the removal of the thorn, irrespective of whether the forbidden action was intended.[11] Furthermore, if we were to conclude from the example of an embedded thorn that R. Shimon holds unintentional bloodletting to be free from liability, why did the *Terumat ha-Deshen* believe that *melechet machshevet* is not needed in the case of circumcision, where there is an intention to wound? Is intention to perform the planned act not a part of *melechet machshevet*?

To reconcile the apparent inconsistency in R. Shimon's position, Rabbi Hershler proposes an important halachic distinction between an intention to perform an action and the purpose of the act. R. Shimon holds that, to incur culpability for wounding, a specific productive purpose is not needed, but in its execution the perpetrator must still intend to wound. Thus, in the case of an embedded thorn, even if hemorrhage were unavoidable, the intent is only to remove

---

10 *Shabbat* 107a, *Tosafot: U'me'mai.*

11 *Keritot* 19b; *Shabbat* 75a, *Mitasek hu*; and *Ketubbot* 5b, *Tosafot: Im timza lomar*. This question is actually raised by *Tosafot* (*Shabbat* 75a: *T'fei*).

the offending object and not to wound. The situation is similar to the Talmud's example of digging a pit only for the purpose of using the earth, e.g., to cover excrement, and not for the sake of the hole.[12] Although the intention is to dig, the malefactor cannot be liable for the Biblical work category of building, as he realizes no benefit from the pit with regard to improvement of the land. But, in the case of a *mohel* who in error circumcised the wrong one of two infants, one who was due to be circumcised on Shabbat and the other after Shabbat,[13] the intention was to create a wound, even though the desired benefit was not, in fact, realized. In this case, according to R. Shimon, the *mohel* would be liable for completing his intended forbidden action, as the planned, constructive *melechet machshevet* purpose of producing a ritually valid circumcision is not needed to make him culpable.

The meaning of the *Terumat ha-Deshen* is now clarified. Although it might be assumed that another *mohel* has less motivation to benefit the infant than the father, in truth, the mere intention to cut the foreskin is sufficient to incur liability in an instance where the mitzvah was not successfully fulfilled. For, according to R. Shimon, the performance of a constructive procedure is not necessary.

Yet, as a consequence of this distinction, the very ruling of the *Magen Avraham* is perplexing, for the productive therapeutic benefit is obtained through removal of the tooth, while the ensuing hemorrhage, although inevitable, is an apparent undesirable result. However, appreciation of the role of hemorrhage in dental extraction does in fact validate the *Magen Avraham*'s position. It is currently maintained[14] that some bleeding after the extraction procedure is desirable. When the site of extraction fills with blood clot, the bone

---

12 *Shabbat* 73b.

13 *Keritot* 19b.

14 As per Dr. Emanuel Moses, Jerusalem, Israel.

is covered, thereby preventing further pain and additional complications. In situations where the bone crater is dry, it may be necessary for the dentist to induce bleeding by incising the surrounding gum in order to cover the bone with blood clot. If the bone remains bare, without formation of protective clot, pain may persist and even intensify after the procedure.[15]

Despite the question raised in the *Biur Halachah*, in the final analysis the *Mishnah Berurah*[16] also follows the more stringent ruling of the *Magen Avraham*. Thus he maintains that when dental extraction must be performed on Shabbat because the patient is in great pain, the services of a non-Jew

---

15 The *Magen Avraham* also rules that a thorn may be removed with a needle, but one should take care not to cause bleeding (*Shulchan Aruch* 328:32). Yet, according to the Talmud (*Sanhedrin* 84b), even if hemorrhage is inevitable, it is surely an undesirable consequence, and why would removal of the thorn not be permitted (*Chemed Moshe* 328:13; *Tehilla l'David* 328:447; and *Mishnah Berurah* 328:11, *Biur Halachah: Ha-Kotz*)? The *Mishnah Berurah* suggests that the *Magen Avraham* cautioned against causing unnecessary bleeding where the thorn is not deeply embedded. But if the thorn is so deep that it is impossible to remove it without inducing some degree of hemorrhage, the *Magen Avraham* would agree that it is permitted, similar to lancing a boil (*Mishnah Berurah* 328:88, and *Sha'ar ha-Tziyun* 63). Rabbi Hershler suggests that the *Magen Avraham's* cautionary ruling refers to an instance where the pain of the embedded thorn is not significant, but bleeding is inevitable with its removal. For according to *Tosafot* (*Shabbat* 107a: *U'me'mai*), removal of a thorn which leads to unavoidable hemorrhage is permitted only because of significant pain. Rabbi Hershler also conjectures that the restriction of the *Shulchan Aruch ha-Rav* (308:35) against removing a thorn which became more deeply embedded during an attempted extraction, so that it was impossible to remove without producing hemorrhage, also applies only to a case where the patient suffers no significant pain despite its entrapment. However, in removing a rusty nail, bleeding may be encouraged even when there is no significant pain, because of the danger associated with such a wound.

16 328:12 and 316:30. Rabbi Hershler notes that there is difficulty in following the more lenient position proposed by the *Biur Halachah*, reasoning that since hemorrhage is not a desirable consequence, dental extraction should be allowed, as the analogy between removing a thorn and extracting a tooth is imperfect. In the former instance the procedure is considered halachically as removal of an irritant, which in the presence of pain is permitted even by a Shabbat observer. Dental extraction, on the other hand, is a therapeutic procedure and, as we have discussed previously (see "Medicines and Remedies on Shabbat"), medical therapy is not permitted on Shabbat for local pain.

should be employed.[17] We might, therefore, infer that when there is actual life-threatening danger, a Jew also would be permitted to perform the procedure. However, the *Mishnah Berurah* adds in the name of *Eliyahu Rabbah* that, even in more serious circumstances, extraction by a Jew would not be permitted, because it is not a definite remedy and, on the contrary, the procedure itself may be a cause of peril.[18]

The position of *Eliyahu Rabbah* can be substantiated by considering the not-infrequent occurrence of disseminated infection following dental procedures in the preantibiotic era. There was also greater danger of breaking the tooth or injuring the jawbone in performing extraction. Nowadays, on the other hand, with the availability of well-trained professionals and the efficacious use of antibiotic therapy and prophylaxis, dental procedures should not be a source of dangerous complications, even in patients predisposed to such an outcome, such as individuals with a previous history of rheumatic fever or of congenital heart disease.

The ruling of *Eliyahu Rabbah* in the preantibiotic era is inconsistent. For if he is concerned that the extraction procedure itself may be dangerous, why does he allow the use of the services of a non-Jew? The *Peri Megadim*,[19] in fact, does not agree with this stringent ruling. He establishes that when extraction is needed to alleviate a life-threatening dental illness, even a Shabbat observer may perform the procedure. Because of the lack of agreement among the authorities and the many problems of Shabbat violation which are associated with dental treatment, Rabbi Hershler is of the opinion that it is preferable to seek the advice of a

---

17 See also *Beit Yosef* 328, and *Darchei Moshe*.

18 *Mishnah Berurah* 328:9. *Shemirat Shabbat k'Hilchatah*, 32:107) is also inclined to be stringent, agreeing with this view. The Maharshal specifically permits a non-Jew to perform Biblically prohibited procedures for a patient in need of dental treatment, but not extraction, because the procedure "is life-imperiling" (Bach 328).

19 *Eshel Avraham* 328:2. See also *Mishnah Berurah* 328, *Sha'ar ha-Tziyun* 6.

non-Jewish dentist when one is suffering from a severe toothache on Shabbat.

In the unusual circumstance of an intensely aching tooth which is already rotted and loose, Rabbi Hershler does not hesitate to permit a Shabbat-observer dentist to remove the tooth on Shabbat when the patient cannot wait. He conjectures that this situation is similar to those of removing a thorn and lancing a boil, which are permitted to alleviate significant pain.[20] Yet it is preferable to do the procedure with a *shinui,* and care must be exercised not to cause hemorrhage.

Nonserious Dental Conditions

Dental conditions not usually of life-threatening gravity include minor gum infection, minor toothache, a broken tooth, and a patient with a previous history of rheumatic fever who requires antibiotic prophylaxis. Mild toothaches are considered minor indispositions, halachically. These usually arise from tooth decay, compaction of food between the teeth, and sensitivity to changes in temperature. In most instances, the ache passes spontaneously in a short time.

For a mild toothache, medical treatment is not permitted on Shabbat. The patient may not use sedatives or analgesics,[21] nor dab alcohol or topical salves on the tooth.[22] However, to ease the pain, he may drink or sip alcoholic beverages which are usually imbibed by healthy individuals who suffer no aches. But he may not rinse the tooth or swish the liquid in his mouth and then spit it out, since it would then be obvious that his intention is therapeutic.[23]

---

20 *Shulchan Aruch* 328:28, *Magen Avraham* 32.

21 *Shabbat* 111a. *Shulchan Aruch* 328:32. Nor may a non-Jew be asked to perform any treatment, even if it is prohibited merely by Rabbinic ordinance (*Mishnah Berurah* 100).

22 *Chayei Adam* 69:3.

23 Ibid., and *Mishnah Berurah* 102.

It is permissible to clean between the teeth with a tooth-pick.[24] or dental floss, taking care not to cause bleeding. [25] One should also not suck blood from his own gums. [26]

Medicated gum or mastic should not be chewed, nor may one rinse the tooth or gums with chemicals or medicines as a treatment.[27] If, however, the intent is to mask a foul mouth odor, rinsing with a mouthwash is permissible.[28]

---

24 *Beitzah* 33a and *Shabbat* 81b (see Rashi; Rambam, *Hilchot Shabbat* 11:8, and *Shulchan Aruch* 322:4. One should be careful not to use items which may be *muktzeh*, such as a splinter of wood not prepared for this purpose before Shabbat.

25 See the comments of *Magen Avraham* on *Shulchan Aruch* 328:22. *Lev Chayim* (182) adds that if bleeding is unavoidable [as in an individual with sensitive gums], a toothpick may not be used. Similar care must be exercised in using dental floss.

26 *Magen Avraham* 328:53. According to Rashi (*Shabbat* 132b), sucking out blood is part of wounding. *Magen Avraham* suggests that, since the intent is to benefit from the procedure, it may even be a major work category which is Biblically proscribed.

27 *Tosefta Shabbat* XIII; Rambam, *Hilchot Shabbat* 21:24; *Shulchan Aruch* 328:36.

28 See also "Medicines and Remedies on Shabbat," in this volume. However, if the mouthwash, which is not a foodstuff, actually "cures" a malodorous pocket in or between the teeth, it would not be permitted (according to *Tosafot, Shabbat* 64b).

Brushing teeth on Shabbat

Translated and adapted from the article
by RABBI CHAIM REGENSBERG in *Halachah U'Refuah* I, 41-43

In the article "Dental Care on Shabbat," we have noted that it is permissible to use a toothpick to clean the teeth and that one may use mouthwash to mask bad breath. Although no clear statement with regard to brushing one's teeth is found in the *Rishonim*, the Rambam declares that one may smear chemicals on the teeth to dispel a foul mouth odor.[1]

Yet, in ruling about the specific issue of brushing one's teeth on Shabbat, Ha-Gaon Rabbi Moshe Feinstein concludes that the procedure is prohibited under the work category of scraping to smooth out a surface (*memachek*).[2] Rabbi Regensberg is puzzled as to the application of this prohibition to brushing teeth. The Biblical work category of scraping pertains to preparing a hide by removing hairs and wool,[3] while removal of particles of food and film coating the teeth by polishing them with a brush and paste is a process of cleaning. Perhaps it is prohibited because of spreading or smearing (*memare'ach*) the paste on the brush, a subcategory of scraping. But in smearing the intent is to produce an even, smooth surface layer which remains in place.[4] In brushing the teeth, paste is put on the brush only for a few moments. The purpose is not to produce an even layer on the brush but, rather, to brush the teeth with the paste.

Others have raised the possibility of forbidding brushing because liquid is inevitably squeezed out of the wet brush

---

1 Rambam, *Hilchot Shabbat* 21:24. The *Shulchan Aruch* (*Orach Chayim* 328:36) similarly rules that one may smear mastic on the teeth for this purpose.

2 *Iggrot Moshe, Orach Chayim* 112.

3 Rambam, *Hilchot Shabbat* 11:5.

4 Ibid., 11:6.

fibers when they are pressed against the teeth (*sechitah*)[5] However, wringing out liquid out of hair is prohibited only Rabbinically.[6] In addition, when water is squeezed out of the wet brush fibers by pressing the brush against the teeth, the act of *sechitah*, which is normally performed by hand, is being accomplished in an unusual manner (*shinui*). Furthermore, the wringing out of the water is unintentional. Admittedly, it is an inevitable consequence of brushing, but Rabbi Regensberg reasons that just as unavoidable results are permitted on *Yom Tov* when the action is performed in an unusual manner,[7] this leniency should apply all the more so to actions which are only Rabbinically proscribed.[8] The *Terumat ha-Deshen* is even more lenient in permitting unavoidable, unintended consequences in all actions which are only Rabbinically proscribed,[9] but the *Magen Avraham* amasses overwhelming evidence contrary to this position.

Nevertheless, in an instance where two Rabbinic injunctions would be required to forbid an action — to refrain from wringing fluid out of hair and to refrain from performing forbidden actions with a *shinui* — we may surely follow the *Terumat ha-Deshen*'s leniency. Rabbi Regensberg contends that the argument for leniency is strengthened by the importance nowadays of not coming among people with a foul mouth odor.

It has also been suggested that the use of toothpaste is similar to that of soap,[10] and the latter was banned on

---

5 *Seridei Esh* II, 28.

6 Rambam, *Hilchot Shabbat* 9:11. Also see the *Maggid Mishneh*. Other *Rishonim* may hold that there is no prohibition whatsoever against wringing out hair (*Avnei Nezer* I, 157). Moreover, since toothbrushes are currently made of nylon fibers which do not absorb water, according to all opinions there should be no prohibition regarding wringing them out.

7 *Bechorot* 25a.

8 See Rashi, *Shabbat* 124a: *Shomta mi-Pesach*.

9 Cited by *Magen Avraham, Orach Chayim* 314:5

10 *Seridei Esh* II, 28.

Shabbat because it is made ready for use by being softened in water. It is *muktzeh* as *nolad*,[11] i.e., an item which was not prepared or ready for use before Shabbat, but came into being on the day of rest.[12] Rabbi Regensberg reasons that toothpaste is, in fact, ready to use as it is, and does not require the softening of water to prepare it.[13] Indeed, mixing with too much water dilutes the paste, impairing its efficacy.

Rabbi Regensberg thus concludes that brushing the teeth with paste should not be prohibited on Shabbat. Of course, as noted previously, one must be cautious not to induce bleeding by brushing too vigorously. In addition, this leniency would not be extended to individuals with sensitive gums which inevitably and unavoidably bleed whenever their teeth are brushed.

---

11 Rama, *Orach Chayim* 326:9.

12 Ibid.

13 The *Aruch ha-Shulchan* (326) also permits using soap already softened the day before for washing on Shabbat.

Bathing and swimming
for paralyzed patients on Shabbat

Translated and adapted from the article by
RABBI JOSHUA MOSHE ARONSON in *Halachah U'Refuah* I, 156-59

Rabbi Aronson deals with the possibility of permitting paralytics to bathe and swim in a pool on Shabbat, since these activities are very important for the recuperation of limbs which have become weakened or atrophied. There is a controversy in the Talmud as to whether it is forbidden to bathe on Shabbat and, if so, whether the prohibition applies only when one uses heated water.[1] The *Shulchan Aruch*[2] rules that one is forbidden to bathe with water that is heated on the fire, but with water that comes from a hot spring or with cold water it is permissible. The *Shulchan Aruch* explains that heated water cannot be used out of concern that one might incorrectly conclude that water could be heated on Shabbat for the purpose of bathing. For this reason, hot spring waters can be used only in their natural environment, but once they were drawn into a tub their use would be proscribed, since there would be no over differentiation between that water and water heated by man-made fire.

From the *Shulchan Aruch* it is not clear whether it is only hot spring water that cannot be used in a vessel, since one might confuse one kind of heated water for another, or if cold water drawn into a vessel would also be forbidden, because bystanders may not realize that cold water is being used. Rabbi Aronson notes that from the *Beit Yosef*,[3] the earlier work of the author of the *Shulchan Aruch*, it appears that one may bathe in cold water in a tub. However, the *Mor-*

---

1 *Shabbat* 39b.

2 *Orach Chayim* 326:1.

3 *Tur, Orach Chayim* 326, *Beit Yosef.*

dechai[4] maintains that one is permitted to bathe in cold water only in a river, but not in a pool set apart from the river, because it appears to a spectator "as though he is washing in warm water,"[5] since the water is gathered specifically for bathing.

The Maharil[6] points out that one should not bathe even in the cold water of a river because of the possibility of wringing water (*sechitah*) out of wet hair or from the towel after its use, because of concern that the bather may carry water on his body more than four cubits from the river, and because of the prohibition against swimming (see below). According to the Maharil, more problems are raised by bathing in a river, while the *Mordechai* is more concerned about bathing in a pool, which is similar to a tub or other vessel.

In recent times, the tendency has been to be more lenient with respect to rinsing in cold water.[7] Rabbi Aronson suggests that it depends upon the climate: in torrid zones the authorities have been more lenient, while in temperate regions the custom is to be more stringent. Rabbi Aronson further proposes that, even in a heat wave, one should take care not to rinse the entire body simultaneously, lest this leads to disrespect for the holiness of Shabbat.

But even if bathing in cold water were permitted, swimming is not, as a precaution lest the swimmer put together a flotation device for assistance,[8] and out of concern that water might be sprayed more than four cubits by the swimmers movements.[9] However, in a pool within an enclosed

---

4 *Shabbat*, ch.3.

5 See *Shabbat* 39b, *Tosafot: V'ha*; and *Shabbat* 109a, *Tosafot: Rochatzin*. See also *Terumat ha-Deshen* 256.

6 *Teshuvot Maharil* 139 (also cited in the Bach on *Tur, Orach Chayim* 326). See also *Aruch ha-Shulchan, Orach Chayim* 326:9.

7 *Olat Shabbat* 17; *Kaf ha-Chayim* 326:25.

8 *Beitzah* 36b.

9 *Shabbat* 40b.

space (where spraying would not be forbidden) and with a raised rim (which is similar to a vessel, in which there is no reason to suspect that the swimmer might assemble a flotation apparatus),[10] swimming should not be forbidden. Modern paved pools which have raised rims and are enclosed should, therefore, present no problem. Yet Rabbi Aronson questions whether a pool with continual turnover of fresh water should be considered as equivalent to a flowing river, even though the portion drained and replenished at each instant is not apparent to the observer. From the Rambam[11] it appears that, in the case of a pool segregated from an adjacent river, the raised rim of the pool merely serves as a recognizable line of demarcation between it and the river and, when it is present, it does not matter whether, in fact, the pool is so constructed as to conceal continuous exchange of its water with that in the river.

The Me'iri[12] further specifies that, in applying the leniency of a pool, it is essential that the total volume of water in the pool should be small enough so that there could be no reason to use a swimming aid. It is thus possible that a large pool could not be used, even with a raised rim, since flotation aids may be used in it when one is learning to swim.[13] However, the *Chayei Adam*[14] does not differentiate as to the size or the construction of the pool. He generalizes that one may not swim on Shabbat out of concern that he may put together a device to assist him.

In the final section of his responsum, Rabbi Aronson

---

10 *Shabbat* 41a, Rashi: *D'let lei gidulei*; and *Shulchan Aruch, Orach Chayim* 339:2. Rashi also adds that where the pool is not paved and the water at the edge is shallower than in the middle, we must also be concerned that the swimmer might dig up or smooth down the earth while seeking a foothold in the sand.

11 *Hilchot Shabbat* 23:5.

12 Me'iri, *Shabbat* 40b.

13 Rashi: *Chavit*. See also *Beitzah* 36b.

14 *Chayei Adam* 44:20.

discusses the halachic implications of therapeutic immersion in water. Therapy is not permitted on Shabbat because of concern that the raw material may be ground up in the preparation of the pharmaceutical, thereby transgressing a Biblical prohibition.[15] This restriction applies even with nonmedicinal treatments, unless the action can be interpreted by an onlooker as other than for the purpose of healing. Thus, a person who had an attack of congestion could be cooled in water, because it is not obvious that his immersion is being done for therapy, while an animal with a comparable affliction could not be treated similarly, because animals are not usually immersed in water for cooling where there is no therapeutic motive.[16] Similarly, when the Talmud rules that one may bathe therapeutically in a hot mineral spring on Shabbat,[17] Rashi points out that it is because people are accustomed to bathe in the springs for pleasure on weekdays. The *Shulchan Aruch*[18] adds that, in a location where such bathing was performed only as a treatment, it would be forbidden to do so on Shabbat. One could, therefore, argue that nowadays, since we are generally more stringent in not allowing total immersion of our bodies in water on Shabbat to cool off, one should also not be permitted to do so therapeutically.

With regard to the situation at hand, Rabbi Aronson would be inclined to forbid the bathing, were it not for the serious nature of the patient's illness. Even though the patients are in the process of recuperating, one should not be stringent in withholding therapy, due to the serious nature of the underlying paralytic illness. But Rabbi Aronson would not permit it for other recuperating patients. Of

---

15 For a more complete analysis, see "Medicines and Remedies on Shabbat" in this volume.

16 *Shabbat* 53b.

17 Ibid. 109a, and Rashi.

18 *Orach Chayim* 328:44. See *Magen Avraham* 49.

course, soaping and wringing water out of hair and towels are definitely forbidden, and the patient should similarly be cautioned not to exercise vigorously.

Use of an electric blanket for the sick on Shabbat

Translated and adapted from the article by
RABBI CHAIM DAVID REGENSBERG in *Halachah U'Refuah* I, 12-13

Rabbi Regensberg points out that an electric heating pad should be prohibited on Shabbat, as are other medical treatments, unless it is needed for a patient who is significantly ill.[1] Although the Talmud states that one may heat a cloth on Shabbat to place it on the abdomen for cramps,[2] *Tosafot* explains that this is permitted because it is not obvious that it is being done as a treatment. However, putting a hot-water bottle on the abdomen, would be forbidden,[3] because it is a more clear-cut therapeutic procedure.

Despite the above considerations, Rabbi Regensberg reasons that using an electric blanket which had been turned on before Shabbat merely to keep warm, with no therapeutic intent, should be authorized. An electric blanket should be no different from other utensils which are used primarily in a manner which would normally be prohibited on Shabbat (*keli she-melachto l'issur*). Although such an implement is set aside from being handled on Shabbat (*muktzeh*), because there would normally be no reason to use it, as it may not be plugged in or switched on during Shabbat, the utensil may be utilized for permissible purposes, such as covering oneself with it.[4]

Rabbi Regensberg further argues that the blanket does not become *muktzeh* as a base supporting the heated electric

---

1 See the article "Medicines and Remedies on Shabbat" in this volume, for a more complete analysis of this point.

2 *Shabbat* 40b; see Rashi and *Tosafot*.

3 *Shabbat* 40b; see *Korban Netanel* on the Rosh.

4 *Shabbat* 124a; Rambam, *Hilchot Shabbat* 25:3; *Shulchan Aruch, Orach Chayim* 308:3.

wires (*basis l'davar ha-asur*), which are themselves *muk-tzeh*.[5] For while candlesticks become a base to the flame above,[6] the heated wires in this case do not glow, and the heat emitted is not an entity which can be prohibited from being moved on Shabbat.

With regard to forbidding its use because of the possibility that one may inadvertently change the setting of the selector switch on Shabbat, Rabbi Regensberg suggests that the switch be tied or taped over as a reminder.[7]

---

5 A *basis l'davar ha-asur* is a non-*muktzeh* object upon which a *muktzeh* article is lying. Once the *muktzeh* item was lying on the base at the onset of Shabbat, the base remains *muktzeh* for the rest of the day, even if the *muktzeh* item fell off or was removed by a non-Jew.

6 *Shabbat* 44a.

7 See *Shulchan Aruch, Orach Chayim, Magen Avraham* 275:2.

Using modern cooking facilities on Shabbat

Translated and adapted from the article
by RABBI YISRAEL ROSEN in *Halachah U'Refuah* II, 245-51

Rashi states that the Talmud permits solar cooking on Shabbat, because "that is not the way [food] is usually cooked, and solar heating is not confused with fire, to necessitate the prohibition of [solar cooking] because of [fire]."[1] But with regard to secondary solar cooking, using intermediary agents which have been preheated by the sun (*toldot chammah*), we rule that it is not allowed, because a spectator observing the cooking process would not be able to tell whether the intermediaries were preheated by the sun or by man-made fire (*toldot ur*).[2] How, asks Rabbi Rosen, should we consider cooking with other sources of heat, using neither fire nor the sun as a primary source of energy, e.g., friction, slaked lime and other chemical reactions, nuclear energy, geothermal energy, high-frequency electromagnetic radiation, electrical-resistance heat, or heat given off when substances undergo a change of physical state (e.g., from vapor to liquid phase)? Are they similar in principle to solar heating or should they be proscribed because they may be mistaken for *toldot ur*?

From the *Tiferet Yisrael*, it appears that heating by friction should be no different from *toldot chammah*. The Mishnah states that one may not put an egg into hot sand or into hot roadway dust so that it should be roasted.[3] Rashi explains that the sand and the road dust were both heated by the sun.[4] However, the *Tiferet Yisrael* comments that the

---

1 *Shabbat* 39a, Rashi: *D'shari*.

2 *Shabbat* 39a; Rambam, *Hilchot Shabbat* 9:3; *Shulchan Aruch, Orach Chayim* 318:3.

3 *Shabbat* 3:3. See the commentary of *Tiferet Yisrael*.

4 *Shabbat* 38b, Rashi: *B'chol*.

sand was heated by the sun, while the road dust was heated
by [the friction of] the wheels of passing carriages. *Shevitat
ha-Shabbat*[5] also derives from this Mishnah that the heat of
friction is considered halachically as *toldot chammah*. But,
Rabbi Rosen observes, according to the Talmud's explanation, the Mishnah forbade setting items into warm sand or
road dust on Shabbat because of the concern that one may
dig out unprepared sand when there is not enough loose sand
to cover the object, or that one may not differentiate between
putting a dish in sand and putting it in hot ashes, which are
similar in appearance. Therefore, there is no proof that it is
forbidden to cook with frictional heat directly.

With regard to chemical reactions, the Me'iri notes,
"lime...when it is boiling is *toldot ur* and it is forbidden to
soft-boil an egg in it on Shabbat..., that is, when [the lime]
is still boiling as a result of the fire [which heated it]; but if
it cooled off and then heated up again to boiling through
[reaction with] the water which quenched it, some authorities are lenient [permitting it to be used for cooking]. But
that opinion is of no value, since even after it has cooled it is
hot internally, and the heat derived from the fire does not
leave it, but is added to at the time of water quenching."[6] The
Me'iri considers the subsequent chemical reaction a derivative of the original fire which prepared the lime.[7] The
authorities who are lenient consider it a novel primary
source of heat, similar to solar energy, which would not be
confused with fire or derivative sources arising from fire.
Other authorities consider all sources of heat other than fire

---

5 *Shevitat ha-Shabbat*, Cooking, note 17.

6 Me'iri, *Shabbat* 39a.

7 Perhaps this argument would apply only to those chemicals that are prepared
by roasting, but not to reactions between chemicals that are not initially
produced by a heating process. However, there is an authority that, surprisingly, maintains that "anything which is naturally cold and boils only when
another substance is placed on it is considered a secondary derivative of fire
and incurs liability for cooking" (*Teshuvot Lev Chayim* III, 74, cited in *Yesodei
Yeshurun*).

and direct solar energy as halachically equivalent to derivatives of solar heating and, therefore, prohibited by Rabbinic ordinance.[8]

The halachic treatment of geothermal energy may be derived from the Talmud's discussion concerning the use of the hot springs of Tiberias.[9] According to the Rabbis, the hot springs of Tiberias were forbidden to be used on Shabbat as *toldot chammah*, while R. Yosi understood them to be *toldot ur*, because the springs "pass by the entrance to Gehinnom [and are heated by the fires there]." The positions of both R. Yosi and the Rabbis are difficult to comprehend. On the one hand, R. Yosi's source of heat is not of this world. On the other hand, what relation is there between hot springs and the sun? Indeed, according to current understanding, hot springs are heated by the molten magma within the earth. Perhaps the position of the Rabbis may be further evidence for the point of view that all sources of heat not derived from fire itself are equivalent halachically to *toldot chammah* even though they are not actually heated by the sun. Support for this notion comes from the Rambam, who rules that both *toldot chammah* and hot springs are prohibited Rabbinically, yet cites hot springs as a separate phrase in the same halachah.[10] Indeed, the *Or Same'ach*[11] predicates a general principle that any natural source of heat which cannot be linked directly to fire is halachically similar to the hot springs of Tiberias.

The status of electric-resistance heating of an element immersed in liquid depends upon the halachic considerations involved in heating metal. Rabbi S. Goren[12] takes the

---

8 *Teshuvot Even Yekarah* 12, cited in *Shevitat ha-Shabbat*, Cooking, note 44.

9 *Shabbat* 39a.

10 *Hilchot Shabbat* 9:3. See *Shabbat* 40b: "R. Chisda said, 'One who cooks with the hot springs of Tiberias....'"

11 *Or Same'ach* on Rambam, *Hilchot Shabbat* 9:2.

12 Rabbi S. Goren, *Lighting Electricity on Shabbat* (Sinai, 5709).

position that electric-resistance heating would be prohibited only Rabbinically, since the heat produced is not a product of fire. Rabbi L. Y. Halperin points out that electric-resistance heating elements which do not glow would surely not be proscribed Biblically.[13] Similarly, Ha-Gaon Rabbi S. Z. Auerbach, discussing the Raavad's viewpoint that kindling does not apply to heating metal, notes that heating a wire by passing electric current through it would be considered halachically as *toldot chammah*, and forbidden only Rabbinically.[14] He further observed that some authorities even hold that since electric-resistance heating cannot be mistaken for *toldot ur*, it would be permissible to cook with it initially, even according to Rabbinic stringency. The *Chazon Ish*, in a novel approach, viewed electric-resistance cooking as cooking with something halachically similar to a product of solar energy, which further "incubates and becomes transformed into fire."[15] In his opinion, just as one is liable for cooking with *toldot ur*, one is also culpable for cooking with fire which "incubated" from a product of solar energy.

Rabbi Rosen suggests that, in analyzing all nonconventional sources of heat, it may be logical to differentiate between cooking with a primary source, using the heat when it is first extracted, and cooking with a secondary source, where the heat is initially stored in some substance before it is utilized. When the Rabbis prohibited secondary sources derived from solar energy, because they may be interchanged with secondary sources derived from fire, their intent was to ban all secondary sources of heating, no matter what the primary source. Secondary sources would include

---

13   Rabbi L. Y. Halperin, *Kashrut v'Shabbat b'Mitbach ha-Moderni*, (Jerusalem: Institute for Science and Halachah), II, chs. 7 and 8.

14   Rabbi S. Z. Auerbach, *Collected Papers on the Subject of Electricity and Shabbat*, (Jerusalem: Institute for Science and Halachah, 1978), p. 85. However, Rabbi Auerbach later understood that even the Raavad (*Hilchot Shabbat* 12;1), who considers causing metal to glow under the work category of cooking, would admit that Biblically prohibited kindling can apply to electricity.

15   Ibid., note 3.

friction-heated road dust, geothermal hot springs, and water warmed by heat emitted when a refrigerant condenses from a gaseous to a liquid state.[16]

On the other hand, with microwave and infrared ovens the cooking occurs at the site where the heat is first generated, i.e., within the food itself. There is no glowing metallic filament, nor is cooking effected by transferring heat from one body to another. Heat is similarly primarily generated within the liquid being heated when, as in some hot-water vaporizers, the fluid completes the electric circuit between electrodes and the water alone is heated by its own resistance to the passage of the electric current. Even in the situation when an electric-resistance wire is immersed in the water being heated, the wire itself does not heat up, for the heat generated within the wire is immediately drawn off into the water being boiled. Perhaps these primary sources may be halachically similar to an initial source of solar energy and, therefore, permissible to use on Shabbat.

With respect to chemical reactions, heat emitted during the actual reaction may be considered a primary source; but when water is added after a heated substance is produced, the water is heated as from a derivative source. Thus, heat emitted through the chemical reaction of water with cold lime may be viewed as from a primary source and, therefore, not likely to be confused with secondary sources derived from fire.

Yet, in the final analysis, Rabbi Rosen wonders whether the primary source of solar energy is unique, because, as noted above, Rashi explains that the reason solar cooking is permitted is because "that is not the way food is usually cooked." One might thus conclude that novel contemporary primary sources of heat which are, in fact, usual methods for cooking food would then be forbidden, perhaps even accord-

---

16 In the latter instance, water circulating around the hot coils of the condensing refrigerant in a freezer or air conditioner is heated and then stored in an insulated reservoir until needed.

ing to Biblical law. Ha-Gaon Rabbi Moshe Feinstein was, therefore, inclined to prohibit a microwave oven as a Biblically bona fide form of cooking.[17] This approach was also cited in connection with the use of a sun-heated boiler, but Ha-Gaon Rabbi S. Z. Auerbach disagreed, maintaining that the distinction between "fire" and "sun" is basic, and not merely dependent on the customs of cooking.[18]

Rabbi Rosen concludes that, in practice, cooking with any of the modern sources should not be permitted initially. They are likely to be proscribed by Rabbinic edict and, in some circumstances, perhaps even by Biblical law.

---

17 *Iggrot Moshe, Orach Chayim* III, 52.

18 See Rabbi Y. Neuwirth, *Shemirat Shabbat k'Hilchatah*, 2nd ed. (Jerusalem, 5739), 1:45. Rabbi Binyamin Silber argued similarly in *Az Nidbaru* I, 34.

Use of an electric oven for cooking and baking on Yom Tov

Translated and adapted from the article
by PROF. ZEEV LOW in *Halachah U'Refuah* I, 256-61.

In *Kashrut v'Shabbat b'Mitbach ha-Moderni*[1] Rabbi Halperin questions the permissibility of raising the current on *Yom Tov* in an electric stove or oven for the purpose of hastening the cooking process. Rabbi Halperin maintains that in a gas or oil stove added fuel is kindled from the already-burning flame, and this is permissible on *Yom Tov*. But any change in the current of an electric stove results in the creation of a succession of new "flames" (electric pulses) which are independent from each other, similar to lighting a series of matches one after the other by means of friction.

Rabbi Halperin limits his discussion to two types of electric ovens. In one, there two heating elements, of which one, or the other, or both may be turned on by means of a selector switch or dial. The temperature of the oven is determined by the particular heating element(s) in the operation. Since each heating element is independent from the other, there is no difference between raising the temperature by causing an additional heating element to glow and starting a cold oven. In both instances the action would be forbidden under the work category of kindling (*havarah*), and perhaps even the category of cooking, since the element softens at high temperatures.

The second type of oven has only one heating element. The temperature may be controlled by changing the current and the voltage drop through the element by means of a variable transformer or resistor. A more sophisticated mechanism uses an electronic circuit to control the fraction

---

1 By Rabbi L. Y. Halperin (Jerusalem: Institute for Science and Halachah).

of time that current flows to the heating element during each cycle of alternating current. In order for current to flow through the heating element, its phase must correspond to the phase of a smaller alternating current within the electronic control circuit. By varying the fraction of overlapping of the phases in the two circuits (from 0 to 100 percent), the temperature within the heating element may be modified. In the operation of the electronic control circuit, the heating element will be conducting current a small fraction of the time at lower temperature settings and for a greater proportion of the time at higher dial positions, but this will not be detected visually since each cycle occurs many times a second and there is no opportunity for the glowing element to cool.

Prof. Low takes issue with Rabbi Halperin's premise concerning an oven of the latter kind, in which the heating element is already glowing before *Yom Tov*. He maintains that while it is true that the primary work prohibited under the major category (*av melachah*) of kindling is dependent upon burning and the creation of a flame, a secondary Biblically proscribed action (*toladah*) subsumed under this category, with no difference in stringency, is the raising of the temperature of a metal until it is glowing, even though there is neither flame nor consumption of matter.[2] Thus, there is no need to continually sustain a "flame" (electric pulse) in order to avoid a new act of kindling, for as long as the metal keeps glowing it should be considered a continuation of the original kindling and usable as a source of heat for cooking on *Yom Tov*. Halachically, we should take into account what is visually apparent — that the heating element merely glows more brightly when the current is raised.

He further contends that there is no reason to view pulsing electric current as though it were composed of separate units. For in discussing the difference in culpability

---

2 The Rambam holds that the *toladah* of kindling relates to the intention of refining metal (*Hilchot Shabbat* 12:1).

between direct action and indirect action, in the case of one
who commits murder by binding an individual below a dam
and then directing a channel of water to drown him,[3] the *Yad
Ramah* establishes the principle that, since the units of
water are adjacent one to another, the entire column of water
is considered one entity, no matter how long it must run
before inundating the victim. Thus, even if the victim were
lying at some distance from the initial burst of flow, as long
as the water had not momentarily stopped its advance, his
drowning would be considered a direct action of the perpetrator. One can argue similarly regarding a current of electricity. Since the initial act of kindling was permissible,
taking place before *Yom Tov*, adding current flow should not
be viewed as a new forbidden act of kindling, but rather a
continuation and augmentation of the original action, as
long as the individual pulses keep moving uninterruptedly.

Even according to the view that the action is considered
a direct one only if the victim was lying immediately in front
of the burst of water, but if he was lying at some distance the
act of initiating the flow is only an indirect cause of his death,
for the subsequent spread of the water is not directly linked
to the criminal's initial action,[4] we should still not forbid
raising the current and the temperature of the oven on *Yom
Tov*. For the current which is caused to flow initially prior to
the onset of *Yom Tov* is sufficient to induce glowing of the
metal, so that subsequent elevation of the current on *Yom
Tov* does not create a new glow within the element, merely
intensification of that which is already present.[5]

The *Chazon Ish*, at first glance, disagrees with Prof.
Low's position. He asserts that even if metal is already
glowing, putting it into the fire on Shabbat to add heat would

---

3 *Sanhedrin* 77b, commentary of the *Yad Ramah*, second opinion.

4 *Sanhedrin* 77b, Rashi and the first opinion of the *Yad Ramah*.

5 In the case of an electronic control which monitors the phase overlap between
   a primary and secondary circuit, the act of turning up the thermostat does not
   even directly affect the current which flows through the heating element.

be proscribed as an act of cooking.[6] But, as Prof. Low points
out, the *Chazon Ish* is only addressing the issue of added
culpability for the work category of cooking on Shabbat, but
he does not indicate that there is a supplementary act of
kindling in this regard. Therefore, augmenting the intensity
of glowing within the metal would not be forbidden on *Yom
Tov*, when cooking is permitted. Additionally, the *Chazon
Ish*'s opinion that completing an electric circuit is an act of
building[7] also does not apply in this situation, since the
circuit is already completed before the onset of *Yom Tov*.
Also, according to the view that completing an electric circuit
is forbidden as an object which was not prepared before the
holiday but became available for use on *Yom Tov* (*nolad*),[8]
this would not apply to an already-completed circuit which
is merely being upsurged. Of course, in the event that the
thermostat was set low so that the metal was not already
glowing before *Yom Tov*, it would be forbidden as an act of
the work category of kindling to amplify the current, even
though the circuit was completed before the beginning of the
holiday.

---

6 *Chazon Ish, Orach Chayim, Hilchot Shabbat* 50.

7 Ibid.

8 *Teshuvot Beit Yitzchak, Yoreh De'ah* II, 31.

Use of automatic electric doors on Shabbat

Translated and adapted from the article by RABBI LEVI
YITZCHAK HALPERIN in *Halachah U'Refuah* I, 361-74.[1]

Automatic electric doors are found at many sites in a hospital: at the entrance of the emergency room, the operating
room, the delivery room, and many other locations. Since the
arrival of an individual initiates the mechanism which opens
the door, a serious issue concerning their use on Shabbat and
holidays is raised. In analyzing the problem, Rabbi Halperin
differentiates between a pneumatic mechanism, which me-
chanically opens the door by direct pressure of the foot on a
pneumatic-sensitive surface; a pneumatic-electric mechanism, which opens the doors electrically through a pneumati-
cally sensitive switch triggered by the person's weight; an
electromagnetic mechanism, which is triggered by a disturbance of electromagnetic reflections within a sensitive spa-
tial volume; and a photoelectric mechanism.

A purely pneumatic device would be permissible on
Shabbat, since no substance is physically altered as the air
is pushed from one point to another. Air that is lost from the
tubing may be replaced by drawing air from a large reservoir
chamber. However, when the chamber is designed so that
loss of air pressure activates an electric compressor, the
system may be used only when an indirect pressurestat
sensor is employed.[2]

With a pneumatic-electric mechanism, the person entering presses on a sensitive area in the floor, completing the

---

1 See also Rabbi L. Y. Halperin, *Ma'aseh u'Gerama b'Halachah*. (Jerusalem:
Institute for Science and Halachah, 1978).

2 A *gerama* device. See the section "Refrigerators" in the author's book *Kashrut
u'Shabbat b'Mitbach ha-Moderni* (Jerusalem: Institute for Science and Halachah) in reference to a *gerama* thermostat.

circuit and turning on the electric motors. Rabbi Halperin
suggests that, if an automatic circuit interrupter is employed, the starting up of the electric motor can appear to be
performed indirectly and independently, so that even in this
instance we may rule leniently.[3] A simple device of this kind
might employ a pulsating light (rather than a continuous
light beam) which shines on a photoelectric sensor. By me-
chanically causing a screen to intervene between the light
source and detector during the interval when the beam does
not shine, no light circuit is interrupted. The screen merely
prevents the next scheduled pulse from reaching the detector, thereby indirectly allowing an automatic circuit to be
closed (*gerama*).[4]

The electromagnetic mechanism relies upon the detec-
tion of the disturbance caused when a person walks into the
sensitive space of the steady state field set up by the transmitter. This disturbance induces a voltage change which
operates the motors, opening the doors. In discussing the
halachic rationale for permitting or forbidding an individual
to disturb the electromagnetic field on Shabbat, Rabbi
Halperin proposes that the issue is similar to the case of one
throwing a rock in a manner which would cause no harm to
another (in our case, the electromagnetic waves transmitted
into the air) and, while the rock was in flight, another person
interposed a barrier which deflected the rock, causing it to
mortally wound a third party (similar to the disturbance
caused by the person entering the field, which leads to the
doors being opened).

The principle is established that one is not responsible
for an indirect action. Thus, if one were to throw a stone
upward and, as it plummeted down, it were to strike and kill

---

3 See the second suggestion in the section "Heating Food for Hospitals" in
Kashrut v'Shabbat b'Mitbach ha-Moderni.

4 Others have argued that this might be a forbidden causation. Perhaps it might
be permitted only when there is some need (see the Rama's gloss on the text
of *Shulchan Aruch, Orach Chayim* 334:22).

another person, the first person would not be responsible.[5] The force of the initial action in propelling the rock upward is expended in midflight, and the direct cause of the mishap is due to the force of gravity, a natural cause.[6] But if the stone continued to travel horizontally as it fell, the thrower would be responsible, because the horizontal motion is directly derived from his initial thrust, even though his major effort was to propel the rock upward.[7] In a somewhat different case, if one flung a stone against a wall, and when it rebounded it caused mortal injury to another, the Talmud rules that the thrower is culpable,[8] for the outcome is considered a direct result of the thrower's force and not an indirect action, even though the stone was redirected in bouncing off the wall.

But what if the injury is a result of a change in conditions, which is effected after the missile leaves the hand of the thrower? The Talmud rules that if an arrow is shot toward an individual who was protected by a shield, and while the arrow was in flight a third person pushed the shield aside, causing the death of the shield holder, the archer is not culpable,[9] because at the instant the arrow was shot it lacked the capability to injure. A similar rule holds with regard to the civil damages incurred when one throws a vessel from a height onto a pillow-covered ground surface and, while the vessel is falling, another removes the pillows, causing the vessel to shatter.[10] However, *Tosafot*[11] and the Rambam[12] caution that when there is reason to believe that the shield

---

5 *Sanhedrin* 77b: "R. Papa says, 'If one threw a stone upward....'"

6 Ibid. 77a, *Tosafot: Sof chama.*

7 *Sanhedrin* 77b and 78a, Rashi: *Ella ko'ach kachush.*

8 *Sanhedrin* 77b: "Rava said, 'If one threw a stone at a wall....'"

9 Ibid.

10 *Bava Kamma* 26b.

11 Ibid. 33a, *Tosafot: Hotzi.*

12 *Hilchot Rotze'ach* 6:9.

or pillows will be removed, the first person is culpable.

Now, what if there is reason to sense that, after a missile will be thrown, another person might interpose a barrier which would deflect the missile and direct it so as to harm someone? Is the missile thrower culpable as in the case of a preexisting wall, or does his responsibility cease with the active participation of the second person? Rabbi Halperin suggests that, if the initial force was sufficient to propel the missile to its final destination, it makes no difference whether a barrier was likely to be removed or to be interposed; the thrower remains culpable, even though the missile is redirected in the latter case. However, in a case where the initial force was not sufficient to complete the action without the interposition of the barrier, which provided augmentation for the first thrust, the thrower would not be culpable, even if such an intervention should have been anticipated. Alternately, perhaps both are responsible, as partners in crime. In extending this analogy to the case at hand, although the "missiles" of electromagnetic waves are propelled automatically with sufficient force without the necessity of human assistance, we should surely attribute the voltage alterations occurring in the receiver to the person who actively deflects the incident waves with his body.

An electromagnetic device would, therefore, be forbidden to be used to operate an automatic door on Shabbat. To circumvent this problem, Rabbi Halperin proposes that, rather than detect an increase in reflections, the mechanism should be altered so as to open the doors when a certain number of reflected waves are prevented from returning to the receiver by the presence of an individual. The mechanism would then be similar to the operation of the pulsating photoelectric device described above, where an individual obstructing the beam does not contribute directly to the resultant action but prevents light pulses from reaching the detector, thereby enabling the device to open the doors. (It is preferable to employ a delay mechanism in addition.) Rabbi Halperin notes that such an action would be a permissible indirect action, similar to closing a window in order to prevent the wind from disturbing a fire, thereby allowing the flame to burn more brightly.[13]

Rabbi Halperin further reasons that, in most cases, the resultant opening of the doors is not premeditated, since most individuals merely intend to approach the door, without considering that this action will cause it to open. Even an individual who knows that the doors will open as a result of his action does not specifically intend to perform a Shabbat-prohibited electrical process. Since we generally rule according to R. Shimon, that an action which produces an unintended proscribed outcome is permissible on Shabbat, we may argue for further leniency in the case of a photoelectric automatic door.[14]

An objection may be raised that, even according to R. Shimon, when the proscribed result is inevitable (*pesik reisheih*), the action should remain forbidden. There is, however, a controversy among the Rishonim whether an action is forbidden even when the proscribed outcome is only probable, or whether it must actually be a certain consequence. The Talmud rules that one may not open a door in a usual manner if a lamp behind the door will be extinguished by the wind gust of the moving door.[15] Rashi and Rabbenu Chananel appear to hold that the action is forbidden, because we are concerned that the candle may be extinguished.[16] However, the Rashba is puzzled as to how such a result can be considered inevitable, since it is possible that the candle will not be extinguished.[17]

---

13 *Ma'aseh u'Gerama b'Halachah* IV, ch. 12; see also footnote 3.

14 *Shabbat* 157a. See the Rashba, Rambam, and Rosh on the text; and also the Rambam, *Hilchot Shabbat* 1:7.

15 *Shabbat* 120b, and the various *Rishonim* on the text.

16 Ibid., Rosh 9 and the Maharsha. The *Shulchan Aruch* in its ruling also states, "lest he extinguish it" (*Orach Chayim* 277:1).

17 The Rambam also forbids the action only when it is certain that the candle will be extinguished (*Hilchot Shabbat* 5:17). The Ritva explicitly states that,

Now, if we adjust the device to open the doors automatically from time to time, it is no longer certain that the person crossing the beam will cause the mechanism to operate (i.e., it is not a *pesik reisheih*), for the person may enter at the precise instant when the doors are already activated to open spontaneously. Even if we were to take the position that a probable proscribed outcome is sufficient to interdict the action, it should still be necessary for the prohibited effect to occur most of the time. But if we set the mechanism to open the doors automatically at specified, fixed-interval times, rather than randomly, we may halachically consider it equally likely that a prohibited or a permitted action may occur,[18] and according to all *Rishonim* the outcome would no longer be considered inevitable.

Among his arguments for leniency, Rabbi Halperin notes also that the prohibition against using electricity may be Rabbinic rather than Biblical in nature. Therefore, when in doubt, there should be less urgency to be stringent, particularly when the door is being opened for the benefit of a patient.

---

if there is even a remote possibility that the proscribed result will not occur, it cannot be considered inevitable (*Shittah Mekubetzet, Ketubbot* 5).

18 Following the principle that, where a minority occupies a set or predicable position (*kavua*), it is considered as equal to the majority (*kol kavua k'machtza al machtza dami*). A classic example of this axiom is seen when a customer cannot recall whether he entered one of nine kosher butcher shops in the vicinity or the sole nonkosher store in order to purchase the meat he is carrying. In such an instance, since the shops are individually recognizable and each is in a fixed position, the Torah decrees that we set aside the axiom of following the majority, and we rule that the meat is just as likely to be forbidden as permitted. On the other hand, a piece of meat found on a thoroughfare in that neighborhood would be deemed kosher, following the principle that an unidentifiable item which has emerged and become separate from a number of recognizable forbidden and permitted entities is considered as having come from the majority (*kol d'parish meirubah parish*). See also *Sanhedrin* 79a.

Scheduling an operation
within three days of Shabbat

Translated and adapted from the article by RABBI MENACHEM
MENDEL SCHNEERSON in *Halachah U'Refuah* II, 77-79

The Lubavitcher Rebbe inveighs against Torah-observant
Jews who schedule elective surgery within three days of
Shabbat. The rule is that one may not set sail within three
days of Shabbat, because it takes time for the body to adjust
to the motion and atmosphere of the sea, and for the first
three days one experiences "discomfort and turmoil which
would interfere with the pleasure of Shabbat."[1] Surely the
same turmoil and mental anguish would pertain to one
entering a hospital, even if only for elective treatment.[2]
Moreover, the loss of Shabbat pleasure would extend beyond
the patient, to include his family as well.

In the immediate postoperative period, it is usual to
undergo many examinations which involve work categories
which are prohibited on Shabbat. If one knew that he was
likely to become critically ill on Shabbat as a result of the
surgery, it is as though he placed himself in danger so as to
profane Shabbat afterward.[3] Since the patient benefits directly from the procedures, one should not undergo elective

---

1 *Shulchan Aruch, Orach Chayim* 248:2; *Shulchan Aruch ha-Rav* 248:61.

2 One cannot argue that, since medical therapy is a mitzvah, it should be
permissible to enter the hospital, just as one is permitted to set sail for a
mitzvah even on Friday (*Shulchan Aruch* 248:1). For according to some
authorities it is important, even when one is traveling for a mitzvah, to obtain
an agreement from the ship's master that he will rest on Shabbat (*Shulchan
Aruch*, ibid.; Rambam, *Hilchot Shabbat* 24:6). But even according to those who
maintain that for a mitzvah one may set sail even when the ship's master
refuses to agree to rest on Shabbat (*Shulchan Aruch* 248:1, *Ba'er Heiteiv* 1),
this may apply only when a mitzvah chanced to present itself at that moment
in time (*Shulchan Aruch, Yoreh De'ah* 266. *Shach* 18).

3 *Shulchan Aruch ha-Rav* 248:61. Also see the *Beit Yosef* on the *Tur* 248.

surgery close to Shabbat even if it could be ascertained that a non-Jew would perform them,[4] and all the more so when they are done by Jewish personnel. Moreover, many postoperative hospital procedures are routine and are not necessary in order to evaluate the danger to the patient, therefore, one should not cause a situation in which these procedures will be performed on Shabbat.

---

4 *Shulchan Aruch ha-Rav* 248:66.

Compensation for medical treatment on Shabbat

Translated and adapted from the article
by RABBI CHAIM PORUSH in *Halachah U'Refuah* I, 184-89

From the Biblical verse forbidding one to "find your own affairs or to speak words [concerning one's affairs],"[1] we derive the principle that it is prohibited to speak about business matters on Shabbat (e.g., to hire laborers on Shabbat).[2] However, the Talmud points out that accounts of a religious nature, e.g., determining charity grants, may be discussed, because these are "affairs of Heaven," which are not forbidden. Therefore, if prior to Shabbat we were to arrange to pay someone to perform a religious duty which is not expressly forbidden on Shabbat, the payment for this service would be permissible. In this vein, the *Mordechai*[3] cites the opinion of his son, Rabbi Shemuel, permitting cantors to hire themselves out to perform the mitzvah of praying on Shabbat.

Although it is the custom to be lenient with regard to hiring oneself out to perform a mitzvah on Shabbat,[4] others feel that even for a mitzvah, payment should not be permitted for services rendered on Shabbat. The Taz[5] questions Rabbi Shemuel's position based on the Talmud's ruling that payment for services rendered on Shabbat is permissible only when one is hired as a guard for a period of one week or longer,[6] because the Shabbat payment is assimilated in the

---

1 *Yeshayahu* 58:13.

2 Mishnah, *Shabbat* 150a.

3 *Ketubbot*, ch.5.

4 *Mishnah Berurah* 306:24.

5 Taz, *Shulchan Aruch, Orach Chayim* 585, note 7.

6 *Bava Metzia* 58a.

weekly wage.[7] According to Rashi,[8] the Talmud's discussion concerns a guard who is enabling a mitzvah to be performed, e.g., looking after a red heifer to assure that it does not become blemished and that no one places a yoke on it. Thus, even for a mitzvah, the Talmud requires Shabbat payment to be subsumed in the weekly or monthly wage. The Taz, therefore, suggests that Rabbi Shemuel's rule, not requiring the inclusion of Shabbat payment in a weekly or monthly wage, applies only to a mitzvah which is specifically related to Shabbat and has nothing to do with the weekdays, such as chanting the longer prayers of the holy day.

In opposition to the Taz, the *Aruch ha-Shulchan*[9] contends that when an act can be performed only on Shabbat, it is all the more reprehensible to accept payment for it. He concludes that Rabbi Shemuel must disagree with Rashi's interpretation of the Talmud, and would require absorption of Shabbat payment in weekly or monthly wages only for services which do not involve a mitzvah; but where any mitzvah is involved, not one specifically related to Shabbat, inclusion in a weekly or monthly payment would not be necessary. However, with regard to the performance of a mitzvah specifically related to Shabbat, such as that of the cantor, the *Aruch ha-Shulchan* justifies payment on these grounds: The recipient is not sinful, as he is remunerated for his preparation and practice during the week; and the one who hires him does no wrong, for he has no choice since hardly anyone is willing to volunteer to perform the services gratis.

Rabbi Porush, in turn, takes issue with this analysis. He maintains that there is no need to presume that Rabbi Shemuel disagrees with Rashi. One may reason that absorption of Shabbat payment for guarding a red heifer is neces-

---

7 Ibid., Rashi: *Notnin lo.*

8 Ibid., Rashi: *Lishmor et ha-parah.*

9 *Orach Chayim* 306:12.

sary because it is merely preparatory to the actual performance of the mitzvah, but, even according to Rashi, Shabbat
payment for the mitzvah itself would be allowed.

The *Shulchan Aruch* first states that it is forbidden to
hire cantors to pray on Shabbat,[10] but later adds that one
who accepts wages to blow the shofar on Rosh Hashanah or
to pray on Shabbat and holidays will see no sign of success
from that endeavor,[11] indicating that it is not clearly forbidden to do so. Because of the conflicting rulings, of which the
more lenient is presented last, the less stringent view is
generally accepted. However, it is best not to allocate initially what will be paid for the Shabbat services, but rather
to accept payment after Shabbat as though it were a gift.[12]

In the case of a midwife, the *Mishnah Berurah* rules that
she is surely permitted to accept payment for services performed on Shabbat. This position follows the ruling of Rabbi
Yisrael Bruna,[13] who claims that her payment is not specifically for services rendered on Shabbat, since she is also
reimbursed in part for her general availability to assist in
childbirth. Payment is also permitted as an incentive, for
fear that, were she not paid, she may procrastinate or be
reluctant to perform her duties on Shabbat, thereby endangering the lives of her patients.

By the same token, physicians also should be permitted
to accept payment for services rendered on Shabbat.[14] This
is true even in the specific instance presented to Rabbi
Porush, where the physician happened to be visiting another
community on Shabbat and, while he was there, he responded to an emergency call. Under this circumstance, we
could not claim that the payment for his Shabbat service is

---

10 Ibid. 306:5.

11 Ibid. 585:5; see also the *Magen Avraham*, note 12.

12 *Mishnah Berurah* 306:24.

13 *Teshuvot Mahari Bruna*.

14 *Tzitz Eliezer* V, 15:13.

included in the remuneration for his general availability, since he is not generally available to the community he is visiting.

Yet, even in this instance, he should be allowed to accept payment as an incentive, lest he be reluctant to respond to similar emergencies in the future. Furthermore, it is a fact that the value a patient derives from treatment on Shabbat extends to the rest of the week, and it is this benefit that may be combined together with the actual Shabbat treatment to warrant payment.[15] The preferred course of action is for the physician to perform a follow-up examination during the week, at which time a single fee would be presented to cover all services rendered.

---

15 *Har Tzvi* I, *Orach Chayim.*

Choosing between an observant and a non-observant physician

Translated and adapted from the article
by RABBI MOSHE FEINSTEIN in *Halachah U'Refuah* I, 130.

Ha-Gaon Rabbi Moshe Feinstein offers a short note regarding a patient who must choose between an observant physician who is not expert and a doctor who is expert but non-observant or an atheist. Rabbi Feinstein reasons that, as the Torah permitted Jews to seek treatment for their illnesses, it behooves one to seek out the most qualified individual, even though he be an atheist or even a gentile. One should not rely on miracles as long as there is a physician who is knowledgeable about the malady, and the requisite treatment is available.[1] One must, of course, pray to Hashem that the physician does not err and that treatment should lead to a successful outcome.

One need not be concerned that a non-observant physician will lead the patient away from his faith, as the vast majority of doctors go about their tasks and are uninterested in provoking questions of faith. However, if it is known that the doctor in the course of treatment will attempt to lead the patient away from his faith, then it is forbidden to turn to him even if no other physician is available.[2]

---

1 *Avodah Zarah* 28.

2 This issue is unlikely to arise in treating organic illness, but may be of some concern in choosing a psychiatrist or psychologist.

The obligation to save life

Translated and adapted from the article
by RABBI MOSHE HERSHLER in *Halachah U'Refuah* II, 27-68

The Rambam rules, "Anyone who can save a life and does not do so transgresses the negative commandment: 'Do not stand still over your neighbor's blood.'"[1] Thus one who sees his fellowman drowning, or attacked by robbers, or by a wild beast, and can save him [but does not] transgresses the commandment...."[2] In the Talmudic source of this ruling,[3] note is also made of an additional positive commandment, "you must return it to him,"[4] which is interpreted to mean "you must return himself to him," i.e., the person in danger of losing his life must be rescued so that his life is restored to him.[5] The Talmud explains that the positive commandment by itself might be taken to imply that the obligation to save a person's life applies only when the observer himself is physically able to intervene. The negative commandment adds the imperative that the observer must do everything in his power to help, even to hire others to save the person in peril.

However, the obligation to save another's life does not merely involve transgressions of positive and negative commandments, but also smacks of the stringency associated with the prohibition against shedding another's blood. This

---

1 *Vayikra* 19:16.

2 *Hilchot Rotze'ach* 1:14.

3 *Sanhedrin* 73a.

4 *Devarim* 22:2

5 Although the directive "you must return it to him" is written in a section of the Torah dealing with lost objects, this particular phrase is superfluous, as the Torah has already commanded in the previous sentence, "you must surely return them to your brother." It is, therefore, construed to charge an individual with saving his fellowman's life.

is implied in the disagreement between ben Patura and R. Akiva in the instance of the two people on a journey who do not have sufficient water for both to make it to civilization.[6] Ben Patura says that even if one of them is in possession of sufficient water to rescue himself, it is better for both to share it, although they will ultimately perish, than for the owner of the water to observe the death of his companion. R. Akiva does not deny that withholding relief is inextricably bound up with shedding blood. He merely rules that, in this particular situation, a man's own life takes precedence over that of his neighbor, for the Torah says, "let your brother live alongside you,"[7] indicating that he, too, has a right to life, but only after your life is assured.[8]

Withholding the Means to Prolong Life

According to the Halachah, a murderer can be executed only if he has caused the death of another by his own hand or through his direct action.[9] If, however, one performs an act which indirectly leads to the death of another, then, even though the murder was premeditated, the perpetrator may not be executed by a Jewish court. Nevertheless, he is considered one who has shed another's blood and, therefore, deserving of Divine punishment.[10] Thus, one who hires another to kill a third party or who binds a victim, allowing him to die of starvation, is culpable in the eyes of Hashem as a shedder of blood. Indeed, the Rivash[11] maintains that just as

---

6 *Bava Metzia* 62a. See also *Chiddushei Ha-Gaon R. Chayim Halevi* on *Hilchot Yesodei ha-Torah*, ch.5.

7 *Vayikra* 25:36.

8 Of course, where an individual is given the choice of actively killing another man in order to save his own life, the heinous crime of murder cannot be overridden to assure one's own life (*Sanhedrin* 74a; see also *Kesef Mishneh* on the Rambam, *Hilchot Yesodei ha-Torah* 5:5).

9 Rambam, *Hilchot Rotze'ach* 2:1 and 3:9.

10 Ibid. 2:2, 3 and 3:10.

11 Rivash 328 and 473. Many authorities also note that one may not save one's

a bystander must stop a pursuer with murderous intent, even at the expense of the pursuer's life, one is similarly required to prevent a person from shedding blood by indirect means.

Similarly, it may be reasoned that a doctor or nurse who withholds food or medicine from a patient would be guilty of shedding blood if the patient subsequently died, even though no direct murderous act could be attributed to them. Moreover, if the patient's death is brought about by discontinuing the supply of oxygen, the crime would be serious, as it is similar to confining a victim in a manner in which the process of dying is immediately initiated.[12]

But what about withholding life support from a patient who is already expiring? The Rama[13] rules that when something prevents the soul of a dying person (*goses*) from departing, such as persistent banging or grains of salt on his tongue, it is permissible to remove these impediments so that the process of dying should not be prolonged. However, one is not allowed to remove the patient's pillow or feather bed, nor shift the individual's position in order to hasten the departure of the soul. The Shach and Taz[14] explain that even though one's motives may be pure, it is forbidden to actively do anything to a patient which may hasten his death. But when the patient is not physically disturbed or is only barely

---

own life if given the choice to shed another's blood, even if the crime will be performed by indirect means.

12 *Sanhedrin* 76b and 77a. Rava differentiates between tying up a victim in the heat of the sun and confining him to a place where the sun is due to appear. In the former instance the perpetrator can be executed as a direct murderer, because injury to the victim proceeds from the moment he is tied up, since the spot is already exposed to the heat of the sun. But if the spot is merely destined to become hot at some future time after the sun strikes the victim, then the victim's blood was shed in an indirect fashion. See Rashi: *Sof Chammah lavo,* and *Tosafot.*

13 *Shulchan Aruch, Yoreh Deah* 339:1.

14 See the marginal note of the *Nekuddot ha-Kesef* regarding removal of salt from the tongue.

touched, stimulants which impeded the completion of the death process may be removed, even though a *goses* is considered a living person in every sense.[15] Physiologically, an external irritant, such as a loud noise, or a chemical irritant, such as salt placed on the tongue, may stimulate a more rapid heartbeat and increase the patient's blood pressure to some degree, thereby facilitating oxygen and nutrient transfer throughout the body, particularly to the centers of life within the brain.

As a consequence of this ruling, one might conclude that it should also be permissible to externally disconnect the oxygen supply from a dying patient, as it would be similar to removing an external stimulant. However, the presence or absence of an external irritant does not actually improve or detract from the overall physiologic state of the patient, while discontinuing the necessities of life, such as the supply of oxygen or nourishment, inevitably leads to physiological deterioration and weakening of the patient's condition. Indeed, as indicated above, removing an oxygen mask from a patient with labored breathing or with poor air exchange in the lungs would be forbidden, as it immediately initiates the process of dying. Moreover, if it were possible through medical intervention to revive an unconscious patient so that he may recognize his surroundings and perhaps reflect on his situation, it would be imperative halachically to expend

---

15 One might be tempted to draw a similar conclusion from the martyrdom of R. Chanina ben Teradyon (*Avodah Zarah* 18a). Although R. Chanina's fiery death was artificially prolonged by the water-soaked tufts of wool placed over his heart, R. Chanina refused to hasten his own demise by actively opening his mouth to enable the fire to enter his body more quickly. Yet R. Chanina readily assented when the executioner asked that R. Chanina guarantee him a place in the World-to-Come (*Olam ha-Ba*) if he were to remove the water-soaked wool, which was impeding the speedy departure of R. Chanina's soul. However, no conclusion regarding a patient may be drawn from this episode. For there is no doubt that when one is given a choice of being executed by painful means during which his life will be prolonged or a quick, painless death, he may surely choose the latter. Indeed, careful reading of the text confirms that not only did R. Chanina agree to the removal of the water-soaked wool but he consented to have the executioner actively raise the flames as well.

every effort to continue his life, even if the benefit may be sustained only for a brief period of time.[16]

On the other hand, if all endeavors to save the patient have been unsuccessful and the doctors abandon hope of saving him or even having him regain consciousness briefly, it would be permissible to cease further medical treatment.[17] Halachically, one is not expected to carry on if there is only a remote possibility of success,[18] and in this circumstance the obligation to "restore the patient's life" would no longer exist. Moreover, it is possible that since the patient is beyond saving, it may not longer be permissible to violate Shabbat on his behalf.

Despite these considerations, one is enjoined from performing any direct action, such as closing the patient's eyes, which may break the patient's tenuous hold on life, or withholding sustenance by disconnecting either the oxygen supply or an intravenous infusion, even if there is evidence that the patient is suffering and that continuation of this state causes grief to his family. However, if it is necessary to start a new intravenous infusion or to replace the mechanical respirator, Rabbi Hershler is less certain of an obligation to do so.

---

16 See below.

17 Rabbi Hershler derives support for this conclusion from the Talmud's comparison between restoring one's life and returning lost property. For abandoning hope of saving a patient would be similar to loss of expectation of retrieving lost property (ye'ush), which removes from the finder the obligation to restore it. Rabbi Hershler also notes that one should be more cautious in abandoning hope in a case of trauma to an otherwise healthy individual, whose internal organs were not known to be damaged previously. Even when coma is prolonged, the outcome in such a case is frequently less certain than in the instance of a comatose, chronically or subacutely ill patient, with documented irreversible changes in one or more internal organs.

18 Teshuvot Chatam Sofer, Yoreh De'ah 338. See also Rabbi Chayim Yosef David Azulay (Chida); Chayim Sha'al 2:25; and Teshuvot Maharatz Chayes 52.

The Obligation to Prolong Life Temporarily

Evidence for the importance of prolonging life temporarily is obtained from the Talmud's discussion concerning the suspension of the laws of Shabbat in order to rescue an individual who is buried under the rubble of a collapsed structure.[19] When it becomes clear that the victim is no longer alive, the body may not be freed from the debris until after the close of Shabbat. But as long as it is possible that he is alive, the debris may be cleared, and if he is found to be alive he may be freed completely, even if it is obvious that he has only a short while to live.

On the other hand, with regard to the Rabbinic injunction against a Jew allowing himself to be treated by a heathen physician who is suspected of desiring the Jew's death, the Talmud states that, if the patient would surely die without the treatment, the prohibition may be waived on the chance that the heathen may respond professionally, without prejudice, to do everything possible to save the Jewish patient's life.[20] True, the heathen may maliciously shorten the little time, be it a day or two, that the Jew has left to live without treatment. Yet, when one has a chance of a normal life expectancy, the risk of losing the surety of a brief remaining time to live is of no consequence.

In comparing the Talmud's disregard for short-term survival in securing the medical services of a heathen physician with the rule that Shabbat may be violated to clear rubble from a victim who has only a short time to live, *Tosafot*[21] notes that in both instances the motive is to maximize the potential benefit to the person at risk. It is entirely possible that the victim's life may not be prolonged, despite the removal of the rubble. Indeed, there is a risk that his life may be shortened were the structure to collapse further as a

---

19 *Yoma* 85a.

20 *Avodah Zarah* 27b.

21 Ibid., *Tosafot: L'chayei sha'ah.*

result of the manipulations of the rescuers. Yet every effort
is extended to free the victim, on the chance that this will
extend his life maximally, even though the benefit may be
only transitory. Similarly, a patient may risk his remaining
short-term survival on a cure that will afford him a relatively
normal life expectancy.

The authorities differ as to the relative possibility of
successful cure necessary to warrant the risk of losing one's
remaining shortened life. The *Mishnat Chachamim*[22] declares that there must be at least an even, fifty-fifty chance
of being cured sufficiently to attain a normal life expectancy
before a patient is permitted to risk the loss of his remaining
shortened life. But Ha-Gaon Rabbi Chaim Ozer Grodzensky[23] maintains that, even if the surgery is very hazardous
and there is a greater likelihood of expiring on the operating
table, the risk of prematurely terminating a shortened life
expectancy is of no consequence when there is a possibility
of securing long-term survival. Rabbi Grodzensky, however,
qualifies his ruling to exclude the situation where there is
doubt as to whether the surgical procedure proposed is in
fact the appropriate treatment for the illness.

Rabbi Hershler suggests that the *Mishnat Chachamim*
and Rabbi Grodzensky differ as to the significance of short-
term survival. According to the *Mishnat Chachamim*, an
individual's short-term survival is significant enough to
warrant the same effort for its preservation as for that of a
normal life span. It may be disregarded only in the reasonable expectation of a complete cure, i.e., at least a fifty-per-
cent chance of success. But Rabbi Grodzensky infers from
the Talmud in *Avodah Zarah* that short-term survival is of
little importance, even though its preservation is sufficient
to demand a violation of Shabbat. Hence, one may risk its
loss even for a faint hope of normal life expectancy.

---

22 Commentary on the Rambam, *Hilchot Yesodei ha-Torah.*

23 *Achi'ezer* 2:16 (10).

The importance of short-term survival may also underlie the discussion between ben Patura and R. Akiva as to the preference of sharing an insufficient quantity of water with one's traveling companion. For, as the Netziv[24] ponders, it is untenable for ben Patura to reason that it is better for both to die in a situation where both cannot be saved. Is a person obligated to bring about the loss of his own life just because he cannot fulfill the precept of "letting your brother live alongside you?"[25] One must conclude that, according to ben Patura, the virtue of sharing the water lies in assuring the short-term survival of the traveler who has no water. The preservation of life, even if only for another day or two, is important enough to obligate his companion to share his meager supply of water, even though the companions own long-term survival is thereby jeopardized. For, as the Netziv explains, where there's life there's hope. Perhaps the travelers may chance upon some water in the desert. Withholding the means of survival by refusing to share the water would be linked by ben Patura to the prohibition against shedding blood, which is not permitted even upon risk of one's own death.

Ben Patura's contention, that no preference should be given to the owner of the water, applies only in a situation where the choice is between the long-term survival of one traveler and the short-term survival of both. But if there is no possibility of short-term survival for both, e.g., where there is a single one-man life preserver, ben Patura would apparently agree that priority is given to the owner of the means of survival.[26] Moreover, an individual with an extra life preserver capable of supporting only one person may, in principle, choose any one of two drowning companions to

---

24 *Ha'amek She'elah* on *She'ilot d'Rav Achay, Devarim* 147(4).

25 From the Midrash (*Torat Kohanim Behar* 3), however, it appears that ben Patura indeed interprets "alongside you" to mean that both must always be equal — either both live or both die.

26 *Binyan Tziyon* 175.

rescue, for there would surely be no purpose in seeing both go under.

R. Akiva, of course, disagrees with the position that the owner has no priority over the water. Although he takes no issue with the importance of short-term survival, he maintains that there is no obligation to save another when one's own long-term survival is at stake. However, if both travelers were joint owners of the same quantity of water, even R. Akiva would concur that each should ensure his own short-term survival, because in this instance the long-term survival of one should not take precedence over that of the other.

On the other hand, following the dictum of the Talmud that temporary prolongation of life is of no consequence where there is an opportunity for long-term survival, if the owner of the water were mortally ill and could live only for a short time even if he were to drink all the water, but his companion would succeed in reaching civilization if the owner were to give him all the fluid, R. Akiva may hold that it is better for the owner to sacrifice his brief remaining time for the sake of a normal life expectancy for his companion. Alternately, R. Akiva may posit that temporary support of life is of no importance only when there is a possibility of a more prolonged life span for the same individual. But when the choice is between the short-term survival of the one who has the water and another's long-term salvation, the owner should still have priority.

However, in a case where there are three traveling companions, and the owner of the water has enough to guarantee his own survival, but the remaining water is not sufficient to enable the other two companions to reach civilization, R. Akiva should surely prefer choosing one to receive all the water[27] over sharing the meager supply with both.[28]

---

27 It is unclear whether the owner should choose by whim, or follow the sequence of priorities in the Talmud, or if they should cast lots.

28 It may even be regarded as bloodshed to preserve both companions' brief life spans at the expense of the long-term survival of one of them.

One could argue that ben Patura also may hold that, when the owner of the water is so ill that he surely would not survive for more than a brief time, while his companion would gain normal life expectancy if the water were given to him, it is better for the owner to sacrifice his brief remaining time to live to assure a normal life expectancy for his companion. It is only when both are equal in life expectancy that ben Patura maintains that one should not be favored over the other. But if we maintain that ben Patura would not favor the one with a possibility of long-term survival even in this circumstance, because it involves a choice between two people, he would surely support the right of one person to opt for his own long-term survival at the risk of losing the little time he has left to live.

The *Chazon Ish*[29] writes that the question of how one should act toward two companions, if he has more than enough water for his own needs but the remaining water is insufficient to insure that both companions will reach civilization, is included in the disagreement between ben Patura and R. Akiva. According to ben Patura, the water should be divided evenly between both companions even though both will die, while R. Akiva would hold that the owner of the water should give all the remainder to whomever he chooses, just as he may in any event take all his own water for himself. The *Chazon Ish* views R. Akiva's dictum as a rule that an individual empowered with the decision to allocate life-saving resources should strive to ensure the long-term survival of at least one member of a group, rather than allow all to perish after a brief respite.

Hence, in a situation where several hospitalized patients are in need of a particular life-saving apparatus, such as an artificial respirator, of which there is only one available, the physician in charge may select the individual who in his judgment will benefit most from the device. If, as a result of using the apparatus, one patient could benefit from a normal

---

29 *Chazon Ish, Bava Metzia, Likkutim* 20.

life expectancy while another's existence would be only temporarily extended, the physician is obligated to provide the
treatment to the one who is expected to be cured. However,
once the apparatus has already been attached to a patient
who does not have long to live, the physician is not permitted
to endanger the patient's short-term survival by transferring
the device to another patient, even though the latter may be
totally cured by the procedure.[30] But if the device is owned
or leased by a particular patient, it is possible that, as with
the water discussed above, his therapy takes precedence
over that of another patient who may recover, even if the
owner or lessee of the apparatus has only a short time to live.

Rabbi Hershler adds that, when doctors have abandoned
hope of reviving an unconscious patient who continues to
survive with the aid of a respirator, demonstrating some
evidence of independent life, such as gasping, when removed
from the device, the patient is considered a *goses*. One is
forbidden to shorten such a patient's life. Halachically, a
great deal of reflection is necessary to determine whether it
would be permissible to transfer the apparatus to another
individual who may recover completely. It is possible that
when the oxygen tank empties and needs to be replaced the
selection process may be reconsidered as though both patients have presented anew simultaneously, in which case
the one who is expected to recover completely may be given
preference. However, a patient whose vital functions are
estimated to have ceased — i.e., he is motionless, with no
sign of spontaneous breathing, no reflexes, no response to
external stimulation, and no other evidence of brain function
— may not need to be maintained for a prolonged period of
time through the use of an artificial respirator, even though
his heart continues to beat as a result of the therapy.

---

30 Even Rabbi Chaim Ozer Grodzensky, who maintains that short-term survival
   is of no consequence when there is a possibility for long-term benefit, would
   differentiate between risking one's own life for an uncertain future and
   requiring an individual to sacrifice his own remaining time to live for another's
   long-term survival.

The likelihood of recovering completely is not the sole criterion which should be used to determine which patient to treat. Preference should similarly be extended to a patient who is in certain peril over one who is only in possible danger. The *Peri Megadim*[31] rules that where there is insufficient medicine to treat two patients, therapy of the one medically determined to be in definite danger preempts treatment of the patient who is only possibly at risk. Yet, even in this circumstance, if the medicine to be used is the property of the patient whose need is less certain, his therapy takes precedence, following the dictum of R. Akiva. This rule would prevail even when it is doubtful whether the therapy would benefit the patient who possesses the medicine, while it is certain that the other patient, who is in greater danger, would be cured.

Is There an Obligation to Jeopardize One's Own Life to Save Another's?

The *Shulchan Aruch* rules, "One who observes another drowning in the sea or beset by thieves is obligated to rescue him, and if he does not try to rescue him, [the bystander] transgresses the negative commandment: 'Do not stand still over your neighbor's blood.'"[32] The *Sefer Me'irat Einayim*[33] adds that, in discussing this issue, the *Hagahot Maymuniyot* notes that the *Yerushalmi* infers that one must even place one's own life in possible jeopardy in order to save another, for, as the *Beit Yosef* reasons, the victim's peril is certain while the rescuer's danger is only a possibility. However, since R. Yosef Karo, the author of the *Beit Yosef*, did not cite this ruling in the *Shulchan Aruch*, and other *Rishonim* ignore the *Yerushalmi*, the *Sefer Me'irat Einayim* concludes that it is not binding. The Radbaz[34] also rules similarly.

---

31 *Orach Chayim* 328, *Mishbetzot Zahav* 1.

32 *Choshen Mishpat* 426.

33 Ibid. See also the Rambam, *Hilchot Rotze'ach* 1:14, *Kesef Mishneh*, and *Yerushalmi, Terumot*, ch. 8.

The *Minchat Chinnuch*[35] is, in fact, perplexed by the *Yerushalmi*'s stringency. Since the potential rescuer performs no forbidden action in withholding his assistance, why should he be required to place his life in possible jeopardy? On the contrary, from the verse: "Keep My decrees and laws, for only by keeping them can a person [truly] live...,"[36] the Sages derive the teaching that one may violate any commandment of the Torah to save a life, including one's own life, even if the loss is only doubtful. True, one is not permitted to sacrifice another's life to save one's own, but only when the choice is between actively murdering someone else or allowing oneself to be killed.[37] But when one is entirely passive, he should not be compelled to become actively involved, thereby jeopardizing his own life. For just as there is no reason to assume your life is dearer than another's, so, too, another's life is not dearer than your own.

In truth, the *Rishonim* disagree as to the extent of the obligation not to save one's own life at the expense of another's. *Tosafot*[38] clearly states that a person is required to give up his life only when asked to kill another by his own hand. But, if he were requested to allow himself passively to be thrown on an infant, he would not be required to sacrifice his life to save the infant. Apparently, *Tosafot*'s position is that one who is under duress to kill another must only withhold all actions, because neither his nor the other's life is dearer in the eyes of Heaven.[39]

---

34 Responsa 3:627.

35 Commandment 327.

36 *Vayikra* 18:5.

37 A classic illustration is cited in the Talmud (*Sanhedrin* 74a) of one who told Rava that the governor of his town ordered him to kill another person, or else he himself would be slain. Rava answered, "Let [the governor] slay you, rather than you commit murder. Who knows whether your blood is redder [i.e., dearer]. Perhaps the blood of the other man is redder."

38 *Sanhedrin* 74b: *V'ha Esther*.

39 Novellae of Ha-Gaon Rabbi Chayim Halevi, *Hilchot Yesodei ha-Torah*.

The Rambam,[40] on the other hand, in forbidding one under duress to sacrifice another in order to save his own life, makes no distinction between active and passive contributions to murder.[41] According to his view, the rationale that no one's life can be dearer than another's is not central to the prohibition against killing another to save one's own life. As R. Moshe Kohen points out,[42] the Rambam's ruling that an enemy's demand to hand over an individual who is singled out to be put to death must be resisted, even if all the inhabitants were to be slain as a result, cannot follow this reasoning. For the other inhabitants are in actuality not saving themselves at the expense of this specific person, since he would in any event be put to death with the other inhabitants of the city. The Rambam, in following the Yerushalmi,[43] must, therefore, subscribe to a more inclusive principle, that one must never, in any manner, whether active or passive, be a party to the shedding of another's blood.[44]

The position of the *Yerushalmi*, disallowing the conveyance of an individual to his death even when resistance could be of no benefit to the victim, is consistent with the rule cited by the *Sefer Me'irat Einayim* from the same source. For the *Yerushalmi* links the obligation to rescue another together with the prohibition against contributing to his death. Had R. Akiva not promulgated the interpretation that "Let your brother live alongside you" indicates that he has a right to life only after your life is assured, one would have been required to attempt a neighbor's rescue even if it meant certain death for both. But the interpretation of R. Akiva

---

40 *Hilchot Yesodei ha-Torah* 5:2.

41 See also *Minchat Chinnuch*, Commandment 327 and Novellae of Ha-Gaon Rabbi Chayim Halevi, *Hilchot Yesodei ha-Torah.*

42 Cited in *Kesef Mishneh, Hilchot Yesodei ha-Torah* 5:5.

43 *Terumot*, ch. 8.

44 See also *Hilchot Yesodei ha-Torah* 5:2, *Lechem Mishneh.*

does not imply that one has a greater obligation to preserve
one's own life than that of another, for the *Yerushalmi*, in
fact, maintains that one must put one's own life on the line
rather than contribute to the death of another who would die
in any event. Hence, according to the *Yerushalmi*, R. Akiva's
interpretation merely grants an individual permission to
save his own life, even when he thereby contributes to the
death of another. However, this permission, to ignore the
transgression of shedding blood, is conceded only when the
risk to both is equal. But, in answer to the *Minchat Chinnuch*'s objection that the potential rescuer performs no forbidden action in withholding assistance, in a situation where
the rescuer would only place himself in possible jeopardy and
the one being saved is in certain peril, the potential rescuer
could not absolve himself of the guilt of shedding another's
blood by doing nothing.

Yet, although the Rambam cites the *Yerushalmi* regarding the prohibition of consigning an individual to bandits,
there is no record in his compendium of a ruling similar to
that of the *Sefer Me'irat Einayim* with respect to the obligation to rescue another. We must, therefore, conclude that the
Rambam views R. Akiva's interpretation as dissociating the
obligation to rescue another from the prohibition of shedding
blood. On the one hand, it would be forbidden to save one's
own life by performing any action which contributed to the
shedding of another's blood, even if the other would have died
anyway. But, on the other hand, where one does not contribute to another's death, a person is obligated to preserve his
own life from possible loss, in preference to averting another's certain peril.

In practice, *Tosafot* would rule similarly, that there is no
obligation to save another in a situation where there is
potential danger to the rescuer. For according to its view R.
Akiva maintains that, whenever the prospective rescuer can
abstain without actively contributing to the victim's death,
the rescuer's life always takes precedence.

The Culpability for Depriving a Goses *or* Tereifah *of Life*

In an all-encompassing discussion of the culpability for contributing to murder, the Talmud relates a controversy between the Rabbis and R. Yehudah ben Beteira concerning ten men who struck a victim, causing him to die.[45] The Rabbis state that all ten perpetrators are exempt from judicial death penalty,[46] since the demise of the victim was not brought about by any one individual. However, R. Yehudah ben Beteira rules that if the victim was struck successively by each one, the last one is culpable, for his was the actual death blow.

In the analysis which follows, the Talmud points out that, on the one hand, if the victim was a *tereifah* (an individual who is suffering from a fatal organic defect), R. Yehudah ben Beteira would agree that the one who struck the last blow is exempt. On the other hand, if the victim was near death through an act of Heaven with no prior human intervention (*goses bi-yedei Shamayim*), such as an infectious disease, even the Rabbis would consider culpable the one who struck the death blow. They differ only with regard to one who was in the throes of dying as a result of another person's actions (*goses bi-yedei adam*) but had not sustained well-defined, fatal injury to a vital organ.[47] Since he has already been injured, the Rabbis compare the victim to a *tereifah*, while R. Yehudah ben Beteira likens him to a person dying naturally, because he has suffered no clear-cut, fatal injury to a vital organ.

The *Yad Ramah*[48] explains that a *tereifah* is surely doomed since there is obvious, fatal injury to a vital organ,

---

45 *Sanhedrin* 78a.

46 But in the eyes of Heaven, all would surely be deserving of punishment.

47 Rashi (*Sanhedrin* 78a: *B'goses bi-yedei adam*) explains that this would include the case at hand, since the victim is near death as a result of the blows, yet the first nine assailants had not made him a *tereifah*.

48 *Sanhedrin* 78a.

while a *goses bi-yedei adam* may yet live. This is elaborated
by the Ri Migash,[49] who points out that, once signs of fatal
injury are evident, a *tereifah* must die, even if he is standing
on his feet at present, for he cannot be cured of his deficit.
But one who is near death as a result of a severe beating may
yet survive his generalized debilitated state, if no vital organ
has been damaged irreparably. Thus, according to R. Yehudah ben Beteira, he is considered fully viable until the
moment of death.

On the other hand, the Rabbis reason that *goses bi-yedei
adam*, which is the result of human intervention, is halachically not equivalent to *goses bi-yedei Shamayim*. As the
Minchat Chinnuch elaborates: "One who kills either a
healthy or a sick person, even one who is a *goses bi-yedei
Shamayim*, is put to death judicially, even though most who
are *goses* will not survive. Yet, since he is now alive and no
injurious action was committed against him, he is considered
alive.... Even if Eliyahu were to come and say that he is
destined to live only for another hour or moment, yet the
Torah did not differentiate between killing a child who has
many years to live and killing a man one hundred years
old.... Here too, although [the *goses*] is expected to die, since
he will live another moment, [the murderer] is culpable. But
with regard to a *goses bi-yedei adam* who was dealt a mortal
blow, or a *tereifah* who has suffered irreparable, fatal damage to a vital organ, even though they may yet remain alive,
we learn from the Torah that one who kills them is not
culpable judicially. The reason is not because they are expected to die, for since they are now alive it does not matter
what will happen.... It is only a Biblical decree that [they]
are not considered alive...and one who kills them is not
culpable judicially. But as to one who has neither suffered
fatal injury to a vital organ nor been dealt a mortal blow,
such as a *goses* who is expected to die, [the killer is culpable,
for] all men are destined to die and there is no difference

---

49 Cited in the *Shittah Mekubetzet, Bava Kamma* 26b.

whether he will live a long time or only a moment longer."[50]

The rationale for the halachic difference between killing a *goses bi-yedei Shamayim* and a *goses bi-yedei adam* lies in the *Minchat Chinnuch*'s observation that a *goses bi-yedei Shamayim* who is expected to die is no different from all human beings, who are also destined to die. *Goses bi-yedei Shamayim* is a natural consequence of the process of living, for throughout one's life there is a progressive loss of vitality which eventually terminates with the demise of the individual. Thus, when the course of events is naturally determined, a person would be considered alive throughout his last moment, even when his hold on life becomes very tenuous. But when an act of violence, capable of killing him, interrupts this normal process, thrusting him into the condition of a *goses*, he is considered already partially dead, just like a *tereifah* who has suffered injury to a vital organ. Thus, the one who strikes the final blow cannot bear the whole blame for his demise.

Alternately, it may be argued that the Rabbis agree that, with respect to actual vitality, there is no difference between a *goses bi-yedei adam* and a *goses bi-yedei Shamayim* As long as the individual is not completely dead, he is still considered alive. Yet, with regard to judicial culpability for murder, the Torah specifically decreed, "he that kills all life (*kol nefesh*) of a man shall be put to death,"[51] implying that the killer must be responsible for depriving the victim of all his natural viability. Hence, each of several assailants would not be culpable judicially for the victim's death, since each is not completely responsible for his demise.[52]

Tosafot[53] apparently follows the latter approach. For in response to the query as to why the first attacker is not

---

50 *Minchat Chinnuch*, Commandment 34.

51 *Vayikra* 24:17.

52 See all the *Yad Ramah, Sanhedrin* 78a.

53 *Sanhedrin* 78a: *B'goses bi-yedei adam.*

culpable even though he has already dealt the victim a blow from which most individuals would succumb, *Tosafot* clearly states that a *goses bi-yedei adam* is as equally alive as a *goses bi-yedei Shamayim*, and is not equivalent to a *tereifah*. Thus, since the first attacker cannot be put to death as long as the victim is alive, and by the time he has succumbed other attackers have already contributed to the loss of his life, no one individual is responsible for "killing all of his life."

An apparent contrary position of *Tosafot*, differentiating between *goses bi-yedei adam* and *goses bi-yedei Shamayim*, may be cited from *Yevamot*, where *Tosafot*[54] rules that a *goses* who is wounded by being cut all over will surely not live, since he is a *goses bi-yedei adam*. However, there is actually no contradiction, for in that instance *Tosafot* points out that the victim was wounded in a manner that made him a *tereifah*. If so, we could conclude that in the case discussed in *Sanhedrin*, if the initial assailant wounded the victim in a manner so as to make him a *tereifah*, the first attacker would be culpable and those who struck him subsequently would be free of a judicial death penalty.

This is, indeed, the position of the *Yad Ramah* and the Rivash,[55] although the latter adds that, in practice, no punishment may be delivered until the victim actually dies. However, Rabbi Waldenberg[56] cites the *Allufei Yehudah* who, surprisingly, maintains that it would appear from *Tosafot* that one who premeditatedly injured another person so as to make him a *tereifah* and not expected to live would be adjudicated to be put to death even before the victim's actual demise. The *Minchat Chinnuch*, on the other hand, is uncertain whether the first assailant would be culpable merely for making him a *tereifah*.

---

54 *Yevamot* 122b: *L'memra*.

55 Responsa 251.

56 *Tzitz Eliezer* X, 25:25.

In opposition to *Tosafot*, the Rashba[57] appears to follow the first explanation given above, that *goses bi-yedei adam* is, in all cases, similar to *tereifah*. In response to *Tosafot*'s question as to why the first attacker is not culpable, even though he delivered a usually lethal blow, the Rashba first raises the practical objection that, since the victim was subsequently struck by several others, it would be impossible to determine accurately whether he would have, in fact, succumbed from the blows of his initial assailant. But, if it were possible to make this assessment, the Rashba would agree with the contention of the query that the first attacker should be culpable, even though the victim retained the residual vitality of a *goses* after the blow was delivered. Thus, he clearly holds that *goses bi-yedei adam* is similar to *tereifah*, and not to *goses bi-yedei Shamayim*.

The Rashha offers a second response to *Tosafot*'s query: that the first assailant would not be culpable according to the Torah's requirement that in order to be punished by a Jewish court, a murderer must be responsible for depriving a victim of all his life. According to this rejoinder, the Rashba apparently holds that, although the first attacker's blows were adequate to kill the victim without the additional blows of the other assailants, as long as the victim had not died before the second perpetrator struck him, the latter's hastening of his death is sufficient to warrant the first assailant's exemption from the death penalty, because he did not "kill all of the victim's life." It is possible that, even if the first attacker made the victim a *tereifah*, who is already considered a nonviable being, the Rashba would take issue with *Tosafot* and the *Yad Ramah* and maintain that the first perpetrator is exempt, because the second assailant accelerated the victim's loss of life.

The Rambam also differentiates between the murder of a *goses bi-yedei Shamayim*, who can be adjudicated for the death penalty, and one who snuffs out the life of a *goses*

---

57 Novellae, *Bava Kamma* 26b.

bi-yedei adam, who cannot be put to death by a Jewish court of law.[58] It is interesting that the Rambam does not lump *goses bi-yedei adam* and *tereifah* together in the same ruling, although he also states that one who murders a *tereifah* is not culpable according to the laws of man,[59] even though the *tereifah* showed no overt evidence of illness or disability in his actions at the time. Rabbi Hershler suggests that, according to the Rambam, there is a fine halachic distinction between the two states. While the murderer of a *tereifah* is not culpable according to the laws of man, the slayer of a *goses bi-yedei adam* is guilty of murder but cannot be put to death by a Jewish court because of a technicality — the Torah's decree that adjudication is not possible unless one person takes away the whole life of the victim.[60]

In discussing the *tereifah,* the Rambam lays down the principle that the classification of well-defined injuries that apply to animals regarding the permissibility of partaking of their flesh does not relate to human beings. The human status of *tereifah* depends only upon the medical determination that a particular affliction is invariably fatal in man.[61] On the other hand, the Ri Migash[62] and the *Yad Ramah* state that a human *tereifah* is precisely one who demonstrates one of the well-known signs of injury which make an animal unkosher, and although he is now alive, he is surely doomed. It is possible that the Ri Migash and the *Yad Ramah* also do not mean that these signs are exclusive evidence of this condition, but that we may add to this basic list any defect or illness which physicians consider fatal. Indeed, Ha-Gaon

---

58 *Hilchot Rotze'ach* 2:7.

59 Ibid. 2:8. The Rambam qualifies this as a Sinaitic decree. For according to the Noachide law the murderer of a *tereifah* would be put to death (*Hilchot Melachim* 9:4) on the basis of "he who spills human blood shall have his own blood spilled" (*Bereshit* 9:5).

60 *Hilchot Rotze'ach* 4:6.

61 Ibid. 2:8.

62 Cited in the *Shittah Mekubetzet, Bava Kamma* 26b.

Rabbi Chaim Ozer Grodzensky[63] rules that one who kills a person suffering from an internal illness is exempted from judicial death penalty, even though the victim has no evidence of a physical injury.[64]

Nowadays, it is very difficult to establish that a human being is a *tereifah*. With recent advances in the medical and surgical treatment of many defects and illnesses which were invariably fatal formerly, it has become more difficult to establish guidelines for determining this state in a person. Indeed, the *Chazon Ish*[65] takes the position that one cannot be ruled a *tereifah* with certainty, even when all physicians available declare that there is no treatment for a specific fatal illness, for it is possible, with the accelerating pace of medical advances, that another researcher may soon discover a cure for the malady. Hence, to rescue and sustain the life of a presumed *tereifah*, one would be obligated to do everything possible, as though he were, in fact, a normal individual.

On the other hand, when treatment for a life-threatening malady has to be instituted immediately, the patient might be considered a *tereifah*, halachically, if the required medicines are not at hand, or a surgeon with the necessary skills is not available to perform the required operation. For with regard to culpability for murder, the Talmud[66] rules that an assailant who mortally wounds another would not be culpable judicially if medicines were readily available to successfully treat the injury at the time the wound was inflicted. From the language of the Talmud, it may be inferred that, if

---

63 *Achi'ezer, Yoreh De'ah* 17:10.

64 This ruling might not be acceptable to the *Rishonim*, who assert that, in the absence of violent human intervention, an internal illness would be considered a natural consequence of the process of life. Yet, perhaps they would agree that an illness which is fatal with absolute certainty is sufficient to confer the status of a *tereifah* on a patient, even though he is nominally a *goses bi-yedei Shamayim*.

65 *Chazon Ish, Yoreh De'ah* 5 and *Even ha-Ezer* 27.

66 *Sanhedrin* 77b.

the treatment could not be obtained in the city where the incident occurred, the attacker would be culpable, even though elsewhere the injury could be cured readily. Furthermore, if the means of treating a life-threatening illness are available but the patient cannot undergo the procedure because he is debilitated by other ailments, such as heart disease or diabetes, he would surely be considered one who has an incurable fatal disease. For, in determining that one is a *tereifah*, we view the combination of the patient's ailments as one complex illness for which there would be no cure in all people similarly affected.

In the final analysis, with respect to the obligation to save an individual from succumbing to his illness, there is little practical difference as to whether the patient is, halachically, a *tereifah* or not. Although one who murders a *tereifah* would not be punished by a Jewish court of law, because he has killed a man who is already dead (*gavra ketila ketal*), in other matters the *tereifah* is considered a living human being, whose wife is forbidden to other men and who may join in a *minyan* and other holy assemblies.[67] He also has the potential for short-term survival, and, if necessary, Shabbat may be violated in order to save his life.[68] Surely, it would

---

67 *Tosafot Rid, Shabbat* 136a.

68 *Yoma* 85a. It is, however, possible that, according to *Tosafot,* Shabbat may be violated for a *goses bi-yedei adam* only where there is some chance of long-term survival. For, in discussing the permissibility of violating Shabbat to save a fetus, *Tosafot* (*Niddah* 44a: I'hu) compares a fetus to a mortally wounded person, for whom Shabbat may be desecrated, because "in matters of saving a life, account is taken of the minority who survive with such injuries." The *Yad ha-Melech* (*Hilchot Shabbat* 5:18) is surprised at *Tosafot*'s reasoning. What difference should it make whether any survive or not? Is not the short-term prolongation of the life of the *goses* sufficient to warrant Shabbat violation on his behalf? Moreover, how can a fetus, who has only a potential to survive, be equated with a *goses bi-yedei adam*, who already possesses short-term survivability? But the *Biur Halachah* (*Hilchot Shabbat* 329) in fact suggests that, according to *Tosafot*, Shabbat could be violated for a *goses bi-yedei adam* only where there is some possibility that the person can be saved. But for an injury which is universally fatal, one would not be permitted to desecrate Shabbat merely to prolong such a patient's dying. Indeed, if we accept the rationale

not be permissible to sacrifice the life of a *tereifah* in order to save another person with a normal life expectancy.[69]

Is There an Obligation to Save a Fetus?

When an unborn child endangers the life of its mother, the Mishnah states, "one may cut the fetus in her womb and remove it piece by piece, because [the mother's] life takes precedence over that of [the fetus]."[70] But once the greater part (or head[71]) has been delivered, it is not permissible to sacrifice either the mother's or the fetus's life for the sake of the other. The Talmud explains that, in the latter instance, the fetus cannot be considered a pursuer of its mother for endangering her life while participating in the natural process of delivery. For the fetus has no intention to harm its mother, and her peril is an act of Heaven.

Tosafot[72] notes that, when the mother's life is not in danger, one is not permitted to kill a fetus in utero, although there is no judicial punishment for the act. In establishing the rationale for this ruling, Rabbi Hershler ponders whether the act of destroying a fetus is, in fact, included in the category of murder, but judicial punishment is not meted out because in order for him to be punished the Torah requires that the murderer take "all life (*kol nefesh*) of a

---

proposed above, that a *goses bi-yedei Shamayim* is considered alive halachically, while a *goses bi-yedei adam* is viewed as already partially dead, the conclusion that Shabbat may always be violated to prolong the life of the former but not that of the latter is quite logical. However, it is possible that this halachic difference between the two conditions may pertain only when the *goses bi-yedei adam* is unconscious, but that if he is still aware of what is happening to him, it would not matter whether or not he could possibly survive. For, as the Me'iri (*Yoma* 85a) explains, a moment of consciousness is invaluable in affording a person in extremis the opportunity to repent and make amends for his shortcomings in life.

69 *Noda bi-Yehudah* II, *Choshen Mishpat* 59; and *Tiferet Tzvi, Orach Chayim* 14).

70 *Ohalot* 7:6.

71 This is the version quoted in *Sanhedrin* 72b.

72 *Sanhedrin* 59a: *Leka.*

man,"[73] and the fetus is not a *nefesh*. Alternately, since there is no judicial punishment for taking a life in utero, it is possible that the deed would not be included in the specific prohibition against murder.

According to the latter explanation, the permission to destroy a fetus which imperils its mother in utero is no different from that granted to violate any other prohibition (other than the three cardinal sins of murder, forbidden relations, and idolatry) in order to save a life. But if aborting a pregnancy is included in the prohibition against murder, one must conclude that the fetus may be sacrificed for its mother's sake only because its life in utero is considered less complete than that of its mother. Hence, where the fetus poses no risk to its mother, one would be forbidden to deprive it of life, even though it is as yet not completely viable.

On the face of it, the position of the *Tanna* R. Yishmael lends credence to the view that feticide is not linked to the prohibition against murder. In discussing No'achide culpability, R. Yishamel[74] maintains that the interdiction against abortion derives not from the general injunction against murder but, rather, from the verse "He who sheds the blood of man [which is] within [another] man shall have his [own] blood shed."[75] Moreover, the discussion of the *Rishonim* regarding the permissibility of setting aside Shabbat and Yom Kippur restrictions to save a fetus[76] also must be predicated upon the presumption that withholding the care and sustenance necessary for its survival does not smack of murder. For, if it did, there would be no question about

---

73 *Vayikra* 24:17.

74 *Sanhedrin* 57b.

75 *Bereshit* 9:6. There is a play on words here. In Hebrew, the word *ba-adam*, which can mean "within a man," can also be interpreted as "by the hand of man." The simple sense of the verse is that one who sheds blood should himself be put to death by the hand of man.

76 See the article, "Are Shabbat Restrictions Set Aside to Save a Fetus?" in this volume.

setting aside other Biblical restrictions to save its life. Indeed, although he cites the *Halachot Gedolot* to the contrary, the Ramban[77] notes that many *Rishonim* conclude that one is not permitted to violate Yom Kippur merely to save the life of a fetus when its mother is not endangered.

On the other hand, the Rambam's explanation[78] that an unborn child which endangers its mother may be destroyed in utero, only because it is considered a pursuer, would support the contention that feticide is also an act of murder.

Inducing Labor for the Convenience of the Mother or Physician

From the discussion in the previous section, there is no question as to the halachic approval for induction of labor which is necessary because of peril to the mother. The question arises where labor is initiated for the convenience of the mother or physician. In fact, some women prefer to plan the time of delivery, because they feel more prepared psychologically to cope with the associated anxiety and pain than when labor is initiated by natural process.

Halachically, a woman in labor is considered to be in a state of danger,[79] despite the fact that it is a natural part of a woman's life and that death of the mother during confinement is unlikely. There is a potential for peril with any alteration of the internal organs[80] and, in truth, neglect of a patient in this condition may result in sepsis, hemorrhage, or other significant untoward developments. Even today, with the great achievements of medical progress, the availability of a more efficacious medical and surgical armamentarium, and an ability to respond quickly to medical emergencies, there would be no change in the halachic view concerning the status of a woman in labor. Now, if there is

---

77 Novellae, *Yoma* 82a.

78 *Hilchot Rotze'ach* 1:9.

79 Rambam, *Hilchot Shabbat* 2:11.

80 *Tosafot, Ketubbot* 83b: *Mita*, and *Or Zarua, Hilchot Yom ha-Kippurim* 280.

danger to the mother and child during delivery, it is logical
to assume that one should refrain from hastening its onset
for frivolous reasons.

Of course, the obvious question as to how one is permitted, halachically, to place oneself in danger by becoming
pregnant is really of no merit. For it is in the order of things
that human beings procreate and inhabit the world in this
manner, following the commandment, "Be fruitful and mul-
tiply."[81] True, the commandment was given to Adam and
Chavah before they sinned and, therefore, prior to the time
when it was decreed that womankind would bear the risk of
"giving birth to children in anguish."[82] But the commandment was repeated later to No'ach and his descendants,
when they exited from the ark.[83] Similarly, no one would
suggest that Jews should refrain from performing the commandment of circumcision, which is clearly demanded by the
Torah, even though the procedure is not without danger.

Ha-Gaon Rabbi Moshe Feinstein[84] reasons somewhat
differently, although he also concludes that labor should not
be initiated for frivolous reasons. He contends that, since
Hashem created the world in a manner that requires women
to give birth, He surely meant it as a blessing and not a
perilous undertaking. The punishment meted out to Chavah
was only that she have increased anguish during labor, but
not that she routinely risk her life in the process. But, adds
Rabbi Feinstein, the blessing of Hashem applies only to
deliveries which are at their natural time. When one wishes
to precipitate labor unnecessarily, the mother is exposed to
greater risk. The gravity of the halachic question is more
readily comprehended when account is taken of specific
complications which may arise from inducing labor, such as

---

81 *Bereshit* 1:28.

82 Ibid. 3:16.

83 Ibid. 9:1.

84 *Iggrot Moshe, Yoreh De'ah* II, 74.

dysrhythmic contractions which interfere with the normal progression of labor, eventually requiring operative intervention, immaturity of the fetus through miscalculation of the due date, and infection of the amniotic contents following a prolonged period of rupture of the membranes. Hence, it is forbidden to precipitate labor when there is no danger in awaiting its natural initiation.

Even when initiation of labor is being considered in order to avert complications, the halachah does not regard all instances of peril as equivalent. For clear-cut danger to the mother, there is no doubt that induction and, if necessary, Caesarean section are permitted. Indeed, as long as the fetus is in utero, a midwife or physician may even extract it piece by piece in order to save the mother.[85] Many authorities even extend the permission to perform an abortion to situations where there is only a possibility of danger to the mother.[86] However, when only the fetus is in danger, Rabbi Hershler argues that it should not be permissible to increase the risk to the mother in order to save the unborn child's life. Even if we were to maintain, as discussed above, that one is permitted to place one's life in jeopardy to save another, this would apply only in the case of rescuing a complete human being, but not a fetus, whose life is not yet wholly formed. Yet, in practice, when the fetus is in danger of losing its life, it would be unusual for the mother not to be placed at increased risk also.

In the final analysis, Rabbi Hershler considers the viewpoint of physicians who maintain that, with careful prenatal assessment and management of the confinement, no significant increase in complications should be noted with induced deliveries. He agrees that when an experienced specialist determines that the time is ripe for delivery, there is no reason to gainsay his opinion. But, he cautions, delivery may not be initiated merely for the physician's convenience.

---

85 *Oholot* 7:6, and *Sanhedrin* 72b.

86 *Achi'ezer* III, 72, and Ha-Gaon Rabbi Moshe Feinstein in *Memorial Volume in Honor of Rabbi Y. Abramsky*.

Halachic issues regarding the treatment of kidney failure

Adapted from the article by RABBI MOSHE MEISELMAN
in *Halachah U'Refuah* II, 114-21[1]

The treatment of kidney failure by transplant surgery and by hemodialysis has been one of the great boons granted us by modern medical research in the past few decades. Side by side with the solution of the many medical problems involved in these two processes, many moral and halachic issues have been raised.

We will first address straightforward cases and then elaborate on more difficult and subtle issues. From the viewpoint of Jewish ethics, the simplest case is transplantation of a kidney between two identical twins. We will initially assume that the twins are adult and mentally competent, to avoid the problem of consent policies for minors and defectives. We will return to these problems at a further point in the discussion. The premise that the donor and the recipient are identical twins is convenient not only from a medical point of view but also from an ethical one, as the success rate in such transplants is very high. At the outset we will assume that hemodialysis is not available to the sick twin and that the only possibility of life for the sick twin lies in a transplant.

An issue that has received much consideration in Christian ethics, that of mutilation, i.e., the permissibility of mutilating a person's body without benefit to that same person, is irrelevant from the Jewish point of view. This is not because of the lack of a doctrine of mutilation in Jewish

---

1 In this English version of his original Hebrew article, the author chose to omit the lengthy, halachically technical details of the Hebrew version and merely to present the conclusions of that article in the perspective of some of the nonhalachic ethical writings on the topic.

thought, but rather because of its lack of applicability to the case at hand. There are no proprietary rights in the human body, and one is not given total freedom in the treatment of one's own body. The Torah tells us that the body is holy and must be treated with respect. Hence, one is not allowed to inflict purposeless injury upon the body. Cutting off one's finger is a crime within the Jewish legal system. This is not only true in the Jewish system but is also implicit in the ethical codes of standard medical practice. No doctor will perform surgery to amputate a finger without medical justification. To remove a kidney from a healthy human being without purpose is absolutely forbidden.

But what if the purpose of removing the kidney is not to benefit the one losing the kidney, but another? Is such surgery ethically justified? The large majority of Catholic theologians, most Protestants, and the Supreme Court of the state of Massachusetts all took refuge in the concept of totality. Briefly stated, this principle says that one can remove a part if the whole is thereby improved. Since loss of the kidney is compensated for by the spiritual and psychological benefit of giving the kidney, one would have to conclude that there was a net gain for the donor and hence the surgery is permissible. Many other Catholic thinkers reject the application of the principle of totality in this case and have, therefore, opposed kidney transplants from live donors.

Jewish ethics needs no such handstands to justify the surgical procedure. The concept of totality is used in Judaism only to justify physical loss which is compensated by physical gain. The compensation for physical loss by spiritual and psychological gain is, from the standpoint of Jewish ethics, a tenuous one at best. Current debates over some plastic surgery procedures involve this problem. The reason that the mutilation problem is irrelevant from the Jewish point of view is twofold. Firstly, mutilation is not a crime where the goal of such mutilation is therapeutic. There is no difference whether the victim of the mutilation is the beneficiary or whether the beneficiary is another. It is still therapeutic mutilation. Secondly, according to Jewish ethics, virtually all moral prohibitions are removed where one acts to save a human life. This reason is paramount, as it applies to Shabbat laws as well as to mutilation laws. Noncritical skin grafts or blood transfusions may be warranted by the first rationale. But as a justification for kidney transplants, the second argument is sufficient.

The major issue from a Jewish perspective is one totally ignored by non-Jewish ethicists: What are the limits of my obligation to save the life of another? This question is a dual one regarding kidney transplants. Is one required to sacrifice a limb to save another's life, and to what degree is one required or even allowed to endanger one's own life to save the life of another? What sacrifices are demanded of a healthy human being, and what is he morally charged to do?

From the viewpoint of common law, Justice Holmes wrote: "Although a man has a perfect right to stand by and see his neighbor's property destroyed or, for that matter, to watch his neighbor perish for want of his help, yet if he once intermeddles he has no longer the same freedom. He cannot withdraw at will. To give a more specific example, if a surgeon from benevolence cuts the umbilical cord of a newly-born child, he cannot stop there and watch the child bleed to death. It would be murder willfully to allow death to come to pass in that way, as much as if the intention had been entertained at the time of the cutting of the cord." Jewish ethics takes an entirely opposite view. Every man is his brother's keeper. He is responsible, not only for the physical well-being of his fellowman but also for the well-being of his property. He cannot stand idly by and watch his neighbor's life, limb, or property be destroyed. One is required by Jewish law to dive in and save the drowning child. If one sees someone's property being destroyed or lost, he is obligated to protect that property and return it to its rightful owner.

However, Judaism also operates with a moral calculus. There are differing levels of moral obligation, and these places varying degrees of responsibility upon an individual and demand of him differing degrees of sacrifice. For certain moral responsibilities, one must martyr himself and surrender his life. For others, he must sacrifice limb and property, but not life. For others, he must sacrifice only property and not limb. For yet others, he must sacrifice some property, but not all. The problem at issue is to access exactly the degree to which one is required or even allowed to sacrifice to save someone else's life.

A famous classic case in Jewish ethical literature describes an oriental despot who summoned two men and told them that if A did not allow the despot to cut off his ear, he would then kill B. There are two separate issues involved in this case. What degree of sacrifice is demanded to save another life? To what magnitude of danger may or must one submit himself to save the life of another? In response to the first question, the general attitude has been that one must sacrifice all of his money and material goods to save the life of another. However, there are certain sacrifices which are greater to the reasonable moral man than his material possessions, such as an irreplaceable part of his body, e.g., an arm or a kidney. When we operate within the area of surrender of one of these parts of the body, one is guided by the response of the reasonable moral man. If there is a part of the body dearer to the reasonable moral man than his material possessions, so that the reasonable moral man would not sacrifice it to save the life of another, then there is no absolute moral requirement upon any man to sacrifice that limb to save another. It is an exalted moral act if he performs the sacrifice, but one is not obligated to offer that much to save the life of another. This position, the predominant one among Jewish ethicists, is generally followed in practice. However, a few have maintained that there is an absolute obligation upon an individual to sacrifice his arm or his kidney in such an instance.

Life is the greatest gift given by Hashem to man. He may not treat it in a trifling manner and is enjoined by Hashem to care for it with the utmost concern. Normally, one may not place oneself in a situation of life-threatening peril. Hence, activities such as smoking should be prohibited according to Jewish law. However, this simple issue becomes more complex when a trade-off between two human lives is involved. As an extension of the above reasoning, many have argued that, although not required to, one may place himself in a position of remote danger to save another from a present, imminent danger. However, the above-mentioned argument weakens here. In the previous situation, one was called upon to sacrifice something concrete and the ethical judgment was to assess the value of that concrete object. Here, on the other hand, we are faced with statistical choices, not concrete ones. Yet, the general opinion in this instance also is that one may, although he need not, submit himself to a remote danger to save his neighbor from a present danger. We have thus arrived at the following conclusion: Where one does not foresee that the healthy twin will develop problems with his kidneys, the healthy twin may, but is not obligated to, donate a kidney to save the life of his brother.

An important point must be made at this juncture before proceeding. Suicide is a moral evil in Judaism, and acting in a suicidal manner is also morally repugnant. A poem by Schiller tells of a knight who jumped into a den of tigers to retrieve the glove that his lady had thrown there. Such an action is morally unjustified within the structure of Jewish ethics. To refuse medical treatment for any condition that may prove fatal also is against Jewish law. Life is the greatest gift that Hashem has given us, and we are duty bound to protect it and preserve it at all times. A physician who refuses to treat a patient is morally responsible for the patient's premature death, as is the patient who refuses to seek treatment. Economic factors do not enter this decision. Life is more precious than any sum of money. A patient who refuses to undergo hemodialysis because of the economic burden that is being placed on his family is as guilty of murder as the one who refuses treatment for the most spurious of reasons. Furthermore, the society that refuses to provide the indigent with proper medical care is also guilty of complicity in their premature death. A man who refuses to undergo dialysis because "this was not the image he wanted his children to carry around; he thought that instead of coming into the hospital two nights a week they should be at dances," is guilty of his own murder. However, an important point must be added. Not only is a person disallowed from committing suicide but he is also prohibited from unnecessarily placing himself in a situation that threatens his life. The donor is allowed to donate his kidney only because of the benefit reaped by the recipient. It would be absolutely forbidden for a donor to give a kidney for anything but the saving of a specific life.

Let us modify the ideal case to consider one of an adult donor relative, other than an identical twin, where again there is no possibility of hemodialysis. As would be expected, much depends upon the medical facility involved, as well as the medical details concerning the patient. Some facilities have told me that their six-month survival rate in such a case was 80%, and that this remained constant over a five-period period. Others have had lower success rates, both initially and over five years. Of course, the life expectancy of a graft or of dialysis being successful also depends on many individual factors, and cannot be predicted simply on the basis of Transplant Registry figures alone. It seems that it would be clearly permissible to offer a kidney when the expected survival rate of the specific patient over the long term is greater than 50%. A survival rate of under 50% is morally questionable. A person is not allowed to endanger his own life unless there is a reasonable chance of saving another's life. Neither the physician nor the donor himself can factor into the decision calculation the relative worth of the donor's and the donee's lives. The ages of the donor and donee are irrelevant, as is any consideration of their social worth. Hashem assigns relative value to the lives of human beings, but man must not play Hashem with human lives, even with his own! When the kidney donor is not a relative, the survival rate is generally similar to the survival rates of cadaver transplants. Since the survival rate for these operations does not generally exceed 50%, such operations must be considered morally questionable.

Let us turn to a specific case with additional complexity. Both kidneys of a sixty-year-old man deteriorated, and there was great difficulty in maintaining adequate renal function using hemodialysis. When cell matchings for tissue compatibility were tested on members of the family, it was found that the twenty-two-year-old grandson's cells were remarkably similar to those of the grandfather. However, because the grandfather's kidney failure appeared to be the result of a genetic defect that runs in the family, the loss of one kidney would probably reduce the life expectancy of the grandson by as much as ten years, at the present level of medical knowledge. Would you recommend to the family that they go ahead with the operation?

Let us first dispose of those factors that are irrelevant from the point of view of Jewish law. The age factor plays no role. Neither does the relative social worth of the grandfather and the grandson. The only factor that disallows a transplant operation in this case is that the danger to the grandson can no longer be called remote. One is permitted to submit himself to a remote danger to save another from a real danger. For a healthy person to offer a kidney is to submit himself to a remote danger. Two factors can make a danger less than remote: statistical factors and the presence of a current condition that will cause the probable danger to become real. These two have a tendency to overlap, and in our situation the surgery could not be allowed.

We have so far assumed that dialysis is not available, in order to simplify our considerations. However, in most real-life situations, dialysis is a real option. Success of dialysis depends on three factors: 1) the physical condition of the patient, 2) the ability of the patient to adhere to the strict regimen required, and 3) the efficiency of the dialysis facility.

If there were no problem of limited resources, the issue would be significantly simplified. Furthermore, if there would be no such problem, then a patient who underwent transplant surgery that failed would have the option of returning to the dialysis machine. If the facility under discussion is one in which the success rate for dialysis over four years approaches 90%, as is seen in some, then one must seriously question the ethical and halachic justification for the operation.

Generally, justification for a kidney transplant where optimal hemodialysis is available relies upon the fulfillment of one of two mandates. First, if successful, the operation should increase the life expectancy of the patient. Regarding this, we must at all times remember that we are talking about statistical averages, and no one has yet determined how to foretell the future with any degree of certainty in any one case. The decision to ask the donor to surrender his kidney would depend on many factors, and it is very difficult to give an opinion in the abstract. It is also unclear whether the permissibility to jeopardize the life of a terminally ill patient for the possibility of a long-term cure applies to the case of one undergoing hemodialysis. A person whose life expectancy is more than a year cannot be considered terminally ill, and the morality of performing a dangerous operation on such a patient to grant him a longer life expectancy, if it is successful, is highly questionable.

The second group of factors that may justify a transplant operation is economic and social, as hemodialysis is expensive and seriously restricts the life of the patient. These considerations are halachically irrelevant. Moreover, in the United States current legislation provides that the expenses of dialysis are borne by the government.

It is an elementary fact of Jewish ethics that a society must care for the physical needs of those members who do not have the means to do so. This includes food, clothing, and medical care. The ceremony of *eglah arufah* teaches us that a society that allows the death of a single person through its own negligence is held responsible by Hashem for that death. The ethical issue raised by some popular writers, whether so many skilled persons should be used to maintain life for so few, borders on the amoral from a Jewish point of view. We are hardly at the point of exhausting our resources. We are, however, at a point where the value of human life has become very cheap, especially the life of the sick, the elderly, and the defective. Society is rapidly moving in the direction of a Spartan mentality, one hardly in consonance with Jewish values. The action by the U.S. Congress, whereby the government has assumed the cost of treatment for renal failure, is an important step in the appropriate moral direction. Proper medical care must be made available to all members of society, independent of their ability to pay.

The shortage of machines that once created serious ethical problems in the United States generally no longer exists. Yet the problem merits discussion, as it does exist in other parts of the world. It should be noted that where there are only a limited number of dialysis machines available, the decision to donate a kidney may not only involve saving the life of the donee but also saving the life of another patient who can now be offered dialysis. However, the decision to perform the transplant must be made with the understanding that the recipient will again be placed on dialysis if the transplant fails. Otherwise, there seems to be very little justification for trying a transplant in a situation of limited resources. The current success rate of transplants does not allow us to take a dialysis machine from someone and urge him to undergo an operation with concomitant risks and no option of reinstatement.

The problem of who gets hemodialysis when machines and facilities are limited may be discussed from the aspect of an ideal society governed by Jewish values and from the standpoint of a pluralistic society, such as one in the United States. The notion of a committee such as the Seattle Committee, made famous by *Life* and *Redbook* magazines, i.e., an anonymous committee operating without explicit guidelines to determine who lives and who dies, is "too Kafkaesque" to fit into any moral scheme. Anonymity may protect the members of the committee from pressure, but it also shields them from reality and the human side of their decisions. One who takes it upon himself to make life-and-death decisions should be man enough to face the implications of such decision-making. The Torah tells us that a court that sentences a man to death must be present during the execution and that the convicting witnesses must be the executioners. It is relatively easy to sit in judgment and sentence a man to death. It is more difficult if you have to be the executioner. Furthermore, the lack of specific criteria makes the decision-making almost arbitrary. A surgeon who served on the Seattle Committee told an interviewer from *Life*, "In my practice as a surgeon, the responsibility of making a life-or-death choice faces me every day, and I can tell you this, I do sleep better at night after deciding on one of these committee cases than I sleep after deciding a case of my own. I'm awfully glad, too, that we just know these candidates by number, not their actual names."

What are the criteria in such a selection? Let us first look at the criteria of the Seattle Committee: age, sex, marital status, number of dependents, income net worth, emotional stability with particular regard to a patient's capacity to accept treatment, education, occupation, past performance, and future potential. From the perspective of Jewish law, most of these considerations are irrelevant. The issue is a classic one in moral discussions: To whom do you throw the life jacket? Who gets saved first from the burning building? Generally, one cannot assign relative value to human life. Hence, if presented with a choice to kill or be killed, one is required to allow oneself to be killed, for no one is permitted to assess the relative value of two human lives. The consequences of this will be shown later, in the discussion on cadaver transplants. However, the principle that is always operative is that the assessment of the relative value of human lives is one that no human being can make. It makes no difference if one is ostensibly the loftiest example of humanity and the other is at the bottom. However, this principle cannot be applied to a case where a decision to act on behalf of one or the other must be made. In the case of two people drowning, to refuse to make a choice between the lives of the two who are in trouble would be to sentence both to death. Morality demands that we make a choice. What are the parameters that govern such a choice?

In Judaism, life is significant because man was created in the image of Hashem. Man lends value to his life through ethical activity. The uppermost quality of life is that which has achieved the highest level of ethical activity and service of Hashem. When a choice is forced upon us, we must evaluate the present ethical quality of life. If two candidates were to impress a committee as being equivalent, the decision would be based upon potential for future ethical acts and achievement. There are a number of other considerations. A healthy patient takes precedence over a terminally ill patient. In a situation where one of the candidates in question is in a direct position to save the lives of many others, he is preferred to others.[2] However, this reasoning would apply only where there is a definite group of people in danger, and the person being saved is in a direct position to help. It should not be applied to a situation of saving one whose line of work may eventually lead to saving peoples lives, e.g., a medical researcher who may someday make a life-saving discovery.

The most serious problem, though, is how to apply an ethical criterion in a pluralistic society. Ethical achievement

---

2 The precedent for this is an occurrence in the Vilna ghetto under Nazi domination. Exit visas had been arranged for a limited number of clergymen from the besieged ghetto. The leading Rabbinic authority of Vilna, Rabbi Chaim Ozer Grodzensky, was given the task of assigning the exit visas. He did not take one for himself. He further opted to save certain older rabbis rather than certain younger ones. When questioned as to his choice, he replied that he felt that the older ones would be more active in securing help for the beleaguered population than the younger ones would be. Hence, saving the older ones would represent a potential for greater saving of life.

and potential presuppose a specific system of criteria. Need-less to say, in the Jewish formulation, the Jewish system is presupposed. How does one operate in a pluralistic society? This problem is faced by any system that decides such questions on any basis other than first come, first served, or by lottery. One of the main criticisms of the Seattle Commit-tee was that it was a group of bourgeois saving the bourgeois, i.e., evaluating persons in accordance with its own middle-class value system. One analysis of the Seattle Committee in the UCLA Law Review concluded that its process "ruled out creative nonconformists who rub the bourgeois the wrong way but who historically have contributed so much to the making of America. The Pacific Northwest is no place for a Henry David Thoreau with bad kidneys." However, there is no alternative if we use any criterion other than first come, first served, or a lottery. Finally, serious constitutional ques-tions of equal protection and due process are raised in the United States by any system based on social worth.

What would the Halachah say if a donor were available for a specific patient who is on dialysis, and the success of dialysis in his case is statistically considered at least equiva-lent to the anticipated success of the transplant, but another patient, for whom a transplant is unavailable, would be able to use the dialysis machine currently being used by the potential transplant recipient if the latter were to agree to undergo the operation? The question is essentially whether the potential transplant recipient may opt for a treatment of equal or lesser efficiency if the intended result is the saving of another patient. If in the halachic order of priorities for the machine the nontransplant patient had precedence, there is no doubt about the permissibility of the operation. However, if priority went to the potential transplant recipi-ent, the only case in which such an operation would be allowable would be if the new dialysis patient were an ideal dialysis patient with a very high statistical chance of success. Otherwise, for the intended transplant recipient to lessen his survival chances would be highly questionable, if not outrightly forbidden.

The issue of transplants obtained from minors or defectives is a serious one. It is paradoxical that in five cases that have been before U.S. courts, three in Massachusetts, one in Kentucky, and one in Louisiana, only the court in the state of Louisiana defended the rights of the defective and refused to allow the transplant. All the cases followed the basic approach of the initial case in Massachusetts. From the viewpoint of civil law, a parent of a minor or a defective can consent to an invasion of the property or person of the minor or the defective if, and only if, such invasion is in the best interest of the minor or the defective. Hence, the question of whether a minor could donate a kidney was essentially whether the donation of a kidney was in the best interest of that minor. The consent of the minor alone could not justify the donation, as the consent of a minor is of no legal significance.

In three different cases in 1954, the Supreme Judicial Court of Massachusetts allowed kidney transplants between identical minor twins. The reasoning of the court followed closely the Catholic principle of totality — that in determining the interest of the minor, one must look at the total self-interest, including both psychological and moral interests. The judge ruled: "I further find, upon the testimony of a highly qualified psychiatrist, that if this operation is not performed and Leon (the sick twin) dies, in his opinion a grave emotional impact on Leonard (the well twin) would result. This would be further aggravated by the realization that it was within his power to have saved the life of his brother had this operation been performed.... I, therefore, find that this operation is necessary for the continued well-being of Leonard and that in performing the operation the defendants are conferring a benefit upon Leonard as well as upon Leon."

Similarly, in 1969 a Kentucky court heard a case in which the donee was twenty-eight years old, married, and a part-time college student. The prospective donor, a year younger, had been in an institution for the mentally retarded for some years and his mental age was approximately six years. When the entire family was tested for tissue compatibility, the incompetent was found to be the only available suitable donor. The county court, on appeal, decided that this procedure was vital to the incompetent's own mental health and decided further that a court of equity did have the power to permit such a request.

The case in a Louisiana court in 1973 was analogous. Roy Richardson, seventeen years old, had the mental capacity of a three or four-year-old child, due to mongolism. An otherwise healthy person with mongolism has a life expectancy of twenty-five years. Roy's sister, Beverly, thirty-two years old, needed a transplant. Dialysis was available but was inconvenient. Furthermore, her medical history suggested that conditions were present that would adversely affect the donated kidney.

One judge pointed out that 1) other relief was available, 2) the "best interest" argument was not present in this case, and 3) the "best interest" argument was not in accord with Louisiana law. A concurring judge disagreed on the final point, maintaining that if no other remedy existed, then the "best interest" argument could be used to justify the operation.

All of the above is irrelevant from a halachic point of view. The "best interest" argument is not really convincing. A dissenting judge in the Kentucky decision argued convincingly: "The majority opinion is predicated upon the finding of the circuit court that there will be psychological benefit to the ward, but points out that the incompetent has the mentality of a six-year old child. It is common knowledge beyond dispute that the loss of a close relative or a friend to a six-year-old child is not of major impact. Opinions concerning psychological trauma are at best most nebulous. Furthermore, there are no guarantees that the transplant will become a surgical success, it being well known that bodily rejection of transplanted organs is frequent. The life of the incompetent is not in danger, but the surgical procedure advocated creates some peril."

The moral issues in the Louisiana case seem clear. The option of dialysis was medically preferable to transplant surgery. There was no benefit — physical, moral, or psychological — to the donating minor. There seems to have been little moral justification for allowing the surgery even if the donor had been a consenting adult; since the donor was a nonconsenting defective, it was out of the question.

However, the Massachusetts cases are not so simply dealt with. The court's opinion was based on a series of premises that can be questioned. First, the court stated, "The operation is usually successful when performed on identical twins." While this is certainly the case in 1980, it was hardly so in 1954. The simple truth that two of the three recipients died within months of the operation is ample proof of this fact. Furthermore, if the "best interest" argument is predicated on the operation being "usually successful," the concept must be more clearly defined, for there are various rates of success.

However, the most serious case against the "best interest" argument was presented by David Daube. Briefly stated, he maintained that, if there would be no option of donation by a minor, then the trauma suffered by the healthy twin would be a normal part of life — a natural trauma at the loss of a loved one. The trauma described in the Massachusetts cases was a special one — that of a person who could save a life and did not. However, Daube pointed out, this special trauma would be present only if the court allowed the operation. If the court refused the operation, then it would not be the potential donor's refusal that caused the loss of life of the prospective donee, and it would have been beyond the donor's ability to help his brother, much as it would be if his brother had cancer.

From a halachic point of view, there is no problem in the three Massachusetts cases in view of the ages of the donor twins. The age of consent in Jewish law is generally thirteen years for a male and twenty years for a female. Sometimes the age of consent is raised to twenty years for a male. However, in my judgment, the lower ages were applicable here, especially since there was parental concurrence. It is interesting that at the CIBA Symposium in 1966, J. E. Murray, Director of Surgical Research at Harvard Medical School and Peter Bent Brigham Hospital, expressed the opinion that twelve to thirteen years is a medically reasonable age of consent. Under this age, he believed, there is no awareness of psychological gain or trauma.

However, the problem still remains with regard to younger children and defectives. The problem is very complex in Jewish law and revolves around the rules of implied and presumed consent. If one places a bowl of fruit in front of a group of guests, he cannot sue them for theft if they eat without his explicit permission. This is the doctrine of implied consent. If one's parents enter his home when he is not present, they can take food from the refrigerator without his consent, based on the doctrine of presumed consent. Generally, presumed consent is insufficient for invasion of person and property. Where the overwhelming majority of people would consent to an invasion of property, one can use a doctrine of presumed consent. If the presumed consent is based on a special feature of the person involved, the Halachah does not recognize a doctrine of presumed consent. Thus, if one can determine that the overwhelming majority of people would agree to donate kidneys to siblings, parents, and children, the invasion could be justified. If not, it could not. Permissibility would depend upon determining whether the facts support an actual contention of presumed consent. Finally, if factually there is no presumed consent, I find it very difficult to justify the operation. Invasion of property without consent is forced seizure. If one cannot morally seize the kidney of an adult, how can one do so to a minor or defective?

The U.S. courts, in my opinion, have been less than zealous in defending the rights of defectives, at least to the

extent of presumed consent. This was clearest in the
Saikewicz case in August 1976, when the Massachusetts
court consented to withhold treatment from Joseph
Saikewicz for his terminal leukemia, even though the majority of mentally competent adults tend to ask for such treatment.

We turn now to a consideration of cadaver transplants.
Where dialysis is not available, the donor is dead, and
consent has been obtained for donation, there is no question
about its permissibility. This is true even though the long-
term survival rate is approximately 40%. Where dialysis is
available and there is no issue of limited resources, and there
is no medical gain to the patient in transplantation as
compared to dialysis, I see no room for allowing the removal
of the kidney of the deceased merely for economic or social
reasons. In the multitude of cases where the issues are not
simply delineated, a case-by-case evaluation is required.
Jewish law does not allow violation of a dead body for
anything other than an issue of saving life or restoring
health.

In all cases, consent is required and must be obtained,
either from the deceased or from the family. Neither has
rights to the body, but they do have an interest in the body,
which allows them to refuse permission. Whether such permission should be obligatory or not is presently a debated
problem. Given the current success rate of cadaver transplants, such donation is highly moral, but it is probably not
obligatory. Donation of blood is obligatory upon every ethical
Jew; postmortem donation of a kidney may not be.

However, the most serious question in cadaver transplantation is the question of the determination of donor
death. Death in Jewish law occurs at irreversible cessation
of spontaneous cardiopulmonary function. Although most
medical opinion views brain death as the termination of
human life, this is halachically irrelevant. Death is both a
normative and descriptive phenomenon. No scientist can
scientifically conclude when the normative results of death

occur, as it is a purely normative decision. A doctor may be able to tell, when a layman cannot, that irreversible spontaneous function has ceased, but he cannot tell when human life has lost its value.

When brain death, or cerebral death has occurred, and the heart continues to function, the patient's life may be ebbing and we may conclude that from the point of view of Jewish law the process of death has begun, but he is still alive. What of removing the kidneys of a dying patient and giving them to a potential recipient? Paul Freund, talking of common law, said, "If a human life is deliberately taken, it is moreover no mitigation of the crime that the victim was, by worldly standards, someone of little merit or someone having little time left to live. The governing principle is not the merit or need or value of the victim, but equality of worth as a human being. The governing principle, it might be said, is that man shall not play God with human lives."

The approach of Jewish law is strikingly similar. To take away five minutes of unconscious life from the donor to grant fifty years of life to someone else is unconscionable. One can never judge the relative value of human life. This is made clear in a striking decision by the Rama, of sixteenth-century Poland. The Talmud tells us that when a woman in labor dies, one must immediately cut her open to remove the child, for it may be that one can still save the child. The Rama rules, however, that in the absence of trained medical personnel to establish precisely the time of death, one must wait until the woman has definitely died, even though such a delay will surely cause the death of the child. One cannot take away one minute of the life of the moribund mother to give the child a full lifetime. All are equal before the law, and one cannot judge the relative value of human life. The combination of this doctrine with the definition of death seriously complicates the issue of cadaver transplant.

There is a final consideration. The fact that the mortality rate from dialysis is so significantly lower than that from cadaver transplantation raises serious moral questions, irrespective of the issue of kidney donation. It is seriously questionable whether one may choose a treatment with a lower projected success rate for anything but compelling medical reasons. Social and economic factors have a limited halachic effect on such a decision. It is possibly true that with proper experimentation the mortality rate for cadaver transplants can be lowered, but this raises a serious issue of human experimentation, which should be discussed elsewhere.

Treatment of kidney patients by modern techniques involves many complex moral and halachic questions, and the care of such patients requires an ongoing relationship between one trained in medicine and one trained in Halachah. A medical man who reaches a conclusion without considering the moral issues is no different from the thinker who contemplates the moral issues without clear medical knowledge.

The Jewish attitude to the deaf

RABBI YITZCHAK SHAPIRO, Rosh Yeshivat Mishkan Ya'akov

The deaf-mute is often referred to in Jewish laws of family life, laws of finance, and laws of damages, and his obligations and exemptions are enumerated at length in halachic literature.

A person has two basic means of communication with the world around him — hearing and speaking — and there are grounds to consider that they are linked together intimately. This is evident from the problems we are confronted with in teaching someone to speak when the person has had hearing difficulties from birth. Speaking ability, based on intelligent thought and understanding, was given by Hashem to mankind only, as it is written in *Bereshit*, "and man became a living soul,"[1] which is interpreted by *Targum Onkelos* as "there was in man a spirit of speech" ("*va-havat b'adam l'ruach memalela*"). According to Rashi, "The soul of man is the most highly developed of all [the creatures], because he · was granted understanding and speech."

How and why does the ability to speak uniquely define man? Aristotle noted that man is a social creature. In the language of the Torah, "It is not good for man to live alone."[2] Man is dependent upon the society of which he is part, and without social interaction he could not exist spiritually and physically. The relationship involves give and take. He is helped by his society, and the goals of his society are, in turn, furthered by him. Social interaction depends on communication. By passing on and receiving information, man develops his intellect. When speech capacity is lacking from birth, man is unable to relate properly to his environment and he suffers from isolation. His fund of information is limited, and

1 *Bereshit* 2:7.

2 Ibid. 2:18.

his curiosity and intellectual growth are impaired. His mentality is frequently similar to that of mentally deficient
persons.

Deficiency in speech capability may also arise from impaired hearing. Even though he may have an organic capability to speak, an individual with impaired hearing becomes
isolated. If this occurs at birth, his development suffers and
the chances of his learning a language are minimal. Thus
one who is deaf from birth is usually mute as well, even
though he may have no physical speech handicap. In the
absence of normal interaction with others, a deaf-mute's
decisions will be based only on his own limited knowledge.
The Rabbis felt that, in the best interests of such an individual, it is necessary for others to examine the validity of the
impaired individual's actions for his own protection. In certain instances, it is possible, through various tests, to assess
the individual in order to ascertain his mental level of
understanding. These cases are touched upon in the Talmud,
but we shall not delve into this here.

It should be noted that, in formulating a halachic approach to the deaf and the mute, the Rabbis tried to care for
the needs of the deaf-mute without making the handicapped
person too dependent. On the one hand, the Rabbis limited
his freedom of action, because of the danger that he would
not be able to function appropriately with a realistic assessment of his own limitations. Yet, on the other hand, they
wanted him to have a feeling of independence, so that he
should feel that he is a person of equal rights. They tried to
find a compromise between these two extremes. The Rabbis
opposed the attitude of their contemporaries, who considered
all deaf persons mentally ill.

There is a wide difference of halachic opinion concerning
the competence of one who is deaf-mute from birth. R.
Yehudah considers a deaf-mute competent and clear-think-
ing, so that his actions are always valid.[3] If his mental level

---

3 *Tosefta Terumot* 1:1.

is sufficiently high, he is considered responsible for his actions. On the other hand, R. Eliezer expresses the opinion that a deaf-mute has limited ability. But the Talmud was not sure whether his thinking is always clouded or if it is erratic, varying from clear to clouded.[4] As his competence is always in doubt, in any given instance one can never be certain whether his capacity to act was or was not impaired. The third opinion, which is more exacting than the above and yet affords the possibility of greater leniency, classifies the deaf-mute with those who are mentally impaired.

Because of his intellectual limitations, the Rabbis were concerned that his ability to plan for goals was constrained, so that the validity of some of his actions could be considered suspect, due to a lack of purposeful planning. As there is a danger that people will take advantage of him, to protect his interests the Rabbis validated only those of his actions and objectives that they felt were clearly for his benefit. For example, the Rambam decides that, even though a deaf person has no judicial standing regarding monetary matters, his business transactions involving movable possessions should be validated, so that he be granted the self-sufficiency to support himself.[5] However, he would still be restricted from trading in real estate, as contracts involving such property require more understanding and forethought. With regard to damages, the Rabbis rule that someone who injures or causes monetary damage to a deaf person is liable, while the deaf-mute himself is released from the obligation to pay for damaging or injuring other people, due to similar deficiency in forethought.

In the case of marriage, the Rabbis felt that a deaf-mute has the capacity to live a full family life, unlike a mentally deficient person, whose marriage is not confirmed. In fact, in order to encourage a man to marry a deaf woman, the

---

4 Ibid. and *Yevamot* 113a.

5 *Hilchot Mechirah* 29:3, 4.

Rabbis abolished some of the financial obligations that a husband usually assumes in the marriage contract.[6]

The disability of the deaf and the mute can be mitigated when the person receives instruction in alternate methods of communication. The Rabbis searched for such alternative ways for the deaf-mute to communicate, to enable him to express his desires and demonstrate his personality, to mitigate his disability, and to permit the Rabbis to assess his capacity to make correct decisions. In fact, the Talmud mentions two methods, both of which are currently utilized, by which the deaf-mute can be taught to communicate.[7] One method, called the manual approach, utilizes a form of sign language, which relies on manipulations of the hands and head; the second, known as the oral method, consists of forming words with one's lips (even with an inability to use one's voice), and presumably reading another's lips. Until recently, the oral method was preferred by those who teach the deaf, even though the procedure was more difficult to teach, particularly to those who were deaf or mute from birth. But at the last Congress on Education for the Deaf, as a result of the research done here and abroad, it was noted that the manual method of communication is more natural and can be taught and used more easily, and that this approach may have advantages not recognized until now. It is interesting to note that the Talmud also prefers the manual approach.

The Talmud recognizes writing as a third method of communication, but, in this regard, the Rabbis differentiate between one who was deaf from birth and one who became deaf at a later age. A person who has had normal intellectual development before his handicap was felt to have a better ability to understand the significance and importance of what he is writing, and to be more responsible for its content.

---

6 *Yevamot* 113a.

7 *Gittin* 64a.

With the development of more expertise in educating the deaf-mute to live in society, recent Rabbinical authorities have tried to accept the educated deaf-mute as a normal person or, at least, to classify him in the category of one who talks but does not hear.

Let us now see how Halachah treats one who is deaf but can speak and one who is mute but can hear. The Rambam[8] considers these individuals as normal people, barring minor exceptions. The mute person who can hear is obligated to keep all the commandments. He may sell real estate, since he is able to understand the economic facts and the happenings in the world at large. This is in contrast to a deaf person who can speak, because the latter individual has more difficulty in receiving information. The Rambam requires that both of these disabled persons pass a test to determine if they are really cognizant of the meaning of their actions and if they can really express their wishes.

That the intellectual ability of a mute who can hear is not impaired is borne out by an incident recounted in the Talmud. Two mutes used to come every day to R. Yehudah Hanasi's yeshivah to listen to the discourses, during which they would nod their heads and move their lips, as if in agreement.[9] As they were so eager to learn, R. Yehudah Hanasi prayed for them, and Hashem cured them. To the amazement of all, when they spoke it was clear that they were well learned in all Rabbinic lore.

On the other hand, no matter what their intellectual level of achievement, mutes are disqualified as witnesses, not because of their handicap but because of the stringency of the laws of testimony. The Torah does not allow a witness's report to be accepted if it was passed on by an intermediary or in writing. The motivation behind this regulation is to enable the judges to evaluate the words as well as the

---

8 *Hilchot Ishut* 2:26.

9 *Chagigah* 3a.

nuances of style when witnesses express their testimony. It was, therefore, also required that the judges be expert in understanding the language of the testimony, without the need for a translator. Therefore, a person who could not speak could not testify.

In summary, we must accept that the handicapped are an integral part of the world Hashem created. Even though they have a physical defect, we must try to compensate for what they lack by our interest in them and by our efforts to create an understanding atmosphere. However, their position in society must be defined in order to safeguard their interests without diminishing the general welfare of society. The Torah advises us to accept reality in our search to help the sufferer; to be especially careful to appropriately limit his privileges, so that his joy of living not be turned into sadness.

May it be the Will of the Almighty to fulfill His pledge: "If you will diligently hark to the voice of Hashem your God and will do that which is right in His eyes and will heed His commandments, and keep all His statutes, then I will not afflict you with any of the illnesses which I have placed upon the Egyptians; for I am Hashem Who heals you."[10]

---

10 *Shemot* 15:26.

Moral problems in the treatment of the elderly

Based on a paper by ARNOLD J. ROSIN, MB, FRCP, delivered at the
Congress on *Halachah U'Refuah*, Regensberg Institute, in Jerusalem,
in August 1980

Consideration of the subject of moral problems in the treatment of the elderly immediately prompts the question: Why
should the moral issues of treating old people who are sick
differ from those involved in treating young sick people? If
old people are infirm or suffering from disease, does society
adopt a different set of moral and ethical norms regarding
their care? This article will indicate how much the moral
attitudes of society influence the practical treatment of the
elderly, and also how some of the medical problems raised
by aging present moral dilemmas to society as a whole.

Old age is characterized by an accumulation of physical
changes which are part of aging, a process which in biological
terms leads to deterioration of function and, inevitably, to
the death of the organism. Although this is an unpleasant
prospect, it is a biological fact, engineered by built-in genetic
programming within the cells, and affected in varying degrees by environmental factors, such as nutrition, prevalent
diseases, and accidents. Man is blessed with a long post-fer-
tile period. Even after fulfilling the biological function of
procreation, many years of physical and physiological activity lie before him, even though he has passed the peak of
fertility and physical prowess. The peaks of mental development and of maturity are also gone at this stage, although
the factor of experience may lend power to one who has
previously been marked for leadership. Along with this,
however, decline of abilities may occur, typically related to
recent memory, speed of reaction in problem-solving, difficulty in adapting to new situations, and psychological rigid-
ity in place of flexibility.

If one presents the features of aging to a society which

looks to physical strength and youthful vitality as the main-spring of its survival and achievement, one can readily see how the elderly will be relegated to an inferior position. It is a well-known historical fact, related in detail by Simone de Beauvoir in her classic book *Old Age*,[1] that primitive tribes often abandoned their old people when they became infirm. An ill or paralyzed parent could have no place in a nomadic existence. The rule of might must end for a chief or king when a younger man, perhaps his son, would assert that he was more powerful and a greater fighter. Some tribes even had ceremonies during which elders abdicated not only their positions but also their lives. Thus, decline in biological function, particularly illness, was equated with relegation to the lower strata in the sociological sphere, or to complete exclusion from society.

The perspective of Judaism on old age stands in stark contrast to the above picture. Length of days was held up by the Torah as a reward for carrying out the mitzvot. "Honor thy father and thy mother so that thy days may be long upon the land which Hashem thy God is giving thee."[2] "Send away the mother bird and take the young for thyself, so that it will be well with thee, and thou will have length of days."[3]

Old age was to be a goal toward which man worked as a sign of his reward. The identification of leaders and lawgiv-ers with the word *zaken*, old man, reflects the psychological quality of consolidation of experience, the ability to contem-plate and to make use of the knowledge and wisdom acquired in earlier years. It is as if one's younger years are devoted to exploring and gaining new information in order to store it for its mature use in old age. The ideal life for the righteous is stated in *Pirkei Avot*: "Rabbi Shimon ben Yehudah says in the name of Rabbi Shimon ben Yochay: 'Beauty, strength,

---

1 Published by Andre Deutsch, Weidenfeld & Nicholson, 1972.

2 *Shemot* 20:12.

3 *Devarim* 22:7.

wealth, honor, wisdom, old age, hoary age, and children suit the righteous and suit the world..."[4] — a picture of spiritual, biological, and material fulfillment at the extreme of life.

The central mitzvah referring to old age, "Stand up before one of hoary age and give respect to an old person (*zaken*), and you shall thus fear your God, I am Hashem"[5] is the focus of an interesting discussion in the Talmud.[6] One opinion holds that a *zaken* is not entitled to respect if he has not acquired wisdom; for the term *zaken* is often used to indicate the possession of wisdom, rather than being merely a description of chronological age. Isi ben Yehudah maintains, on the other hand, that all aged individuals are included. Age itself demands respect. It is stated elsewhere that an old person serves, to those who behold him, as a kind of witness of the wonders of the Creator of the world. How much more has the old man been exposed to the signs of the Master of the world and the miracles of everyday life! In honoring him, we are paying tribute to his Creator.

It is noteworthy that the ruling is that any old person except a criminal is worthy of respect according to the law of the Torah. This basic attitude of the Torah found its expression in the patriarchal society of Biblical times, and later in the social organization of the communities in the diaspora. Throughout the Jewish communities, there was widespread development of charity kitchens, funds for the needy, and institutions which included a legitimate place for the old, the weak, and the destitute. The moral basis was laid down with the stricture "and you shall thus fear your God," "for in this matter only the one who does the deed knows what is in his heart [i.e., the motive that prompts him]...and in [such] matters the Torah states 'and you shall fear God, Who knows your thoughts,'" so beware against acting as if you do not see

---

4 *Pirkei Avot* 6:8.

5 *Vayikra* 19:32.

6 *Kiddushin* 32b.

Him.[7] On this foundation, the social attitude was translated into administrative and political terms, resulting in the allocation of priorities, and therefore budgets and economic resources. The fundamental assumption was that society is obliged to initiate support economically and socially for its elders, where this was not forthcoming from the family. This assumption, expressed nowadays in the ramification of services, aids, homes, and facilities for the aged, springs from a fundamental moral and philosophical outlook.

What was known and practiced regarding the elderly from ancient times within Jewish communities began to appear in Western society in postmedieval and modern times. Starting from the relative benevolence of the harsh Poor Laws in 1601, England advanced to the point where legislation for the elderly could be reckoned as a worthwhile political platform. The English word "care" expresses two attitudes: care is treatment; and caring is also an approach of identifying with the problem, and resolving to solve it. The movement "Age Concern," which has become widely known in the last fifteen years in England, is — as its name reflects — the plight of old people and is motivated to do something about it, through education, publicity, and practical projects.

One of the advancements in concern for the aged, which has developed in many countries in the last thirty years, has been the practice of geriatrics as a branch of medicine. A particular contribution of this specialty has been to view the functional problems stemming from the multiple diseases to which elderly people are prone as medical problems in their own right. With due attention to the general disability of the person, as well as to a specific diagnosis of his disease, considerable benefit was realized from rehabilitative techniques and psychological and social manipulation. The structural framework of geriatric hospital units in Britain, for example, grew out of chronic sick wards. These were repositories of people who had nowhere to go outside of the

---

7 Rashi, *Vaykira* 19:32, from the *Sifra* and *Kiddushin* 32b.

hospital, because of crippling physical, psychological or social problems. The growing responsibility of society for its elderly was thus shown by an active policy of intervening to improve the lot of these people, instead of condoning passive custodial care.

The results have been amply illustrated by the large body of theoretical and practical knowledge gained about the potential of recovery from disease in old age. A surprising degree of social and physical competence can be displayed by elderly people stricken by accidents, strokes, and heart disease, in a carefully planned treatment setting. Improvement of the quality of life, which can result from successful medical treatment and adequate social backing, obligates municipal and state authorities to allocate the required resources in their financial planning.

In the discipline of medicine, preventive measures are as important a dimension of treatment as are diagnostic and curative steps. An interesting point of contact between the biological consequences of imprudent behavior and moral attitudes is illustrated in the Talmudic comments on the response of Barzillay in *Shemuel* II.[8] When offered the rewards of his support of David by having a place at the royal table, Barzillay describes the plight wrought by age: "I am eighty years old today; am I still able to discern between good and bad? Or can your servant taste what I eat and what I drink? Or can I still hear the voice of singers and songstresses? Why then shall your servant be a burden to my lord, the king?" The Talmud, however, comments that the depredations of Barzillay's old age were brought about by a feckless life in his younger years. He was highly promiscuous and, therefore, aged rapidly.[9]

A similar comment, applied by the Talmud to the verse "For the childhood and youth are vanity,"[10] notes that the

---

8 19:36.

9 *Shabbat* 152a.

10 *Kohelet* 11:10.

things a man does in his childhood are wont to darken his face at the time of his old age.[11] The famous allegorical, chilling description of old age in *Kohelet* is preceded by the sage advice "And remember your Creator in the days of your youth before the days of evil come and years will arrive about which you will say I have no desire in [living] them."[12] Remember! Investment of spiritual efforts toward moral rectitude in one's youth will ensure that one's old age will be years of wisdom and balanced moral outlook.

On the question of actual illness and degeneration brought about by aging, traditional Judaism has a positive and definitive outlook. This is shown in the laws relating to dementia, a disease of degeneration of brain neurons, prevalent in significant degree in approximately five percent of the elderly population in Western societies. Such a disease, during its long course of three to ten years, presents to those who care for or treat the patient the sight of a gradual breakdown in intellect, personality, social behavior, and physical functions. It requires a strong moral foundation on the part of the treating personnel to retain respect and the awareness that the patient also remains a human being, whose plight demands appropriate application of social services or institutional placement. The aim is to allow this individual, such as he is, to retain his self-respect and to benefit from the world as we know it.

The *Shulchan Aruch* states, "One whose father or mother has become deranged should try to deal with them according to their understanding, until Heaven shows them mercy. And if it is impossible for him to deal with the situation, because they have changed so dramatically, he shall go away and leave them, and arrange for others to treat them in a fitting manner."[13] Here we find a clear directive as to the

---

11 *Shabbat* 152a.

12 *Kohelet* 12:1.

13 *Yoreh De'ah, Hilchot Kibud Av v'Em* 240:10.

obligation to care about and care for an elderly parent in his greatest disability. Together with this, the Halachah recognizes that not everyone is psychologically capable of coping with the problem, or that it may be physically too demanding. Therefore, the possibility of other caretakers or referral to an institution is broached. The Ra'avad is quoted as questioning how such a provision is made. He asks: If the old person is such that nothing can be done for him, what instructions can be given to another person about his care? If something has to be done, why then can the child not do it, instead of handing it over to someone else?

Perhaps the modern answers to these questions are in the necessary cooperation between the family and the treatment team of the geriatric unit or old-age or nursing home, which now should be competent to deal with the care of the demented. It is, again, social attitudes that determine whether such homes are maintained at a minimum standard of care, or less than that, or whether, as we see sometimes in this country and elsewhere, the standard of physical comfort and treatment is deliberately placed at a premium, despite the indifferent mental state of the inhabitants. Moral attitudes determine whether such patients can receive the environmental treatment appropriate to them — food, physical care, kindness, and occupational activity. Deficient morality will allow exploitation of this sector of the population, who literally have no voice, and need protection, and whose relatives must pay for it. Avoidance of the financial temptation to profit from the lot of those afflicted with dementia is not easy when managers, nurses, or doctors are faced with a disease for which there is no cure. Only a sound moral understanding of what quality of life one wishes to achieve for these sufferers can prevent the social shame that accompanies bad standards of institutional or community care.

These principles apply in another common dilemma presented by the aging — the management of the dying patient. Not only is the death rate higher among the elderly, but there is a larger proportion of individuals in this population in whom the dying process is prolonged over weeks or months. This may occur in the context of a progressive chronic disease, such as vascular degeneration of the brain or the heart, or of organ failure, such as chronic heart failure or chronic lung disease. In these conditions, recurrent episodes of acute disease are usually superimposed on a progressively crippled state. It may appear, through the eyes of a healthy individual, that such chronically ill people are not worth treating, especially if they are very old! This attitude might even be reinforced by the patient himself, who declares that life is not worth living. But the Halachah clearly maintains that the value of sustaining any degree of life, even for a brief period (*chayei sha'ah*), is immeasurable. We see this in the Talmud in the discussion of the extreme case of rescuing a person trapped under a rockfall on Shabbat.[14]

The question of how an individual who is progressively wasting away and slowly dying should live, the treatment he should receive, and the quality of life one should plan for him are problems thrust upon society that it must face, and not dismiss because of the nature of the disease or disability. It is a normal psychological characteristic of aging for one to take account of the reality of death, to appreciate its occurrence, and even to expect it. But this does not make the actuality of living any less valuable, as long as the person remains on this earth. The practical problem of managing a chronically ill or dying patient from this viewpoint is to assess realistically the aims of treatment, in order to promote some measure of patient participation in social functioning. At least, one could attempt to have the patient achieve meaningful verbal contact with his family, or, at a minimum, even encourage the family members to hold the hand of the dying person. More significantly, it may be possible to afford him some further happiness. Halachically speaking, his life may be more meaningful, as the additional level of functioning may allow him to perform more mitzvot.

---

14 *Yoma* 83a.

The prayers of a sick person are thought to be more effective, as their power is enhanced by his sickness.

Thus, the question of whether to treat an incurable or chronic disease should be judged clinically by the potential of the individual for any degree of living, however limited. Modern medicine and social advances provide the technical means to fulfill this aim. The moral stance of the doctor and of his culture is what motivates him to consider the aim as worthwhile in the first place. One should reiterate that although cure will not be achieved, society is still responsible to deliver good care to the chronically ill person.

A particular problem of treating the terminal stage of a dying person is that of deciding when not to treat too much or too intensively. The dilemma is to strike a balance between undue interference and needless procedures, which may cause suffering while attempting to relieve the sickness or prolong life, on the one hand, an a policy of passivity, which might bring about neglect and loss of an opportunity for clinical improvement, on the other. The solution to this dilemma demands a finely-tuned ethical and humane approach, tempered with clinical insight into the projected course of the disease. The problem is often resolved through what is called symptom control. Here, the doctor does not ignore the hopeless prognosis of the disease, but rather accepts the fact of the dying process and concentrates on relieving uncomfortable symptoms directly or indirectly connected with the underlying disease. In this way, needless heroics may be avoided, while allowing a more peaceful or tranquil course toward the end of the patient's life. The decision is not that of abandoning treatment — as if throwing up one's hands — but of concentrating on what appears to be the relevant treatment for what is troubling the patient.

Such decisions of humane, and effective, treatment of dying persons imply that every case should be judged on its own merits, with due recourse to the Halachah on issues of life and death. A common example is palliative surgery in an old person, in whom the danger of an operation may be equal to that of his untreated disease, or in whom another disease makes meaningful recovery unlikely. One has encountered, for example, the question of whether to allow an amputation in a person suffering from a severe stroke. In some cases, it may be worthwhile; in others, clinical sense would stay the doctor from further interference.

Effective medicinal treatment to relieve symptoms is often prone to cause side effects or unwanted effects. The question arises frequently as to whether the treatment might hasten the death of the patient, even while relieving his symptoms.[15] On the one hand, it is reasonable to assume that morphine given to alleviate chronic pain from cancer will not kill the patient, who will die from the inexorable progress of his disease. On the other hand, many treatments, such as cancer chemotherapy, are given with the awareness that there is a significant number of patients who will suffer complications. Treatment is nevertheless given in the hope of improving the course of the disease and with the expectation of overcoming any complications. In old people, this treatment is even more problematic because of their generally poorer immune resistance and often inadequate response to some chemotherapeutic regimens. No definitive or general answer can be offered here, save to emphasize that the moral considerations, in both prolonging life and ensuring a good quality of life, must occupy a prominent place in the medical appraisal of the patient.

A semilegal, semimedical problem which a doctor might face in caring for the elderly is that of involving the patient in the decision-making process. A patient is often thought of as a passive recipient of care, for whom decisions are made to be carried out. This is often true regarding the delivery of medical treatment; for surgical treatment he clearly has to

---

15 Rabbi A. Nebenzahl, "The Administration of Toxic Drugs to a Dangerously Ill Patient," *Assia* 7 (1980): 39-41. See also Dr. Avraham S. Avraham, *Lev Avraham*, vol. II (Jerusalem and New York: Feldheim, 1978) ch. 29.

sign consent. But why should the patient not be among those who initiate and are actively concerned with the planning for his care? Should he not participate in decision-making regarding change of location, type of care and environment, and matters pertaining to and connected with the disabilities of aging? A doctor may advise, but what authority gives him the power to dictate to the old person?

One might answer that the weakness and impotence of a disabled old person might leave us no choice but that he should be told what to do, and not asked. But by law an adult's right to decide for himself may be taken away only in specific circumstances, e.g., when he is committed to prison or when he is medically certified as incompetent by reason of mental illness. Age is not a factor, nor is physical illness! Yet medical caretakers use their authority frequently to usurp the power to relegate an old person to a poor-quality institution, or even to a psychiatric hospital. On the other hand, a caring medical attendant may use his authority to attempt to work with, or even against, the patient's relatives, to add dignity to the patient's life. It is the moral rectitude behind that authority that will ensure that only the best will be done for the old person. The easy way out might be not to address the problem at all; or to see only how much of a burden the patient is to the family, without seeking physical, psychological, and social solutions for assistance, that might yet allow him to remain at home.

On the subject of family, an important facet of medical treatment of the elderly is consideration of the family's wishes and of their problems. While it is true that the contract in the patient-doctor relationship is only with the patient, the latter's dependency on his family often makes the doctor duty bound to have the family as a partner in the treatment process. This inevitably increases the doctor's work in fact-finding, and in deciding objectively how well the interests of the patient are served by the family's attitudes and efforts, or otherwise. This is, in fact, part of the essence of geriatrics — the diagnosis of the disability and illness in relation to the social context. Making such appraisals involves judgment and the ability to size up a fellowman's standards. The objectivity of this assessment and the astuteness of the judgment required are much influenced by the moral approach of the responsible doctor.

An example of a conflict of interest that might arise can be seen in connection with a family's request that resuscitation not be performed, should sudden death occur in the relative. Halachically, such a request carries little weight, unless it is backed by strong medical evidence supporting the possibility of sudden death as an expected terminal event of a known disease or one of the diseases from which the patient suffers.[16] From the medical standpoint, such decisions may be clear-cut, although in some instances a preterminal state might give rise to uncertainty as to whether life might be meaningfully prolonged, should resuscitation take place. A more serious moral dilemma may arise, however, when considerations may be based mainly on social or logistic circumstances. For example, there might be no home to which to return, or no one to care for the old disabled person who is occupying a valuable bed in a hospital. These cases demand a pure medical appraisal which must not be influenced by what is, in reality, society's failure to provide for such a person. The logistic difficulty might be the actual problem, rather than the decision whether to resuscitate or not, and as such it should be faced up to in an honest manner.

From these principles of caring about the aged as well as caring for them, it is clear that those who treat these patients must possess certain moral qualities based on a philosophy which allocates a place of honor to the elders of society. They must aim to improve the quality of life threatened by disease or disability, so that the old person can live meaningfully and not merely await the coming of death. They must steel

---

16 Dr. Avraham S. Avraham, *Lev Avraham*, vol.II, ch.29. See also Dr. Avraham S. Avraham, "Treatment of the Dying and the Definition of Death," *Assia* 6 (1979): 30-36.

themselves against the picture of declining human faculties, in order to retain respect for the human being. Above all, they must work with humility and the view that, in striving to improve the lot of the old people, they are acting as messengers of the Almighty.

Surrogate motherhood

by RABBI ELIYAHU REFAEL HEISHERIK

Before we consider the difficult and complicated issues of assigning paternity and maternity in the case of a child born to a surrogate mother, let us first make mention of some of the halachic questions which arise with respect to the subject of surrogacy: Which of the possible processes of fertilization are halachically permissible and, of these, which is the preferred method? Is it one which involves an act of sexual intercourse between husband and wife, or one which is conducted in the laboratory? May a non-Jewish woman serve as a surrogate mother and, if so, is the child that is born to her Jewish? If first a son and then a daughter were born to a couple through two different surrogate mothers, are the two treated as brother and sister (regarding the prohibition against incest and other matters)? If a woman served as a surrogate mother for two different sets of biological parents, successively, are the children born to her at the conclusion of each pregnancy considered to be siblings?

Although the halachic questions regarding surrogacy are many, as we have just noted, the critical problems, the resolution of which might allow us to go ahead and resolve the others, relate to the personal status of the child born to the surrogate mother. Who is regarded as the child's father according to Jewish law and, more importantly, who is reckoned as the child's mother? These two issues are at the heart of our discussion here. Each will be analyzed separately, for the factors to be considered when assigning paternity are not necessarily the same as those which are to be considered when assigning maternity, as will be explained below.

The Question of Paternity

What is the relationship between the father and the off-spring when conception does not result from an act of inter-course but through artificial insemination, by having the medical practitioner introduce sperm into the woman's uterus or oviduct? According to most authorities,[1] the sperm donor is regarded for all purposes as the father of the child conceived with that sperm. The same conclusion was reached by Rabbi S. Z. Auerbach in a lengthy and detailed article dealing with the subject.[2] Some authorities adopt the more stringent position that the child must be treated as a *shetuki* (a child whose mother is recognized but whose father's identity is not), while other authorities are in doubt about the matter.

There are some authorities who suggest that this issue should be considered in the light of the regulation concerning a Jew who had sexual relations with a non-Jewish maidser-vant. In such a case, the Jew is not regarded as the father of the child who may result from that union, because "the Torah dispossessed him of his sperm." It has been argued that the principle underlying this rationale can be explained as fol-lows: The Jew is not recognized as the child's father because his sperm was introduced into the body of the non-Jewish maidservant, who is not governed by any of the rules of lineage. Perhaps then this principle can be applied in the case of artificial insemination as well. If sperm was ejacu-lated into a receptacle which is not governed by the rules of lineage, we might reason that the Torah has also dispos-sessed the donor of his sperm, so that the child born to a woman artificially inseminated with that sperm would not be regarded as the descendant of the donor.

Since most authorities rule that a child resulting from

---

1 *Chelkat Mechokek* and *Beit Shemuel, Even ha-Ezer* 1:8; *Benei Ahuvah; She'elat Ya'avetz* II, 97; *Turei Even, Chagigah* 15; *Shoe'l u'Meshiv, Mahadurah T'lita'ah* III, 132; *Penei Moshe* 1; and others.

2 *No'am* 1, p.165.

artificial insemination is treated in all respects as the offspring of the sperm donor, it stands to reason that the sperm
donor is regarded as the child's father also where gestation
takes place in a surrogate mother's womb, for the man plays
an identical role in the two cases. The process by which
fertilization took place is irrelevant.

The Question of Maternity

The question of maternity is a much more complicated, for
it is far less clear what factors determine motherhood according to Halachah. Is maternity decided exactly like paternity,
so that, just as fatherhood is assigned to the sperm donor,
so, too, motherhood is credited to the woman who contributed
the egg, even if the fetus was later implanted in the uterus
of another woman, who carried it to term and gave birth to
the child? Or perhaps there is room to distinguish between
paternity and maternity, for the simple reason that even in
the usual case of conception and childbirth, the function of
the father is very different from that of the mother. After the
father contributes his sperm, he does not play a direct role
in the later development of the fetus. Thus, even when the
process of fertilization, the site of pregnancy, and the method
of childbirth are extraordinary, it is reasonable for the Halachah to regard the sperm donor as the child's legal father.
But the mother's role in the ordinary development of a fetus
does not end with the contribution of her egg. Conception is
followed by additional, essential stages of pregnancy, during
which the fetus develops inside the womb, and of childbirth, at
which point the fetus emerges into the world as a viable infant.
Thus, there are grounds to claim that motherhood should be
assigned to the woman who carries the fetus inside her body
and gives birth to it, even if she did not contribute the egg and
the genetic material from which the infant had been formed.

　　If we accept this approach, the question remains whether
it is the period of pregnancy which determines motherhood
or the stage of childbirth? Is the woman who carried the fetus

in her uterus, where it grew and developed, regarded as the child's mother, even if, in the end, it was not she who gave birth to the child, or is bringing the child into the world as a viable infant, at the time of birth, the critical determinant of motherhood? If pregnancy is the determining factor, or one of the determinants, how long a period of time must the fetus be in the womb for Halachah to regard the gravid woman as its legal mother? Perhaps motherhood can be established only if the woman both carries the fetus inside her body and then gives birth to it. Or must all three factors — genetic motherhood, pregnancy, and childbirth — be satisfied before maternity can be assigned with certainty? If any one of these stages is missing, are the criteria for assigning motherhood in doubt? In summary, there are several possibilities as to the essential factors in determining halachic motherhood: 1) genetic contribution of the egg; 2) pregnancy alone; 3) childbirth alone; 4) pregnancy and childbirth together; 5) genetic motherhood, pregnancy, and childbirth all together.

Let us consider some of the Talmudic passages and the halachic discussions of classical and contemporary authorities which appear to shed light on our questions.

I. The Mishnah states: "If a river swept away someone's olive trees and deposited them within his fellow's field [and they took root there and produced olives], and one says, 'My olive trees produced [the olives],' and the other says, 'My land caused the [olives to grow],' they must divide [the olives between them]."[3] Thus, both the owner of the olive trees and the proprietor of the field which nourished them can lay claim to the olives which grow on those trees. From the ensuing discussion in the Talmud and the commentators, it appears that, for at least the first three years, the original owner of the olive trees has a stronger claim than the proprietor of the field, for the trees and any olives which were on them belong exclusively to the owner of the olive trees. Indeed, were it not for the mitzvah of ensuring the settle-

---

3 *Bava Metzia* 8:6. See also the Talmud 100b.

ment of *Eretz Yisrael*, the owner of the olive trees would have the right to reclaim his trees even after they took root. The proprietor of the field has a claim only to the increase in the value of the olives resulting from the growth which took place while the trees were in his field.

If it is at all possible to draw an analogy between the question of surrogacy and this issue of the olives, it would seem that the woman who donates her eggs parallels the owner of the olive trees, and the woman in whose uterus the fertilized egg is implanted corresponds to the owner of the field. Thus, it would follow that either both women have an equal claim to the title of motherhood, in which case the child would have two halachic mothers, or that preference is given to the woman who donated her egg over the woman in whose uterus the fertilized egg was implanted, in which case only the woman who donated the egg can claim motherhood. The surrogate who offered the use of her uterus could only demand monetary compensation for her share in the growth and development of the fetus.[4]

There is, however, a general rule that conclusions regarding matters of ritual law may not be inferred from rulings regarding matters of civil law.[5] Since the issue of personal status falls under the category of ritual law, the conclusion regarding title to the olives cannot be applied to the case of surrogacy, to determine which woman should be

---

4 One could contend that the case of the olive trees is not equivalent to that of an egg, for the commentators remark that the position of the owner of the trees is justified only when clods of earth immediately surrounding the trees remained attached to the roots when the trees were uprooted initially, for these clods are able to keep the trees alive, even though the olives could not grow without the added nourishment from the soil of the field. But if the river washed away the soil surrounding the roots, the trees are the sole property of the owner of the field, as the owner of the trees has already despaired of their survival. Here, too, one could reason that the fertilized egg is similar to an olive tree with bare roots, in that it would not survive outside the uterus of the surrogate. — Ed.

5 See Rabbi Moshe Hershler, *Torah she-b'al Peh*, vol. 25; *Halachah U'Refuah* I, p. 308.

considered the mother of the child.

Even if it were legitimate to draw comparisons between matters of ritual law and points of civil law, it might still be argued that a distinction can be made between the case of the olive trees and the case of surrogacy. For when fully grown olive trees belonging to one person take root in a field belonging to another person, it is clear that the trees are more significant than the ground, and that the owner of the trees should have greater claim to the olives than the owner of the field. But it is likely that the law would be different where one person's seeds became implanted and sprouted in another person's field, an instance which parallels the case of surrogacy more closely.[6]

II. The Mishnah states: "If the daughter of an ordinary Jew married a priest and the priest died while she was pregnant [with his child], her [fixed-value] slaves [which she brought into the marriage and are now part of her late husband's estate] may no longer eat *terumah* (the agricultural tax which must be given to the priests and which may be consumed only by the priest and his household), because of the fetus's share [of ownership] in the slaves [as an heir]. For a fetus disqualifies his mother [from regaining her right to eat *terumah*], if she is the daughter of a priest who was married to a non-priest and became widowed or divorced [while she was pregnant with the non-priest's child], and does not qualify her [to continue] to eat *terumah* [if she is the daughter of a non-priest who was married to a priest and became widowed or divorced while she was pregnant with the priest's child]. This is the position of R. Yosi. The Sages said to him, 'Now that you have testified before us regarding the daughter of an ordinary Jew who was married to a priest, it follows that even if the daughter of a priest was married to a priest and [her husband] died while she was pregnant, her slaves also may no longer eat of *terumah*, because of the

---

6 See *Techumin*, vol. 5, pp. 269 and 272, editor's note and response of Rabbi Z. N. Goldberg.

share of the fetus [in ownership of the slaves].'"[7]

The Talmud examines the rationale of R. Yosi's position. Does R. Yosi maintain that, while the born child of a priest takes on his father's priestly status even if his mother is the daughter of a non-priest, the unborn fetus of such a union is not considered a priest as long as it is still in its mother's womb; and since the fetus, as an heir, has a share of his father's estate, the slaves are forbidden to eat *terumah*, as they are partly owned by a non-priest? Or does R. Yosi hold that the fetus has priestly status already in its mother's womb, but a slave is qualified to eat *terumah* only if he is owned by a born priest, and not if he is owned, even in part, by an unborn priest? The Talmud notes that there is a practical difference between these two possible rationales in the case where the mother of the fetus is, herself, the daughter of a priest, for in such a case, the fetus surely has priestly status in the womb, but still may not qualify the slave to eat *terumah*, if complete ownership by a born priest is required.

The *Rishonim* similarly differ about the position of the Sages who disagree with R. Yosi. According to *Tosafot*, the Sages deem the fetus of a priest to be a priest even when it is still in the womb of its mother who is not of priestly descent. But the Rif holds that the Sages agree with R. Yosi, that such a fetus has non-priestly status in the womb, but they maintain that the fetus does not share in the father's estate until after it is born, and so it does not disqualify the slaves from eating *terumah*, as the slaves are completely owned by the fetus's already-born priestly brothers.

Rabbi Avraham Bornstein of Sochaczew was hard pressed to understand the mechanism by which an unborn child of a priest can be regarded as a non-priest while it is still in its non-priestly mother's womb and assume his fathers priestly status from the instant he is born.[8] He rea-

---

7 *Yevamot* 7:3, and in the Talmud 67a.

8 *Avnei Nezer, Yoreh De'ah* 443.

soned that after birth, when a child's parents are related to him by virtue of the fact that they were responsible for his conception, the father is given precedence over the mother, so that the child assumes his father's, and not his mother's, status. But as long as the fetus is in its mother's womb, the mother's status is given precedence over that of the father, because the mother has an added relationship by virtue of the fact that she is carrying the fetus inside her body. *Avnei Nezer* adduces support for this argument from the following passage in tractate *Yevamot*: "If twin brothers converted to Judaism or twin slaves were emancipated,...the one brother is not punished with *karet* if he had sexual relations with the wife of the other. If their mother converted after their conception, but prior to their birth...the one brother is liable if he had sexual relations with the wife of the other."[9] Rashi notes: "The one is punishable with *karet* for having engaged in sexual relations with the wife of his maternal brother, for the mother is treated like a Jewish woman who gave birth to twins."[10] Thus, even though the twins are not brothers by virtue of their conception, for all family connections are severed at the time of conception, it is sufficient that they were together in their mother's womb.

The *Avnei Nezer*'s comments have implications regarding our issue. For it follows from what he says that the mother-child relationship exists already while the child is inside his mother's womb. Not only is the woman already considered the child's mother, but she even determines the child's personal status (for, as we saw above, all agree that the fetus inside the womb of a woman of priestly descent assumes its mother's status). Thus, pregnancy and childbirth appear to be the critical factors in assigning maternity and halachic status. For at the time of conception the mother was a non-Jewess, regarding whom we apply the halachic principle

---

9 *Yevamot* 97b.

10 Rashi: *Aval chayavin.*

that a non-Jewish parent is legally dispossessed of his biological offspring. Were we to adopt the position that maternity is always assigned to the biological mother who
contributed the egg, then the child conceived to a woman
before she converted should always be regarded as a non-
Jew, for he developed from the egg of a non-Jewish woman.
Moreover, if maternity is determined at the time of conception, then that relationship should have been severed at the
time of the mother's conversion (in keeping with the rule that
all family ties are discontinued following conversion), during
the period of her pregnancy. Thus, we are forced to the
conclusion that maternity is assigned during pregnancy or
at the time of childbirth. It may further be argued that, since
the Talmud does not specify at which stage during her
pregnancy the mother converted, the fraternal relationship
between the two brothers is not based upon the fact that they
developed together in their mother's womb but, rather, that
the maternal and fraternal ties are established at the time
of childbirth.

Rabbi Z. N. Goldberg[11] rejects the proof from *Yavamot*
(he apparently did not see the discussion in the *Avnei Nezer*),
arguing that perhaps that passage follows the view that "a
fetus is an integral component of its mother." Since the fetus
is indivisible from its mother, it stands to reason that halachic maternity should be determined when the woman
separates from the fetus, at the moment of childbirth. But
in the case of surrogacy, when a woman gives birth to a child
which has developed from an egg which had been donated
by another woman and was implanted into the surrogate's
uterus after fertilization, maternity might not be assigned
to the surrogate just because she gave birth to the child. Only
according to the halachic view that "the fetus is not an
integral component of its mother" can proof be brought from
Yevamot that childbirth is the critical factor in determining
motherhood. (Rabbi Goldberg himself concludes, however,

---

11 *Techumin*, vol. 5, p. 249.

that the woman who gave birth to a child is regarded as the child's mother, even if she did not contribute the egg from which it was formed.)

Rabbi Elchanan Wasserman[12] also deals with the concept of the fetus as an integral component of its mother in discussing a ruling found in the *Roke'ach*. The *Roke'ach* declares that the pregnant wife of a priest is permitted to enter a structure containing a dead body without being concerned that her fetus is forbidden to contract ritual impurity, for there is only a remote doubt (*sefeik sefeika*) as to prohibition: first of all, the fetus may not develop into a viable infant, and, secondly, the woman's offspring might be female. Rabbi Wasserman cites a question that was raised regarding that ruling: Why did the *Roke'ach* base his allowance on the concept of a remote doubt? The woman should be permitted to enter a structure containing a dead body because as long as the unborn fetus is still in its mother's womb it has no priestly status. After answering that the *Roke'ach*'s ruling might have restricted practical ramifications in a case where the priest's wife is herself of priestly descent, Rabbi Wasserman suggests that the viewpoint that a priest's unborn fetus has non-priestly status as long as it is still in its mother's womb might follow only from the opinion that a fetus is an integral component of its mother's body. But according to the position that the fetus is not an integral component of its mother's body, a priest's unborn fetus might, in fact, already assume priestly status when it is inside its mother's body.

Thus, according to Rabbi Wasserman, the Talmud can surely be explained according to the opinion that the fetus is an integral part of its mother's body, but the question arises whether the Talmud can also be interpreted according to the opinion that the fetus is not an integral part of its mother's body. Thus, we might arrive at the novel conclusion that the status of the priest's unborn fetus has nothing to do

12 *Kovetz Shiurim* II, 41.

with the assessment of whether its mother's or its father's status has more potency while it is in the womb but with the fact that it is not yet regarded as an entity separate from its mother. But this conclusion leads to an inescapable difficulty, for why should a fetus of a priest inside the body of a woman of priestly descent be assumed to have priestly status, so that its mother would be forbidden to enter a structure containing a dead body? Even if the fetus is not yet regarded as a separate entity but, rather, as an integral component of its mother, she is not prohibited from contracting ritual impurity from a dead body! Thus, we are forced to the conclusion that what Rabbi Wasserman meant to say is that, according to the view that the fetus is an integral part of its mother's body, it is clear that the fetus assumes its mother's personal status, but according to the view that the fetus is not an integral part of its mother's body, the matter is in doubt. And so the proof which the *Avnei Nezer* brought from the passage in *Yevamot* stands.

III. The Talmud states: "The firstborn son of the daughter of a Levite need not be redeemed from a priest (even if the child's father is an ordinary Israelite)...for the Torah made the obligation dependent upon 'that which opens the womb (*peter rechem*),'[13] and since the womb of this woman is that of a daughter of a Levite, the child need not be redeemed, as other Levites are also exempt." Rabbi Avraham Weinberg (a disciple of the *Avnei Nezer*) asks in his work on tractate *Bechorot, Reshit Bikkurim*: Why is there no obligation to redeem such a firstborn? Surely, a child assumes the status of his father, and so this firstborn should be treated as an ordinary Israelite who must be redeemed from a priest! Rabbi Weinberg explains the matter by referring to the *Avnei Nezer*'s reasoning that the rule that a child assumes his father's status applies only after the child is born, for when we consider the child's relationship to each of his parent's by virtue of being responsible for his conception, the

13 *Bechorot* 4a.

father is given precedence over the mother. But as long as the child is in his mother's womb, so that she is related to him not only because she once conceived him, but also by virtue of the fact that she is now carrying him inside her, the mother is given precedence over the father, so that the child assumes her status. Thus, it follows that at the very moment when the womb is opened the firstborn son of the daughter of a Levite has his mother's status, so that he is exempt from redemption, even though his Levitical status is removed from him immediately after he is born.

It may, therefore, be concluded that the halachic maternal tie is established through pregnancy and childbirth, and that maternity is not necessarily assigned to the biological mother who contributed the original egg from which the child developed. Thus, maternity should be assigned to the surrogate mother who carries the fetus inside her body during the pregnancy and then gives birth to it, even if the fetus developed from an egg which had been contributed by another woman and then was implanted in the surrogate's uterus after fertilization. But a question remains regarding maternity in a theoretical case where a fetus developed from a fertilized egg which was first implanted into one woman's uterus and then was removed from her body and reimplanted into the uterus of another woman who then carried the child to term and gave birth to it. Do we give priority to the woman who first carried the fetus in her womb, or to the one who carried the fetus longest, or do we favor the woman who both carried the child and brought it into the world at the time of birth?

IV. The Talmud states: "A non-Jewish minor undergoes immersion for the sake of conversion on the authority of the court."[14] *Tosafot* understands that, in such a case, the child is regarded as a convert only by Rabbinic decree. But, it adds, if his non-Jewish mother converted to Judaism while she was pregnant with him, "the child born to her after her conver-

---

14 *Ketubbot* 11a. *Tosafot: Matbilin.*

sion is not required to undergo immersion,"[15] and the minor
is then considered a convert by Torah law. *Tosafot* maintains
that such a child is entitled to inherit its mother's estate by
Torah law, even though we normally hold that a convert is
considered as a new person with no relatives.[16]

Rabbi Shmuel Strashun questions the assumption that
the son of a woman who had converted while she was
pregnant with him Biblically inherits her estate upon her
passing, even though his conception preceded the conversion.[17] He suggests that the source lies in the Talmudic
ruling cited previously, that if the mother of twin brothers
converted to Judaism after their conception but prior to their
birth, each brother is liable if he has sexual relations with
the wife of the other.[18] Just as the twins are regarded as
brothers through their shared mother, even though their
mother was not Jewish at the time of their conception, so,
too, the woman is regarded as the mother of each of them,
and they each inherit a share of her estate upon her death.
It follows also that, in such an instance, the son would be
disqualified from testifying against her.[19] He would, similarly, be liable for the death penalty if he had sexual relations
with the woman, as he would be guilty of incest.

We see that Rabbi Strashun based his argument on the
same Talmudic passage that the *Avnei Nezer* cited, contending that it is the basis for *Tosafot*'s statement in *Ketubbot*.
To sharpen the debate, it could be claimed that the section
in *Yevamot* regarding the twin brothers proves only that a
fraternal relationship exists between two twins who developed together in the same womb, but that it provides no

---

15 *Yevamot* 78a.

16 *Tosafot: Ela* (*Yevamot* 78a) argues that this applies even according to the
    authority who maintains that a fetus is not regarded as an integral component
    of its mother's body.

17 *Hagahot v'Chiddushei ha-Reshash, Ketubbot* 11a.

18 *Yevamot* 97b.

19 *Shulchan Aruch, Choshen Mishpat*, Shach 33:7.

evidence that conception and pregnancy do not matter and only childbirth determines maternity. But, from the words of *Tosafot*, Rabbi Strashun proves that childbirth is, indeed, sufficient to determine maternity regarding all aspects of Jewish law, including succession, testimony, and incest.[20]

A similar argument was put forward by Rabbi Itzele of Ponevez:[21] If a man converted to Judaism together with his son, the father-son relationship is severed, because a man is regarded as his offspring's father only on account of his role in the child's conception, and in this instance conception took place prior to their conversion. But if a non-Jewish woman converted while she was pregnant, she is regarded as the child's mother, because the mother-son relationship is based on the woman's role during childbirth, and here childbirth took place after she had already converted to Judaism. The reasoning is essentially the same as that put forward by Rabbi Strashun.

V. Another Talmudic passage which must be considered in this context is the objection raised in opposition to the view of R. Sheshet that a fetus in the womb is capable of acquiring rights.[22] For R. Sheshet himself explains the Mishnah's statement that a one-day-old child can inherit and bequeath property[23] teaches that a one-day-old child inherits his mother upon her death, so that, even if he died immediately after birth, he bequeaths the right of succession to his heirs on his father's side. Now, the fact that the Mishnah limits this regulation to a child who is at least one day old implies that a fetus who died in its mother's womb would not have inherited and bequeathed the right of succession to those who would have been its heirs had it been born alive, apparently in contradiction to R. Sheshet's view that a fetus is

---

20 See also Rabbi Klav, *Techumin*, vol. 5, p. 260.

21 *Zecher Yitzchak* 4.

22 *Bava Batra* 142a.

23 *Niddah* 44a.

capable of acquiring rights. The Talmud rebuts the objection by explaining that a fetus might, indeed, be capable of acquiring rights in the womb. But where the fetus died before its mother, a son "in the grave" cannot be considered his mother's heir, so as to bequeath his mother's estate to his paternal brothers.

Now, from the fact that the Talmud invokes the principle that a son in the grave does not succeed his mother, who died after him, so as to transmit his estate to his paternal brothers, it follows that a living fetus would indeed inherit its mother.[24] We must, therefore, deduce that maternity is assigned even before the fetus is born. For if the mother-child relationship does not exist while the fetus is in its mother's womb, it is not necessary to invoke the principle that a son in the grave does not succeed his mother, who died after him, so as to transmit his estate to his paternal brothers. The Talmud could have stated simply that a fetus cannot inherit from the woman who is carrying him, because that woman is not yet regarded as the fetus's mother. Hence, we are forced to conclude that the mother-child relationship does already exist while the fetus is in its mother's womb, as argued by the *Avnei Nezer*.

VI. Rabbi Yosef Engel[25] tries to establish a definition of motherhood on the basis of a comment of Rashi in the tractate *Megillah*. Referring to the phrase "And when her father and mother were dead,"[26] which appears to be superfluous, as it has already been stated in the same verse that Esther had no father or mother, R. Acha said: "When Esther was conceived, her father died, and when she was born, her mother died."[27] Rashi comments: "'When Esther was conceived, her father died' — hence, she had no father from the

---

24 Rashbam, *Bava Batra* 142a.

25 *Beit ha-Otzar, Av* 4.

26 *Esther* 2:7.

27 *Megillah* 13a. See Rashi.

moment that he was fit to have been called her father; 'and when Esther was born, her mother died' — and was never fit to be called her mother." Rabbi Engel infers from Rashi that, although the man who contributed the sperm is regarded as a father during the fetal stage, a woman is not legally treated as a mother until the moment of birth. The distinction here is that while the fetus is in its mother's womb it is regarded as an integral component of its mother's body, and so a mother-child relationship cannot be assigned before childbirth. It is still possible to argue that this source does not prove that childbirth is the sole factor in determining maternity. Maternity might be assigned to a woman only if she conceived a child, carried it, and later brought it to the world.

In truth, Rashi's comment poses some difficulty. For if maternity is assigned at the moment of birth, then the woman who brought Esther forth into the world should have been eligible to be called her mother, for she was still alive at the instant that she gave birth to Esther. *Tosafot*[28] notes that it is possible for a child to be born after its mother is already dead. If this had happened in the case of Esther, her mother would never have qualified as a legal mother. But it stands to reason that in a case of natural vaginal childbirth the mother would be alive at the time of birth. For if not, then we would be able to decide our question on the basis of a discussion in tractate *Chullin*[29] Referring to the verse "When a bull, a sheep, or a goat is born, it shall be seven days under its mother, and from the eighth day onward it shall be acceptable as a fire offering to Hashem,"[30] a *barayta* taught that the expression "under its mother" is intended to exclude the case of an animal whose mother died.[31] The Talmud concludes that the *barayta* could not have expected

---

28 *D'hu* (*Bava Batra* 142b) and *Ela demaisa* (*Chullin* 38b.).

29 *Chullin* 38b.

30 *Vayikra* 22:27.

31 *Chullin* 38b. See Rashi.

a newborn animal to be fit for sacrifice only if its mother remained alive the entire seven days; even if the mother died shortly after birth, it should still qualify. Thus, the expression must be referring to a case where the mother died before she gave birth. One might then infer that the title of motherhood can be assigned even without any event of childbirth. Rashi, however, remarks that the Talmud means that the young animal was surgically removed from its mother at the moment of her death. Apparently, Rashi understood that natural birth is not possible after the mother's death. Thus, it cannot be concluded from here that the title of motherhood can be assigned even without there having been any birth, for the surgical removal of the young from its mother surely qualifies as a form of birth, as is evidenced by the fact that there is no question that maternity is assigned to a woman who gives birth by caesarean section. If a woman conceived a child and later brought it into the world, she should surely be regarded as the child's mother, the precise method by which the child emerged from her body being a purely technical matter.

As noted above, Rabbi Engel posited that motherhood is assigned at a different time from fatherhood, because a fetus is regarded as an integral component of its mother's body and maternity cannot be established before the child is actually born. It follows from this that, according to the opposing opinion, that a fetus is not regarded as an integral part of its mother's body, a woman may be considered her child's mother even before the child is born.[32] Moreover, even according to the opinion that a fetus is an integral part of its mother's body, we commented previously that the Talmud implies that a fetus of the daughter of a priest has priestly status even while it is inside her womb, so that she is forbidden to enter a structure containing a dead body, since the fetus is forbidden to contract ritual impurity. Now, this is only possible if the fetus has a separate identity, for if it

---

32 See the arguments of the *Avnei Nezer* and the *Reshit Bikkurim* cited above.

is totally regarded as an integral part of its mother's body, why should the mother, who is not prohibited from contact with the dead, be forbidden to enter into the structure containing the dead body? Thus, it appears that a definition of motherhood cannot be established on the basis of Rashi's comment.

VII. The *Shulchan Aruch* comments: "If one eats meat which was cooked in milk that was removed from a dead animal, he is not [Biblically] liable for eating a forbidden mixture of meat and milk."[33] The source for this ruling is a Talmudic derivation regarding a number of exclusions from the prohibition of cooking meat with milk. The Talmud remarks: "[The phrase] 'in its mother's milk' excludes [from the prohibition] milk which was obtained from a slaughtered animal."[34] Rashi explains that the Scriptural reference to the animal's mother implies that the prohibition is limited to milk derived from an animal which is fit to be a mother, to the exclusion of a slaughtered animal, which is no longer fit to be a mother.

Commenting on the *Shulchan Aruch*'s ruling, Rabbi Akiva Eiger[35] raises a question regarding meat cooked in milk derived from a *tereifah* (an animal afflicted with a severe organic disease or congenital defect, which, according to the Talmud, is incapable of giving birth). Is such an animal considered unfit to be a mother, so that meat cooked in its milk would not be Biblically forbidden? In his response, Rabbi Eiger points to the reasoning behind a unique law pertaining to a rebellious son. The Talmud notes that the period of culpability can apply only between the age of thirteen (at which time he shows physical evidence of maturity) and thirteen plus three months, since by the latter age he may no longer be viewed as just a "son" — he is also

---

33 *Yoreh De'ah* 87:6.

34 *Chullin* 113b. See Rashi.

35 Novellae on *Yoreh De'ah*.

fit to be a "father."[36] For if he had sexual relations with a woman when he reached the age of thirteen and she became pregnant, he would already be recognized as a "father" three months later, when the woman would begin to show her pregnancy. Rabbi Eiger determines from this that a man is regarded as a father even prior to his child's birth, when it is still in the fetal stage. Similarly, although a *tereifah* is incapable of giving birth, it can still conceive[37] and should, therefore, be regarded as fit to be a mother. Thus, meat cooked in its milk should also be forbidden. But Rabbi Eiger himself suggests that the proof is not conclusive, as an animal might be regarded as fit to be a mother only if it could possibly give birth to its young, but a *tereifah* which cannot possibly give birth might not be regarded as fit to be a mother merely by virtue of the fact that conception is still possible. Rabbi Eiger notes that the *Issur v'Heter*, in fact, rules that the milk of a *tereifah* is included in the Biblical prohibition of cooking meat with milk,[38] for if an animal conceived before it became a *tereifah*, it would be able to give birth to its young. On the basis of this, Rabbi Eiger concludes that a distinction should be made between a *tereifah* which became afflicted with a severe acquired organic disease, whose milk would be included in the Biblical prohibition, and a *tereifah* with a congenital defect, for which no punishment would be incurred if meat were cooked in its milk.

Rabbi Eiger's comment that, since a *tereifah* can conceive, it should be considered fit to be a mother even though it will not deliver, has been cited in support of the position that maternity is established at the moment of conception. Thus, in the case of surrogacy, maternity should be assigned to the woman who donated the egg, even though the fertilized egg was later implanted into the uterus of another

---

36 *Sanhedrin* 69a.

37 *Yoreh De'ah*, Shach 57:45.

38 *Issur v'Heter* 31:14.

woman.[39] This conclusion is, however, unwarranted. For the *tereifah* discussed by Rabbi Eiger might indeed be regarded as fit to be a mother, for it is capable of conceiving and carrying its young in its womb for the entire fetal stage. It is only the final stage of childbirth that it is incapable of implementing. Thus, it does not follow that conception, in and of itself, is sufficient to determine motherhood.

Moreover, Rabbi Eiger himself concludes that, in a case where the *tereifah* is incapable of giving birth to its young, the animal is not regarded as being fit to be a mother merely because of its ability to conceive and carry its young during the fetal stage. Thus, in the case of surrogacy, where the woman who donated the egg is incapable of carrying the fetus in her womb to the point of delivery, maternity should not be assigned to the egg donor. Rabbi Goldberg argues that perhaps Rabbi Eiger only meant to say that a *tereifah* is not regarded as a fit mother because its fetus will not ultimately be born alive. But in the case of surrogacy, where the surrogate mother who carries the developing fetus in her womb gives birth to a live infant, perhaps the donor of the egg could indeed be regarded as the child's mother. There is, however, no support for this novel interpretation. On the contrary, it stands to reason that conception by itself does not determine motherhood, for childbirth is a critical stage in the ordinary process of bringing a child into the world, and so the woman involved in the actual birth must be reckoned with in determining maternity. Indeed, the *Issur v'Heter*'s ruling cited by Rabbi Eiger, that the milk of a *tereifah* is included in the Biblical prohibition against cooking meat and milk because a *tereifah* is fit to be a mother if it conceived before it developed the defect, suggests, in fact, that we must take cognizance of childbirth itself when deciding maternity. At the very least it proves that there are multiple factors which determine maternity: conception, pregnancy, and birth.

VIII. The rulings regarding artificial insemination using

---

39 Rabbi Z. N. Goldberg, *Techumin*, vol. 5, p. 249.

the semen contributed by a non-Jew also seem to be relevant
to the matter under discussion here. The Talmud rules that
the offspring of a non-Jew and a Jewess is a legitimate Jew.[40]
According to most authorities, the offspring is a full- fledged
Jew who does not require conversion.[41] Yet the *Shulchan
Aruch* rules that a priest may not marry such a daughter.[42]
Rabbi S. Z. Auerbach[43] further decides that, when the non-
Jew's sperm was contributed by artificial insemination, even
the *Shulchan Aruch* would agree that the female offspring
of the Jewess is permitted to a priest.

It would appear from these rulings that in a case where
a child cannot assume his father's personal status by virtue
of his conception (for "the Torah dispossessed a non-Jew of
his sperm,"[44] the child takes the personal status of the
woman who gave birth to him. Furthermore, even though
the egg from which the child was formed came from a Jewish
woman, it would be reasonable to conclude that just as the
child does not assume his father's personal status merely
because he was responsible for his conception, so, too, the
child should not assume his mother's personal status merely
because she was responsible for his conception. Thus, maternity should only be assigned at the time of birth. The rulings
regarding artificial insemination support these arguments,
but do not incontrovertibly prove them.

IX. Rabbi Yitzchak Dov Berger[45] proposes that a question

---

40 *Yevamot* 45b.

41 *Shulchan Aruch, Even ha-Ezer* 4:5; *Pischei Teshuvah*, note 1.

42 This issue is in fact summarized by the *Beit Shemuel* (4:2) as a dispute among
the *Rishonim*: the Rif is in doubt about whether such a daughter is permitted
to a priest; the Rambam rules that she is permitted; and the Rosh maintains
that she is not permitted to a priest. The *Beit Shemuel* adds that, because of
the conflicting opinions, if the marriage took place the priest is not required
to divorce her ex post facto.

43 *No'am* I, 165.

44 *Yevamot* 98a.

45 *Seridim* (Journal of the Association of European Rabbis) 5743, no. 4.

posed by Rabbi Akiva Eiger[46] sheds light on the issue of when a mother-child relationship starts according to halachah. Rabbi Eiger asked: How is a man permitted to have sexual relations with his wife while she is pregnant; should he not be considered as having sexual relations with a woman and her daughter? Rabbi Berger contends that Rabbi Eiger's question presupposes that the mother-child relationship exists even before birth, while the fetus is still in its mother's womb.

In truth, this premise does not necessarily follow from Rabbi Akiva Eiger's question.[47] For upon closer examination it becomes clear that Rabbi Eiger, in actuality, asked how it is possible for a man to have sexual relations with his wife while she is pregnant, for in so doing he is in effect having sexual relations with his daughter. With regard to this question, it has already been reasoned above that the father-child relationship is not dependent upon birth but upon conception, and, therefore, a female fetus would already be his daughter. But no conclusion may be drawn from Rabbi Eiger's question regarding the relationship between mother and child. On the contrary, it might be argued that Rabbi Eiger's question proves that the mother-child relationship does not exist before childbirth, for he bases his question on the prohibition against a man engaging in sexual relations with his daughter, and not on the prohibition against engaging in sexual relations with a woman and her daughter. This reasoning, however, cannot serve as conclusive proof that there is no mother-child relationship before birth, for one might counter that although Rabbi Eiger formulated his question one way, he could just as well have based his question on the other prohibition.

Rabbi Yitzchak Berger refers also to the Talmudic section dealing with the theoretical situation of one who joined

---

46 *Teshuvot*, no. 172.

47 Although it appears to be correct as determined by *Avnei Nezer* and *Reshit Bikkurim*.

together the wombs of two animals, so that when one animal's firstborn emerged from its mother's womb it entered
directly into the womb of the second animal, and only then
was delivered into the world.[48] Is only the first animal viewed
as having given birth to a firstborn, or is the second animal
also viewed as having done so, so that it, too, will be excluded
from the laws of firstborns the next time that it gives birth?[49]
Rabbi Berger notes that, although one could posit that since
the second animal gave birth to the first animal's young and
delivered it into the world firstborn sanctity would be be-
stowed upon the first animal's young and the second animal
should be excluded from the laws of firstborns the next time
that it gives birth, yet the Talmud explicitly describes the
first animal's young as "not being the young of the second."
Thus, it follows that birth is not the determining factor in
the mother-child relationship.

Rabbi Berger's conclusion, however, is unwarranted. It
is beyond all doubt that, in such a case, motherhood is
assigned to the first animal who conceived the young animal
and later sent it forth from its womb. It is equally clear that
there is no reason to assign motherhood to the second animal
just because the newborn animal entered its womb immediately after it left the first animal's womb. The issues under
discussion in this case are the sanctity of the firstborn and
the mother animal's exemption from the laws of firstborns
the next time it gives birth. Those issues are dependent upon
the concept of "the one who opens the womb," i.e., the animal
which opens its mother's womb has the sanctity of a firstborn
and exempts its mother from the laws of firstborns the next

---

48 *Chullin* 70a.

49 The question is not resolved in the Talmud. But, from alternate sequences of
the possible rulings presented in their commentaries, it has been deduced that
Rashi seems to understand that the Talmud is inclined to assume that the
second animal would not have discharged its firstborn sanctity obligation
through the young of the first animal, whereas Rabbenu Gershom grasps that
the Talmud is disposed to the position that the second animal would discharge
its firstborn sanctity obligation through the first animal's young.

time she gives birth. The question arises regarding the second animal, into whose womb the young animal entered immediately after it emerged from the first animal — whether or not we view the second animal's womb as also being opened by the newborn that later comes out. We might regard the second animal's womb as having been opened with respect to the laws of the firstborn even if we do not view the second animal as having given birth to the young animal and even if we do not assign maternity to it.